Speech for the Deaf Child:

Knowledge and Use

Leo E. Connor, Ed.D.
Editor

Alexander Graham Bell Association for the Deaf
Washington, D.C.

First Edition

The Alexander Graham Bell Association for the Deaf, Inc.
3417 Volta Place, N.W., Washington, D.C. 20007

Library of Congress Catalogue Card Number 71-175247

Lithographed in U.S.A. by
EDWARDS BROTHERS, INC.
Ann Arbor, Michigan

Acknowledgments

The authors, the editor, and the publisher thank the publishers and authors who gave permission to quote their published and unpublished work in this monograph. Particular acknowledgment is made of the following, which appear on the pages indicated:

p. 22 Fairbanks, G., and Grubb, P. A psychological investigation of vowel formants, *Journal of Speech and Hearing Research*, 1961, **4**, 203.

p. 121–122 Charles Van Riper, SPEECH CORRECTION: Principles and Methods, 4th ed., © 1963, p. 75. Reprinted by permission of Prentice-Hall, Inc., Englewood Cliffs, New Jersey.

p. 127 Reprinted from ON HUMAN COMMUNICATION by C. Cherry by permission of the M I T Press, Cambridge, Mass. Copyright © 1961 by the Massachusetts Institute of Technology.

p. 137 From D. McCarthy, "Language Development in Children" in P. H. Mussen, CARMICHAEL'S MANUAL OF CHILD PSYCHOLOGY, 3rd ed. Copyright © 1970 by John Wiley & Sons, Inc.

p. 139 Brain, Sir R., "Speech Disorders: Aphasia, Apraxia and Agnosia" (1961, Butterworths, Toronto) p. 16.

p. 140 *The Child Who Does Not Talk.* Ed. by Catherine Renfrew and Kevin Murphy. Published by Clinic No. 13. Published by Spastics Society/William Heinemann Medical Books Ltd.

p. 145 From H. L. Teuber, "Effects of Brain Wounds Implicating Right or Left Hemispheres in Man," in V. Montcastle (ed.) INTERHEMISPHERIC RELATIONS AND CEREBRAL DOMINANCE. Published by Johns Hopkins Press, 1962.

p. 147 From: LANGUAGE DISORDERS OF CHILDREN: The Bases and Diagnoses, Copyright © 1969. Reprinted by permission of Appleton-Century-Crofts, Educational Division, Meredith Corporation.

p. 149 *The Child Who Does Not Talk.* Ed. by Catherine Renfrew and Kevin Murphy. Published by Clinic No. 13. Published by Spastics Society/William Heinemann Medical Books Ltd.

p. 151 Reprinted from ON HUMAN COMMUNICATION by C. Cherry by permission of the M I T Press, Cambridge, Massachusetts. Copyright © 1961 by the Massachusetts Institute of Technology.

p. 171 From: THE PSYCHOLOGY OF COMMUNICATION by John Eisenson, J. Jeffrey Auer, and John V. Irwin. Copyright © 1963 by Meredith Publishing Company. Reprinted by permission of Appleton-Century-Crofts.

p. 221 From *Curriculum: Design for Living,* by Donald F. Cay, copyright © 1966, by the Bobbs-Merrill Company, Inc., reprinted by permission of the publisher.

p. 228 John B. Carroll, *Language and Thought,* © 1964, p. 74. Prentice-Hall, Inc., Englewood Cliffs, N.J.

p. 231 From Fry, D. B. (1968). *British Journal of Disorders of Communication.* 3,1. 13–90. Edinburgh: Livingstone.

p. 270 From *The Psychology of the Child* by Jean Piaget and Barbel Inhelder, Translated from the French by Helen Weaver, Basic Books, Inc., Publishers, New York, 1969.

p. 322 McConnell, F. (Ed.) Proceedings: Current practices in educational management of the deaf infant (0–3 years). Nashville, Tenn., 1968.

TABLE OF CONTENTS

PART IV. ORGANIZATIONAL PATTERNS

Foreword

LEO E. CONNOR, ED.D.

The publication of *Speech for the Deaf Child: Knowledge and Use* is both timely and essential. Timely because it presents a modern review of a complex subject and confronts proponents and detractors with the realities of this most needed of human skills. Its appearance is essential since recent stress on language mastery, on auditory and acoustical advances, and on technological innovations has distracted many educators and parents of deaf children from a vital area of our mutual concern.

A close review of the 16 chapters in this monograph impresses one with the scientific advances, the varieties of the technical information available, and the necessity for precise knowledge and scientific mastery by teachers of speech to the deaf. The clear and objective descriptions of research results, teaching techniques, problem areas, and necessary new knowledge contribute an impressive display of scholarship and expertise to the literature of this field. I envision the widespread usage of these chapters in the 50 or more United States college and university programs where teacher preparation for the deaf takes place, in the hundreds of programs where speech pathology and audiology sequences are offered, and in the thousands of classrooms where hearing impaired children are educated.

In a wider sense, however, this publication arrives on the American scene when teachers of the deaf must be renewed in their efforts to teach speech to the deaf, both those many deaf children with some functional hearing and those few deaf who still cannot benefit from amplification to a significant degree. The value of this monograph will not be to those teachers alone who teach speech as the major mode of communication, but to all teachers of the deaf, deaf or hearing, who owe to each deaf child the fulfillment of his right to speak as clearly and as effectively as possible. The appearance of this handbook reminds educators, clinicians, researchers, parents, and deaf persons of all ages everywhere of their obligation not to deny the necessary skill of oral language to any deaf child by creating a spirit of divisiveness and an attitude of failure or rejection.

Authors

The authors of this monograph are specialists in the fields of speech pathology, education of the deaf, audiology, speech science, and communication skills; they are classroom supervisors, researchers, teacher educators, clinicians, parent counselors, and state department consultants. The chapters represent their best insights, the latest available research results, their extensive experience, and current work. Some of the material overlaps, because it is presented from several viewpoints and with different emphases; some of it is speculative and new; much has been tried and proven; all of it is important to the teaching-learning process of deaf children. This handbook is deliberately a mixture of practice and theory; it offers a "how to do it" picture as well as a status report on the art and science of the topic.

Trends

What is happening in the teaching of speech to the deaf in the United States? My own impression is that currently we have two contrasting trends, one that is loud and negative while the other is quiet and revolutionary.

The former is comprised of contemporary publicity for such ideas as "Cued Speech" and "Total Communication." Essentially Cued Speech represents another form of fingerspelling, and Total Communication is a new name for the simultaneous method or a combined system. These rather strident and persistent programs are, in the long run, enjoying a popularity which is a direct result of the failure of teachers of the deaf who have done a poor job in producing results under oral-aural methods. General educators and parents should not be blamed for looking elsewhere after 60 or more years of trying to establish the principles of Alexander Graham Bell as the major objective for the education of deaf children. The inability of "true oralists" to produce generally impressive results for the deaf, and the lip service paid to oral methods by many poorly prepared, superficially convinced teachers have allowed the organized advocates of the combined methodology the opportunity for a current public affirmation of their deeply held convictions.

A second set of circumstances is leading toward an optimistic and long-term strengthening and improvement of the speech skills for deaf children. These factors revolve around the advances being made in acoustic, tactile, and visual sensory learning techniques and in the direct stimulation of the auditory nerve. All of the above, plus the early intervention procedures of educators from birth onward, add up to the gradual increase in the number of deaf children who can be reached through functional auditory inputs. Therefore, the goals of educational and social integration of the deaf into nonhandicapped schools and neighborhoods should become more of a reality in the near future. I predict that one of the next large-scale movements in the education of the deaf in this country will be an increased emphasis placed on meaningful and effective regular school programs for deaf children. The success of deaf children in regular schools will be impressive because current day programs for the deaf in the United States have achieved only a spotty record of achievement to date, while the residential schools for the deaf, as a whole, have resisted the "graduation" of their best pupils at as early an age as possible.

Thus, the teaching of speech to the deaf should be viewed as a means to an end, (i.e., the transfer of deaf children into regular school programs at an early age). The concomitant task of organizing regular schools for the advent of deaf children and providing the best educational services possible should be the major task of parents' groups everywhere.

Conclusion

Understandable and effective speech stands out as the greatest achievement that a deaf person can reach because it is so difficult. It represents the giving back to the deaf person one of the two most valuable human skills which he has lost. The other is his use of hearing. However, both of these vital activities are but the means to the end of restoring the deaf individual to his highest level of achievement in the world in which we all live.

No person should be forced to make personal choices in his life based on the lack of effort of another individual. When we, as educators of the deaf, know better ways of achieving normalcy for the deaf and have the opportunity to make these effective, we owe to our deaf students the best efforts we can make in their behalf. Such work must begin early, be carried on efficiently and with knowledge of the multiple factors involved, and must be surrounded by an optimistic social and learning environment that applies speech techniques for the deaf consistently and completely.

The Authors

Conway Studio Corp.

Leo E. Connor, Ed.D.

Leo E. Connor, Ed.D., editor of *Speech for the Deaf Child: Knowledge and Use,* is executive director of Lexington School for the Deaf, New York, New York. He is president of the Alexander Graham Bell Association for the Deaf and is a member of the executive committee of the Council on Education of the Deaf and the National Advisory Committee on Education of the Deaf. He served as president of the Council for Exceptional Children 1967–68. Dr. Connor is the author of many articles on the education of deaf children which have appeared in professional journals, and also has been director or assistant director of a number of research projects. He received his Ed.D. from Teachers College, Columbia University.

Gardy Daniels

Arthur Boothroyd, Ph.D.

Arthur Boothroyd, Ph.D., is director of the C. V. Hudgins Diagnostic and Research Center at Clarke School for the Deaf, Northampton, Massachusetts. A native of England, he received an honors degree in physics from the University of Hull, and, after working as a high school physics teacher, took a research position at the University of Manchester under Sir Alexander Ewing. While at Manchester he conducted research on the influence of the earmold on hearing aid performance, which involved the development of a test of speech sound recognition, a statistical theory of the speech discrimination score, and extensive studies of the effect of filtering on speech sound recognition by partially hearing children. He received his Ph.D. degree from the University of Manchester.

Jean Utley Lehman, Ph.D.

Jean Utley Lehman, Ph.D., is director of the teacher preparation program in the area of the hearing impaired at California State College at Los Angeles. Dr. Lehman has taught in Dayton (Ohio) Day School for the Deaf, and the Wisconsin, Florida, and New Jersey state schools for the deaf. She was supervising teacher at the South Carolina School for the Deaf; resource teacher in the hearing conservation program of the Evanston (Illinois) public schools; and a teacher of lipreading at the Chicago Hearing Society. She received her Ph.D. with majors in hearing and speech at Northwestern University. Dr. Lehman is the editor of *Selected Readings in Language for Teachers of the Hearing Impaired.*

R. J. Mason Studio

Harry Levitt, Ph.D.

Harry Levitt, Ph.D., is an associate professor in the doctoral program in speech at City University of New York. A native of Johannesburg, South Africa, he received a degree in electrical engineering from the University of Witwatersrand. In 1960 he was awarded a Beit Fellowship to study binaural discrimination. After receiving his Ph.D. from the Imperial College of Science & Technology in England, he joined the speech and auditory research group at Bell Telephone Laboratories. Dr. Levitt is currently engaged in conducting research on the speech of the deaf and in developing speech training aids for the deaf. He is a member of the National Academy of Engineering CIEBM Subcommittee on Sensory Aids.

James M. Pickett, Ph.D.

James M. Pickett, Ph.D., is professor of speech communication research at Gallaudet College. He has been a research psychologist at the U.S. Air Force Operational Applications, Bolling Field, and at the U.S. Naval Research Laboratory. Dr. Pickett, who holds a Ph.D. from Brown University, has been a research fellow at the speech transmission laboratory of the Royal Institute of Technology, Stockholm, Sweden. Prior to joining the faculty of Gallaudet, Dr. Pickett was a research psychologist at the speech research branch of the Air Force Cambridge Laboratories at Bedford, Massachusetts, and at Melpar, Inc., Falls Church, Virginia. His professional contributions have been in the fields of acoustic and phonetic factors in speech communication, auditory psychophysics, the nature of deafness, and special speech aids for the deaf.

Boyd V. Sheets, Ph.D.

Abey Photography

Boyd V. Sheets, Ph.D., is professor of speech pathology at Brooklyn College of the City University of New York; director of the Speech and Hearing Center, Brooklyn College; and area chairman of speech pathology-audiology, speech and hearing science, Brooklyn College. Dr. Sheets received his Ph.D. from the University of Minnesota. His teaching and clinical experience has been at the University of Minnesota, University of Utah, and City University of New York; and he has been professional consultant, narrator, and moderator of films and television series on speech and hearing. Dr. Sheets has also headed or been a member of various research teams, and has contributed to a number of professional publications, including the *Journal of Hearing and Speech Disorders, Archives of Otolaryngology,* and *The Journal of Applied Physiology*.

John W. Black, Ph.D.

John W. Black, Ph.D., is Regents' Professor and director of speech and hearing science at Ohio State University. He was president of the Speech Association of America in 1966 and a vice president of the American Speech and Hearing Association in 1964. Dr. Black is a fellow of the Acoustical Society of America, the American Speech and Hearing Association, and the American Association for the Advancement of Science. He has taught at Adrian and Kenyon colleges, and is the author of three textbooks and numerous other publications in the areas of experimental and linguistic phonetics. Dr. Black received his Ph.D. from Wabash University and has studied at the Catholic University in Milan, Italy, under a Fulbright research grant and a National Science Foundation fellowship.

Freeman McConnell, Ph.D.

Freeman McConnell, Ph.D., is chairman of the division of hearing and speech sciences, professor of audiology, and associate professor of otolaryngology at Vanderbilt University School of Medicine, Nashville, Tennessee. He is director of the Bill Wilkerson Hearing and Speech Center in Nashville, and actively supports improved educational facilities for deaf children in Tennessee. He received his Ph.D. in audiology from Northwestern University, Evanston. From 1962–1969 he was a member of the National Joint Committee on Audiology and Education of the Deaf, and was its chairman for four years. Dr. McConnell is co-editor of *Deafness in Childhood* and is the author of numerous professional articles and chapters in books and manuals.

Darcy M. C. Dale, Ph.D.

Darcy M. C. Dale, Ph.D., is senior lecturer in education of deaf and partially hearing children at London University, Institute of Education, London, England. A native of New Zealand, Dr. Dale received his Ph.D. from the University of Manchester after completing post-graduate research work under Sir Alexander Ewing. Returning to New Zealand, he trained teachers of deaf children at Christ Church Teachers' College and, in 1961, became superintendent of the school for deaf children in Auckland. In 1964 Dr. Dale visited schools and universities in the United States under a three-month Carnegie Travel Award, and has taught summer courses at a number of universities in the United States and Canada. He is the author of *Applied Audiology for Children* and *Deaf Children at Home and at School*.

Sophie L. French, M.A.

Sophie L. French, M.A., assistant professor of special education at Eastern Michigan University, Ypsilanti, is coordinator of the university's deaf education program and founder and co-director of its preschool parent counseling clinic. She has taught in the preschool program at Lexington School for the Deaf and served as supervising teacher for the deaf preschool and elementary grades at the Rackham School of Special Education, Ypsilanti. Mrs. French is the author of articles on the education of the deaf; and she has presented papers at national and international meetings of professional organizations.

Altman-Pach Studio

Eleanor Vorce, M.A.

Eleanor Vorce, M.A., is supervisor of the preschool department of Lexington School for the Deaf, New York, New York. She previously taught at the Michigan School for the Deaf and at the Alexander Graham Bell School, Cleveland, Ohio. Miss Vorce is also instructor in speech for the deaf at Teachers College, Columbia University. Also at the college level she has been an instructor at Hunter College and a guest instructor at a summer session of the University of Alberta, Edmonton, Canada, and a lecturer on speech for the deaf at the University of Washington summer school. Miss Vorce is a member of a number of professional organizations and has served on many committees, including the certification committee of the American Speech and Hearing Association. She has delivered papers and taken part in panel discussions at national and international meetings and conferences.

Marjorie E. Magner, M.E.D.

Marjorie E. Magner, M.E.D., is the coordinator of the speech program at the Clarke School for the Deaf, Northampton, Massachusetts, and instructor in the Smith College-Clarke School graduate study teacher-education program. Before joining the Clarke School faculty in 1944 she taught at the Nebraska School for the Deaf. Miss Magner has conducted courses and workshops in schools and universities throughout the United States and Canada. She attended the University of Manchester on a Fulbright scholarship. Her articles have appeared in *The Volta Review, The American Annals of the Deaf,* and *Exceptional Children.*

Henry Verby Photography

Pauline M. Jenson, Ph.D.

Pauline M. Jenson, Ph.D., is professor of special education and coordinator of the education of the hearing impaired program at Trenton State College, New Jersey. Prior to this she was research associate at Lexington School for the Deaf and lecturer in the department of special education, Teachers College, Columbia University. Dr. Jenson received her Ph.D. from Columbia University. She holds the Certificate of Clinical Competence in Speech Pathology and in Audiology from the American Speech and Hearing

Association. She has written extensively on the improvement of oral communication skills in the education of deaf children.

Audrey Ann Simmons, Ed.D.

Audrey Ann Simmons, Ed.D., is director of aural rehabilitation and early childhood education at Central Institute for the Deaf, St. Louis, Missouri, and is associate professor and coordinator of practicum for the teacher education program at Washington University in St. Louis. She is a fellow in the American Speech and Hearing Association, and is a member of the Society for Research in Child Development, the National Association for the Education of Young Children, and the Advisory Board of the Alexander Graham Bell Association for the Deaf. She has served as a consultant for numerous workshops and has contributed articles to several professional journals.

EPS Studios

Patricia A. Scherer, Ph.D.

Patricia A. Scherer, Ph.D., is director of the program for education of the hearing impaired at Northwestern University, Evanston, Illinois. Her experience includes classroom teaching of hearing children, deaf children, children with learning disabilities, and multi-handicapped deaf children. Dr. Scherer's major interest is in the learning processes of young hearing impaired children. She received her Ph.D. in education of the deaf from Northwestern University. The title of her dissertation was "Visual Learning Processes of the Deaf."

Winifred N. Northcott, Ph.D.

Winifred N. Northcott, Ph.D., is a consultant in early education programs for the handicapped, and project director, UNISTAPS Model Demonstration Project for Hearing-Impaired Children (0–6) and their Parents (P.L. 90–538), Minnesota Department of Education. Dr. Northcott has also served as preschool director of the Minneapolis Hearing Society, and has taught at Lexington School for the Deaf. She has taught in the Minneapolis public schools and was formerly coordinator of programs for the hearing impaired in the Minneapolis public schools. She has written articles for professional journals, including *The Volta Review*.

Leonard L. Greif, Jr.

William G. Hardy, Ph.D.

William G. Hardy, Ph.D., is director of the Hearing and Speech Center and audiologist-in-charge at Johns Hopkins Hospital, Baltimore, Maryland. Dr. Hardy has served as consultant in communicative disorders to numerous organizations, including the National Institute of Neurological Diseases and Stroke, U.S. Children's Bureau, Acoustical Audiology Section of the Veterans Administration, and the U.S. Naval Medical Department. He is a past president and fellow of the American Speech and Hearing Association. Dr. Hardy, who received his Ph.D. from Cornell University, is the author of numerous articles that have appeared in professional journals, including *The Volta Review*.

Part I. Speech Science

CHAPTER I

Acoustics of Speech

ARTHUR BOOTHROYD, PH.D.

Speech sounds are a special class among the variety of sounds to which our ears are exposed. What makes them special is not so much their acoustical features, but their function as a link in the chain of verbal communication. The sounds of speech contain, in coded form, information about phonatory and articulatory activities which themselves represent an encoding of linguistically organized thoughts.

A study of the acoustics of speech must therefore involve a description not only of the acoustical features of speech sounds, but also of the way in which these features relate to the phonatory and articulatory activities which generate them. This is the field of acoustic phonetics. It is important to realize that speech sounds basically carry information about *only* phonatory and articulatory activities. They are a way of informing a listener of the movements and activities of the various parts of the speech mechanism. If they do carry information about linguistic structures or thought processes, it is because the phonatory and articulatory activities themselves carry this information.

Several techniques have been used in determining the acoustical correlates of speech activities. One is to analyze the speech of a number of people and look for consistent features. An example of this approach is the work of Potter, Kopp, and Green (1947) aimed at learning the recognition of speech from a real time visible display of its acoustical features. A second approach is to take real speech and degrade or distort it in some way, thus removing certain features. By having listeners attempt to recognize what remains, an assessment of the important features can be made. Some results from this kind of experiment have been presented by Fletcher (1953, chap. 18). Another, and basically different, approach is to create artificial speech sounds using mechanical or electrical analogues of the speech mechanism, and to incorporate a limited number of features in these sounds. The extent to which the synthetic speech is recognizable is a measure of the importance of the features which were incorporated. A review of speech synthesis methods has been given recently by Fant (1968). The results of these various techniques have provided consistent information about the more important features which the normal listener uses in speech recognition, although the picture is far from complete.

The end product in teaching speech to the deaf is sound, and the success of the venture will depend on the extent to which this sound conveys the intended information. An understanding of acoustic phonetics is, therefore, a valuable addition to the equipment of a speech teacher. Unfortunately, most teachers of the deaf do not have a technical background and may find it difficult to read much of the published literature in this field. For this reason, I have chosen to write this chapter in as nontechnical a manner as possible. In addition, I have omitted most of the detail of experimental procedure in describing research results and trust that the interested reader will go to the original articles for further information.

The material which follows is divided into three sections. In the first, I have described the basic physical principles involved in speech production and explained their operation in the generation of speech sounds. In the second, I have discussed the acoustical properties of speech. Starting with an overall description of the frequency and intensity characteristics, this section continues with a description of the various classes of speech sound, and the features which have been shown to aid the normal listener in their recognition. The final section deals with points which are of specific relevance to the teaching of speech to the deaf.

1. Basic Physical Concepts and Their Operation in the Speech Mechanism

1. 1. Natural Frequencies of Vibration

Many systems have a particular position or condition which they adopt in the absence of outside disturbances. For example, a weighted string hangs vertically downward, a stretched string forms a straight line between the points of attachment, and the air in a tube lies stationary. This is the *rest condition.*

When such a system is temporarily disturbed, it returns to its rest condition. It may do so in a single movement (for example, the weighted string if the weight hangs in syrup) or after going through a series of vibrations. When these vibrations occur, they have a definite frequency which is known as a natural frequency of vibration.

A useful way of illustrating vibrations is by means of a displacement/time graph, which shows the distance of the vibrating object from its rest position as a function of time. For example, Figure 1. (b) shows a displacement/time graph for a weighted string whose natural frequency of vibration is 2 Hz (i.e., two cycles of vibration in each second). The effect of hanging the weight in syrup is illustrated in Figure 1. (a); and Figure 1. (c) shows what happens if there are no energy losses within the system, for then it continues to vibrate indefinitely and never returns to the rest condition. The energy losses in a vibrating system are referred to as *damping.*

Some systems such as the weighted string have only one natural frequency of vibration. Others have several, each one corresponding with a different way (or mode) of vibrating. The stretched string, for example, can vibrate so that the whole string moves from side to side in step, or each half can vibrate exactly out of step so that the center remains stationary. Similarly it can vibrate in thirds, quarters, etc., each mode having a different natural frequency. It should also be noted that the string can vibrate in several of these modes at the same time.

The vocal tract from larynx to lips is an air-filled tube. If disturbed, the air will vibrate backward and forward as it returns to its rest condition. Assuming a uniform diameter and a length of 17 cm, the natural frequencies of vibration of this air can be shown to be approximately 500 Hz, 1500 Hz, 2500 Hz, and so on in steps of 1000 Hz.

A region of frequencies extending from just below to just above a natural frequency of vibration of the vocal tract is referred to as a *formant,** and the term *formant frequency* may be used interchangeably with "natural frequency of vibration." The lowest frequency formant is called the *first formant* (F1) the next is the *second formant* (F2) and so on. The frequencies of these formants will be referred to as F_1, F_2, etc.

*The word "formant" has been used in several ways to describe different but related aspects of vocal tract resonance. A discussion of this has been given by Stevens and House (1961).

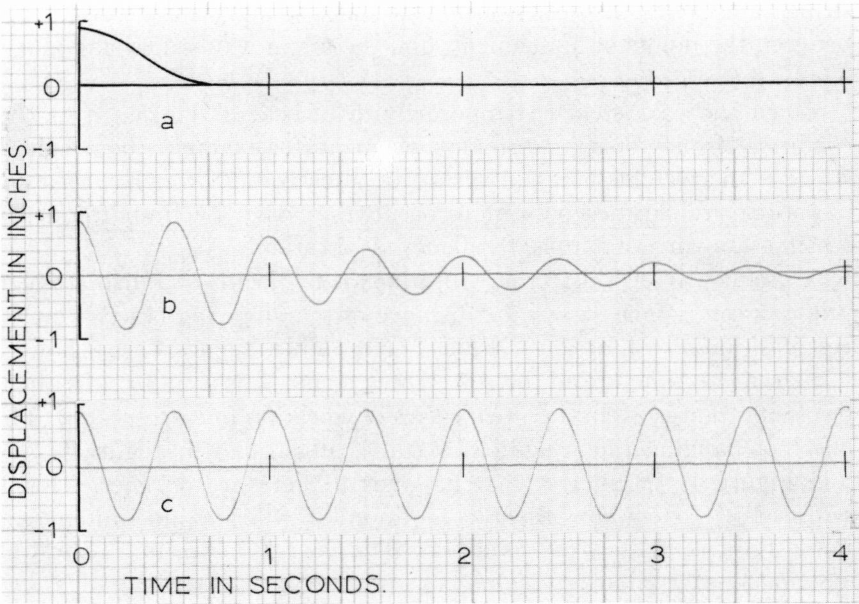

Figure 1. Displacement/time graphs for a weighted string. The curves illustrate the movement of the weight after it has been pulled to one side and released. In the first curve (a) it is assumed that the weight hangs in a viscous fluid such as syrup, and it simply returns to its rest condition. The second curve (b) shows what happens under normal circumstances. The weight vibrates backward and forward as it slowly returns to its rest condition. The third curve (c) illustrates what would happen if there were no energy losses. The vibrations continue indefinitely, and the weight never returns to its rest condition.

In curves (b) and (c) it will be seen that there are two full vibrations in every second. Thus the natural frequency of vibration is 2 cycles per second, or 2 Hz.

Because of the vocal tract's mobility, the formant frequencies can be changed. This is accomplished by changing the shape and size of the lip opening, by raising the tongue to divide the tract into two sections, by changing the position of the raised portion of the tongue, or by lowering the soft palate. The possible ranges of the first three formant frequencies are shown in Table I. Different configurations of the vocal tract result in different combinations of values for the formant frequencies. Conversely, a knowledge of the formant frequencies provides information about the configuration of the vocal tract.

Table I. Frequency Ranges of the First Three Formants

Formant	Frequency in Hz	
	Lowest	Highest
1	150	850
2	500	2800
3	1700	3600

Note: These values are taken from a variety of experimental data obtained with many different speakers. The ranges would not be so great for a single speaker.

1. 2. Resonance

If a system such as we have discussed is forced to vibrate at a frequency other than a natural one, considerable energy will be required and only small vibrations produced. However, as the stimulating frequency is brought closer to a natural frequency, it will be found that the system vibrates more easily, and the largest vibrations will be produced when the stimulating frequency equals a natural frequency. This phenomenon is known as *resonance.* It is the production of large amplitudes of vibration in a system by stimulating it at a natural frequency of vibration. Because of this phenomenon, a natural frequency of vibration may also be called a *resonant frequency.* The amount of damping in a system affects its resonance. With a lot of damping, the vibrations at a resonant frequency will not be very much greater than at other frequencies. With less damping, however, the system will be more selective.

In some experiments on the vocal tract, its resonant characteristics have been investigated by attaching a vibrator to the throat at the level of the larynx and generating vibrations of various frequencies. The response of the air in the vocal tract was determined by measuring the sound radiated from the subject's lips (Fujimura and Lindqvist, 1965).

1. 3. Spectral Composition of Complex Sounds

Certain vibrations are simple and regular and can be specified by a single frequency. These are called *simple harmonic vibrations* and when they are in the range of audibility result in a *pure tone.*

Most of the sounds we hear are not so simple, but it has been shown that a complex sound can be analyzed into (or built up from) a mixture of pure tones of various frequencies. When the sound is *periodic,* that is to say when the displacement/time graph shows a repeated pattern, the component pure tones have frequencies which are whole number multiples of the basic repetition frequency. For example, a complex vibration which repeats itself at the rate of 150 Hz will have components of frequency 150 Hz, 300 Hz, 450 Hz, 600 Hz, etc. Such a series of numbers is a *harmonic series.* The lowest is the *first harmonic,* the next is the *second harmonic,* and so on. (The first harmonic is also called the *fundamental frequency,* and second and higher harmonics may be referred to as *overtones.*)

Periodic vibrations are generated by the vocal cords when they are brought together with suitable tension and air is forced between them. A typical fundamental frequency for a male speaker would be 125 Hz, which gives a harmonic series of 125 Hz, 250 Hz, 375 Hz, etc. During speech, the fundamental might vary between the limits of 80 Hz and 250 Hz, as vocal cord tension is changed.* A typical average value for the fundamental frequency of a woman's voice would be 250 Hz and for a child's, 300 Hz. A common symbol for the fundamental frequency of voiced sounds is F_0.

A vibration in which no repetition can be observed in the displacement/time graph is random or *aperiodic.* It can still be analyzed into a series of pure tones, but now these pure tones are continuously distributed across a wide range of frequencies. Such sounds can be generated in the vocal tract by forcing air through a narrow constriction. When the constriction is small enough and the rate of air flow high enough, the air flow becomes *turbulent.* This turbulence, or random movement, results in an aperiodic sound whose intensity and frequency characteristics depend on the size, shape, and length of the constriction.

1. 4. Resonance of the Vocal Tract

When complex sounds are generated in the vocal tract, these components which fall at, or close to, a formant frequency will cause resonance, and will therefore be effectively transmitted to the surrounding air. Other components will be less effectively transmitted. Thus, the sound radiated from the lips will contain more energy at the formant frequencies than at other frequencies. In this way a listener is given information about the configuration of the vocal tract. It is important to remember that the sound heard by the listener is a combination of two things—the generated sound and the modifications imposed on it by the resonant characteristics of the vocal tract.

*Fundamental frequency is also affected slightly by the air pressure in the lungs.

1. 5. *Spectrographic Analysis*

Spectrographic analysis is a process by which sounds are analyzed to show how much energy they contain at various frequencies. When the measurements are recorded in visible form, the result is a *spectrogram.* The spectrograms shown below are intended to illustrate the various features discussed in this section and were prepared with a Kay Sona-Graph. This machine records a 2.4-second sound sample and then uses an electrical circuit to examine the various frequencies, the results being recorded on paper. Time is shown horizontally, and different frequencies correspond with different vertical positions. When energy is found at a particular frequency, the machine leaves a dark trace in the position corresponding with that frequency, the darkness of the trace being decided by the amount of energy (see Koenig and others, 1946).

In Figures 2–6, a displacement/time graph is shown below each spectrogram. Figure 2 shows the spectrographic analysis of a pure tone. A single horizontal line is seen, corresponding in position with the frequency of vibration of the tone. A spectrogram of a complex vibration is shown in Figure 3. The vibration is periodic and repeats itself at the rate of 250 times per second. The spectrograph finds energy at the fundamental frequency, 250 Hz, and also at twice this frequency, three times it, etc. The following diagram, Figure 4, shows that when the vibration is aperiodic, having no repeated pattern, energy is distributed across a broad range of frequencies. The spectrograms in Figures 5 and 6 were prepared from real speech sounds. The first was a sustained vowel / **ε** /.* The complex vibration of the vocal cords produces a series of harmonics, but those harmonics falling close to a formant frequency appear stronger than the others. Figure 6 shows a spectrogram of the same vowel, but this time it was whispered. The noise source is now aperiodic, but again those frequencies close to a formant frequency are stronger than the others.

Figure 7 shows how the formant pattern is retained independently of changes in fundamental frequency. The spectogram is of a sustained vowel spoken with rising intonation. In preparing the spectrogram of Figure 8, the fundamental frequency of the voice was held constant, but the tongue "hump" was moved from the front to the back of the mouth, resulting in the word "you." This time the formant frequencies change, but the harmonic pattern does not. Pronouncing the word "you?" with rising intonation causes the harmonic and formant patterns to change simultaneously and independently, and the picture becomes somewhat

*A key to the IPA symbols used here and their equivalents on the Northampton Charts is given at the end of this chapter.

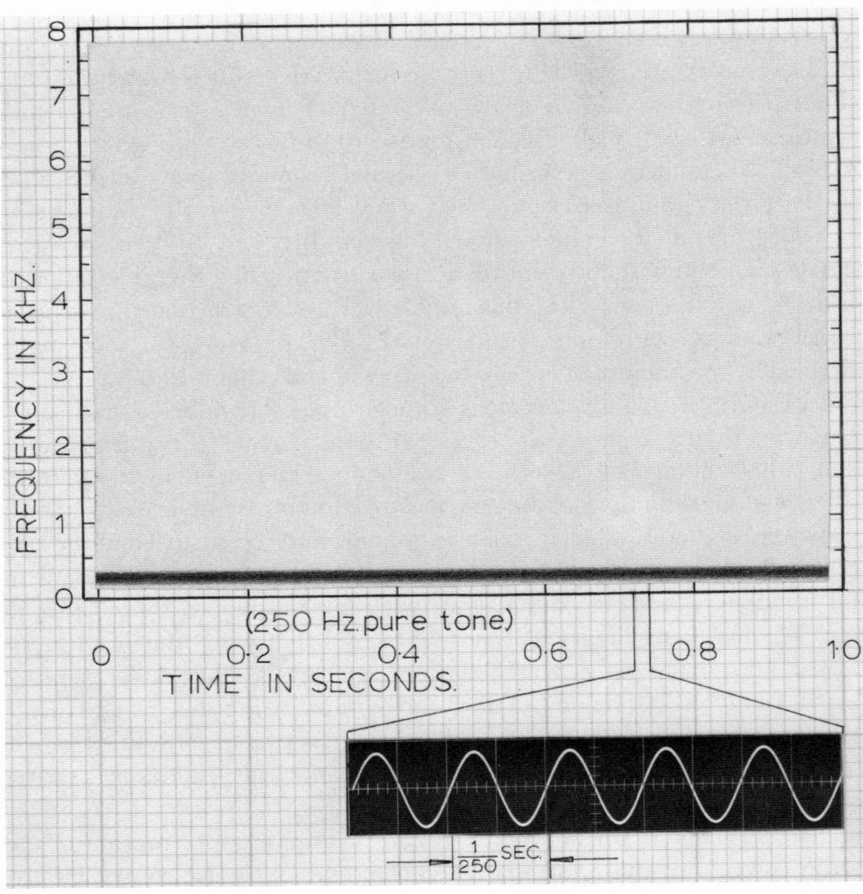

Figure 2. Spectrographic analysis of a pure tone. The tone lasts for just under one second, and the movement of the air particles for one fiftieth of that time is shown in the displacement/time graph at the bottom of the figure. There are 250 cycles of vibration in each second, so the spectrograph finds energy at 250 Hz. Because this is a pure tone, no energy is found at any other frequency.

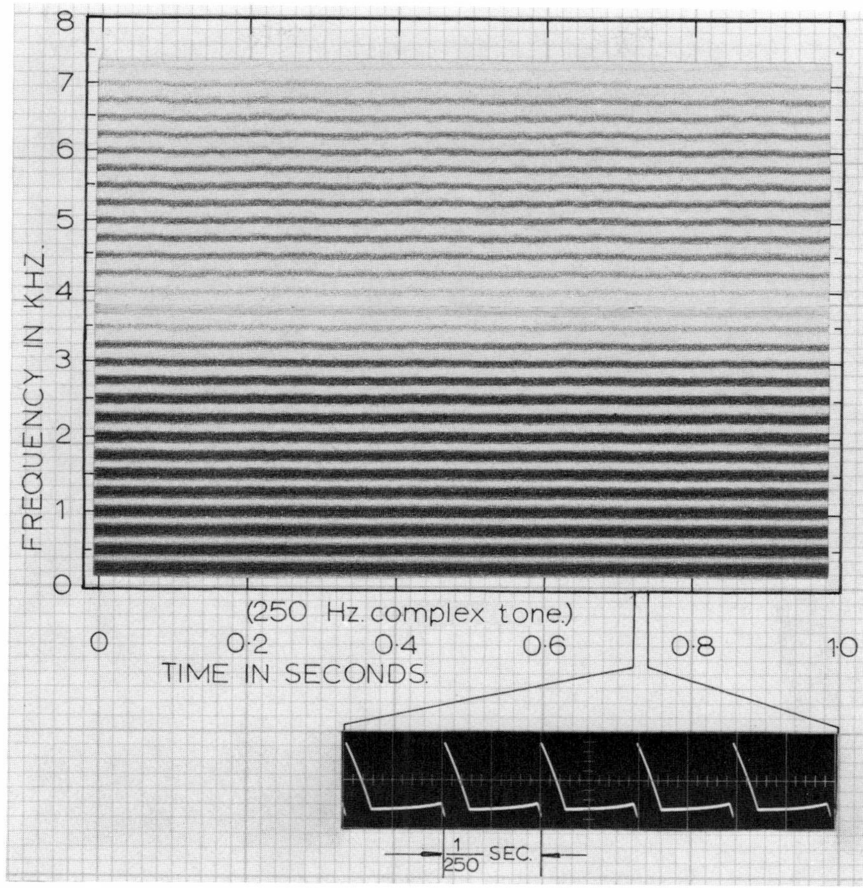

Figure 3. Spectrographic analysis of a complex tone. This diagram is similar to the previous one, but now the displacement/time graph shows a more complicated vibration pattern (similar to the vibrations of the vocal cords during voiced sounds). The pattern repeats itself with a definite period (1/250th of a second) so the spectrograph finds energy at a frequency of 250 Hz. However, in contrast to the pure tone, there is also energy at 500 Hz, 750 Hz, 1000 Hz, etc. all the way up to 7,250 Hz. This diagram illustrates the fact that a complex periodic sound contains frequency components which form a harmonic series.

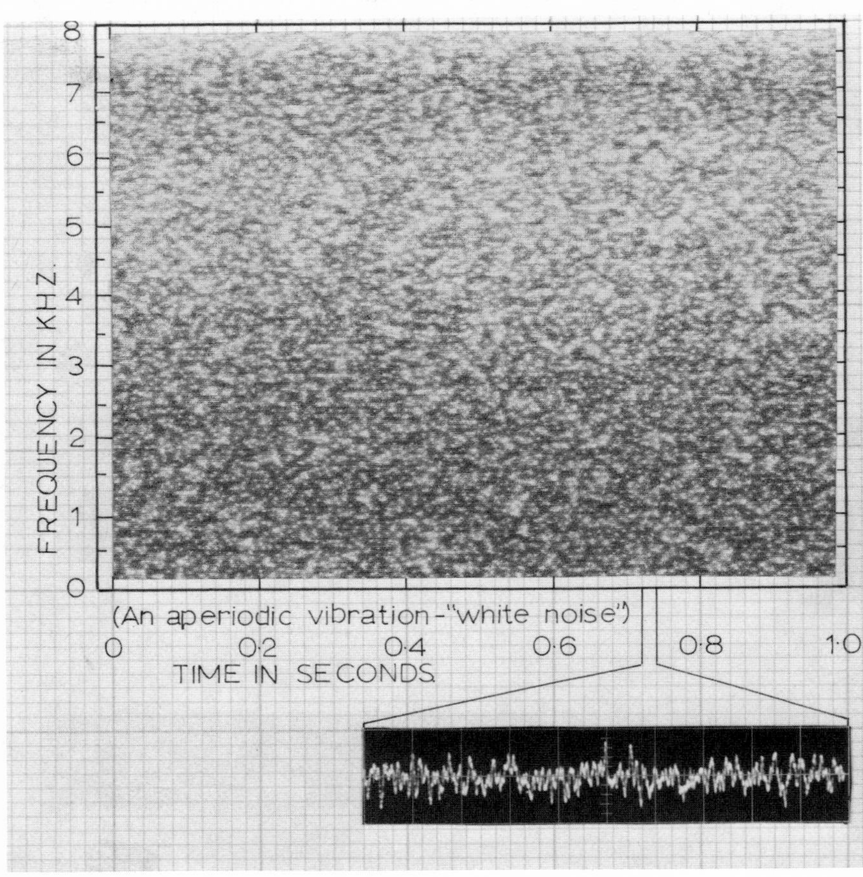

Figure 4. Spectrographic analysis of an aperiodic vibration. The displacement/time graph shows vibrations of the air particles but no repetitive pattern can be observed. Energy is found by the spectrograph across a wide frequency range, but it is continuously distributed—there being no harmonic structure.

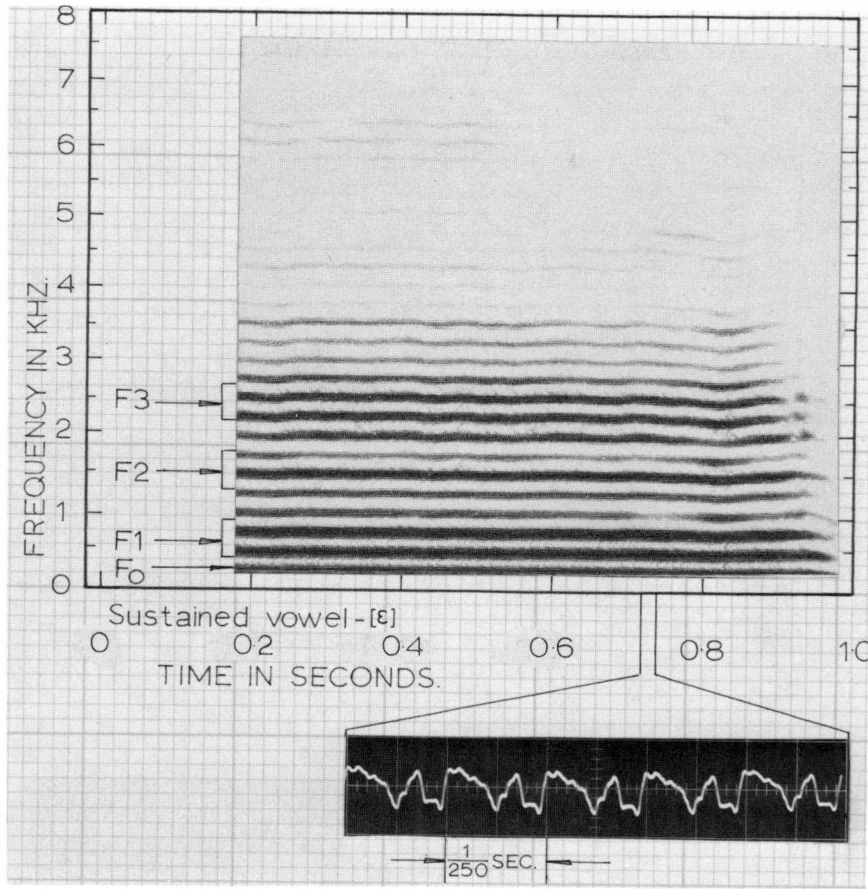

Figure 5. Spectrographic analysis of a sustained vowel. The vocal cord vibrations are periodic and have a fundamental frequency of 250 Hz. Thus the spectrogram shows a series of components forming a harmonic series. However, the resonances of the vocal tract modify the sound, those harmonics falling at or near a formant frequency being stronger than those which do not. For the particular configuration of the vocal tract chosen for this illustration the resonant frequencies were the same as those of a uniform tube of length 17 cm, open at one end and closed at the other. They are 500 Hz, 1500 Hz, 2500 Hz, 3500 Hz, etc.

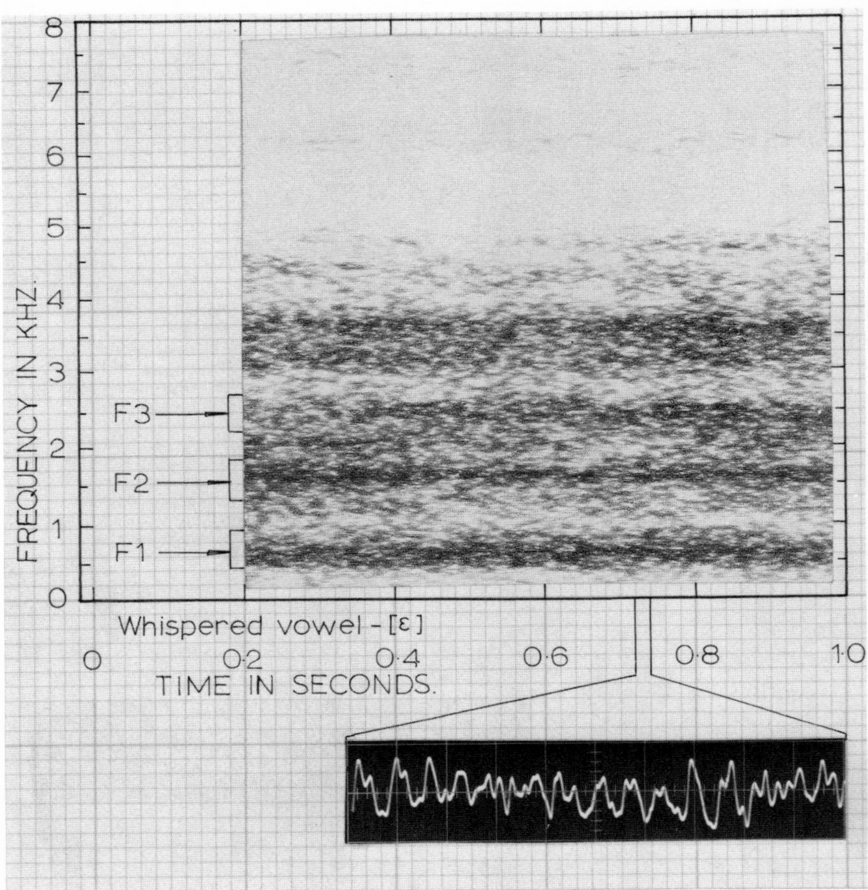

Figure 6. Spectrographic analysis of a whispered vowel. In whispering, air is forced through a narrow space between the vocal cords to cause turbulence. The resulting air vibrations are aperiodic and show a continuous distribution of energy as in Figure 4. However, the vocal tract resonances again come into play and result in some frequency regions being stronger than others as the sound emerges from the lips. The vocal tract configuration was the same as for Figure 5, and consequently the regions of maximum energy correspond in the two illustrations.

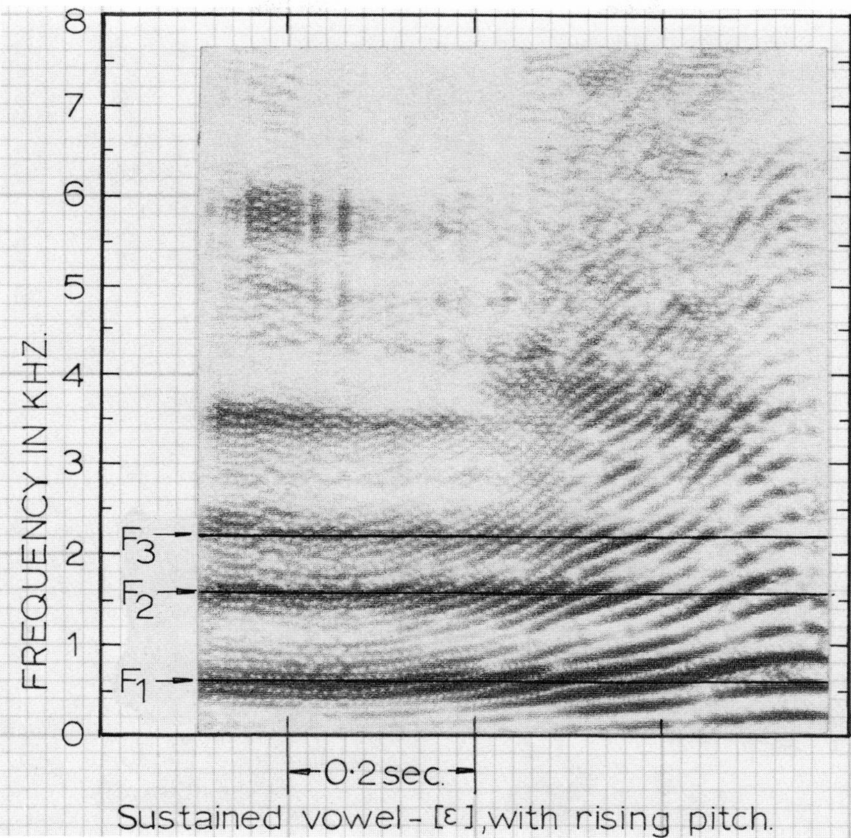

Figure 7. The effect of changing vocal cord frequency without changing vocal tract configuration. To prepare this spectrogram, a steady vowel was uttered but with rising inflection. At the beginning the frequency of vibration of the vocal cords was 100 Hz, but by the end it had risen to 300 Hz. As each harmonic reaches a frequency which is close to a formant frequency, it becomes stronger. Thus at the beginning it is the 15th harmonic which corresponds with the second formant frequency, but at the end it is the 5th. Note that on only a few occasions do a harmonic frequency and a formant frequency coincide exactly.

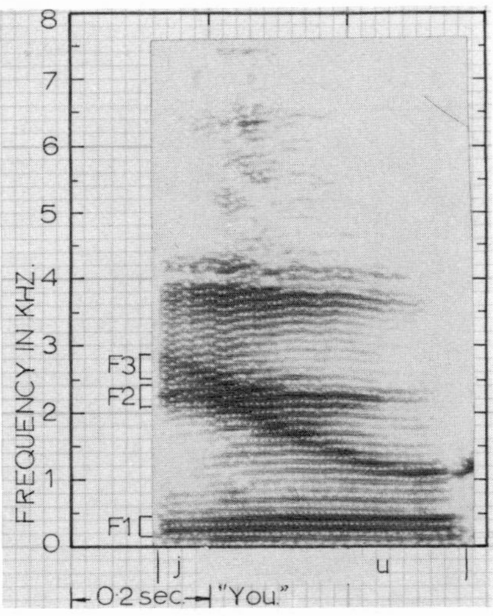

Figure 8. The effect of changing vocal tract configuration without a change of vocal cord vibration frequency. This is simply an utterance of the word "you" at constant pitch. During the utterance, the tongue "hump" moves from the front to the back of the mouth, causing changes of formant frequencies. The biggest change is of F_2 which starts at 2,300 Hz and ends at 1,100 Hz.

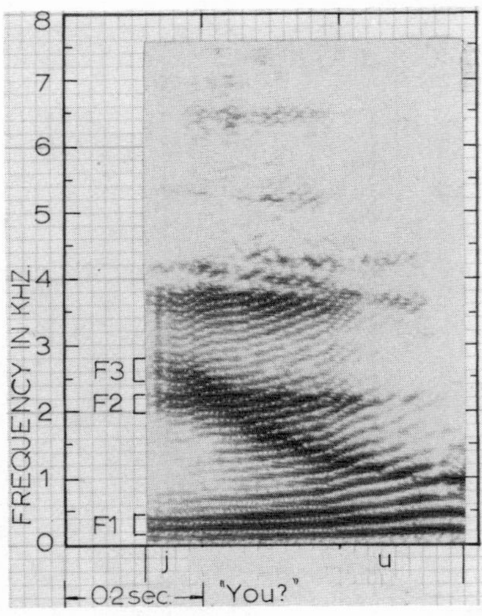

Figure 9. The effect of changing fundamental frequency and vocal tract configuration at the same time. To prepare this spectrogram, the word "you" was again spoken, but this time with rising intonation, as if asking a question. The fundamental frequency rises from 130 Hz to 250 Hz, but the formant frequencies follow the same pattern as in Figure 8. This and the previous two spectrograms illustrate the important point that the sound radiated from the speaker's lips is a combination of two things—the generated sound and the modification introduced by vocal tract resonances—and that these factors can change independently of each other.

confusing (Figure 9). However, by arranging that the analyzing filter of the spectrograph accepts several harmonics at the same time, the harmonic pattern can be suppressed while the formant pattern remains (Figure 10). This is the most suitable arrangement for illustrating the effects of articulatory changes. It does not work very well with high-pitched voices, however, as the harmonics are more widely spaced and still stand out separately (Figure 11). For this reason it is sometimes difficult to interpret spectrograms of women's and children's speech.

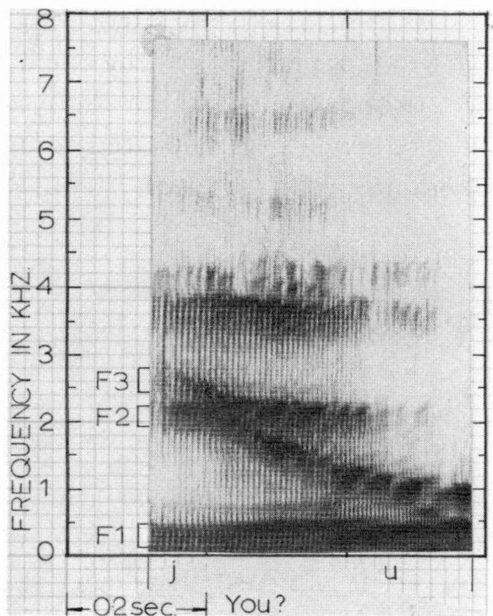

Figure 10. *The effect of decreasing the "selectivity" of the analyzing filter. This is a spectrogram of the same utterance as that used in Figure 9, but the analyzing filter was arranged to accept more than one harmonic simultaneously. The result is that the harmonic structure becomes less obvious, but the formant patterns stand out clearly. In addition, the analyzing filter is able to respond more rapidly to time changes, and shows vocal cord vibrations as a series of vertical stripes. The rising inflection of the word "you" in this spectrogram is shown by a closer spacing of the vertical lines toward the end of the word.*

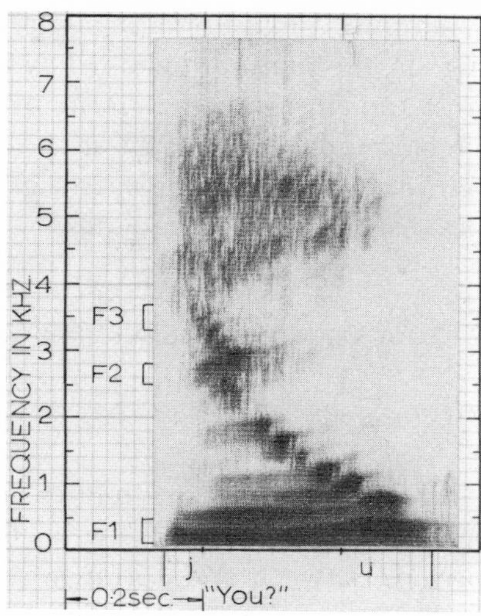

Figure 11. *Analysis of the high-pitched voice. This is a spectrogram of the word "you," spoken with rising intonation by a woman. Even with the least selective filter setting on the machine used for these analyses, each individual harmonic is seen. The combination of harmonic and formant patterns can often be confusing and makes it difficult to interpret the analyses of women's and children's voices.*

1.6. Section Summary

In this section I have tried to explain the basic physical principles involved in the production of speech sounds. To summarize, we use two basically different methods of generating sounds within the vocal tract, vocal cord vibration and turbulence.* Both result in complex sounds

*Actually there is a third method used in stops. It is the sudden release of pressure causing excitation of the vocal tract resonances and gives spectral characteristics similar to those of turbulence. Other ways of generating sound, such as whistles, clicks, implosions, are not used in the English language, but do appear in other languages.

containing a mixture of many frequencies. As it passes to the surrounding air, the sound is modified by the resonant characteristics of the vocal tract and emerges with a formant structure. In the spectrographic analysis of speech, the energy at the different frequencies is measured and recorded. The resulting spectrograms provide information on the acoustical features of speech sounds.

2. Acoustical Correlates of Speech Activities

2.1. Intensity

Measurement of speech intensity is complicated by its rapid variations with time, differences between frequencies, and the presence of silent periods between and within words. However, if a measuring device is used which collects all frequencies, and averages intensity over a long period of time, an average intensity level is obtained. Data from such measurements were obtained in connection with early research into the design of communication systems and have been reviewed by Fletcher (1953, chapter 4). The results indicate that the average sound pressure level* (SPL) measured at a distance of one meter from the lips of a speaker is approximately 65 dB. By deliberately raising or lowering one's voice, levels 20 dB above or below this figure can be obtained, and persons with normally loud or quiet voices might have average levels 10 dB above or below this figure.

2.2. Intensity and Distance

As the measuring microphone is moved closer to the speaker's lips, the average sound pressure level increases by approximately 6 dB for each halving of distance. Thus, by moving to 50 cm, an average level of 71 dB would be obtained, while at 25 cm (a typical distance for a lavalier microphone) the level would be 77 dB. By holding the microphone very close, say 6 cm, the level can be raised to approximately 90 dB. Wedenberg (1954) has recommended the use of speech directly into the ears of "severely hard of hearing children" and provides data based on a distance of 2 cm from the speaker's lips. Under this condition, reflection from the child's head also gives an increase in sound pressure level

*"Sound Pressure Level" is based on a physical reference level of 0.0002 μbar pressure amplitude. A sound pressure level of 65 dB is roughly 55 dB above the normal threshold of hearing.

(approximately 3 dB) and on the basis of the above figures an average level of approximately 100 dB would be expected. If the measurements are made in a typical room, distances of more than one meter from the speaker's lips will not necessarily give levels less than 65 dB because the problem is complicated by reflection of sound from the room boundaries (reverberation). After a certain distance the measuring instrument will effectively detect only the reflected sound and this will remain relatively constant from place to place.

2.3. Intensity and Orientation

When the measuring microphone is moved in a horizontal circle with the speaker's lips at the center, the average level remains fairly constant, being only some 5 dB lower at the back of the head than at the front. This does not mean that microphone position is unimportant, however. Speech at the back of the head is deficient in high frequencies, by some 30 dB as compared with the front (Dunn and Farnsworth, 1939).

2.4. Intensity and Frequency

By using filters, the average sound pressure level in various frequency bands can be measured. Such measurements have been made by Sivian (1929), Dunn and White (1940), Stevens and others (1947), and Benson and Hirsh (1953). Many of the findings are again reviewed in Fletcher's book (1953, chap. 4). The results show that most of the energy in speech is concentrated in the lower frequencies, as illustrated in Figure 12, which is derived from the data given by Fletcher. The graph shows the average sound levels in bands, each half an octave wide, expressed with reference to the normal threshold of hearing (British Standard). Displaying the results of speech analysis on an audiogram form makes it possible to compare them with pure tone thresholds.

2.5. Time Variations

So far we have only discussed long-term averages of the speech intensity. If, however, we use a measuring device which responds rapidly (say in 1/10 second), it will follow the intensity variations within individual

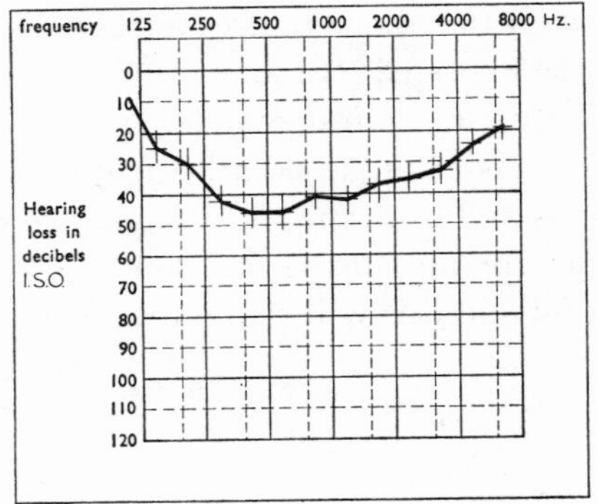

Figure 12. The average intensity level of continuous speech at various frequencies. The overall average is 65 dB (SPL) and is the level which would be measured at a distance of 100 cm from the lips of an average male speaker. The curve shows the levels in frequency bands, each one half an octave wide. These levels were expressed with reference to normal hearing threshold so that they could be displayed on an audiogram form. (Derived from data given by Fletcher, 1953, chap. 4.)

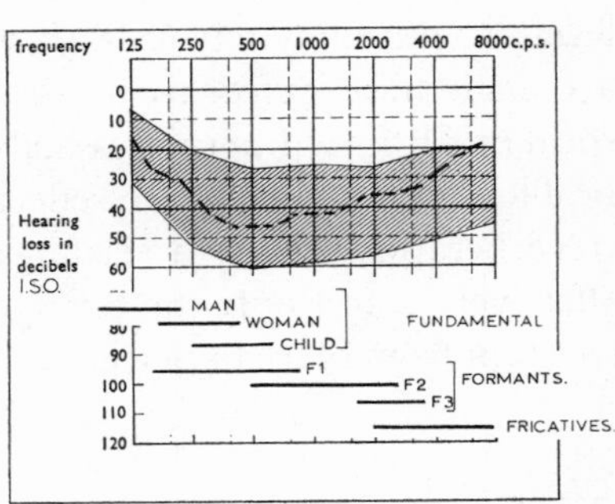

Figure 13. The frequency and intensity ranges of continuous speech at a distance of 100 cm. The shaded area is derived from data given by Wedenberg (1954). It shows the range of intensities covered by speech at various frequencies. The average curve of Figure 12 is also shown for comparison.
In addition, the diagram shows the frequency ranges of the fundamental of voiced sounds, the first three formants, and the main energy content of fricative sounds. The data was expressed with reference to normal hearing threshold and can be compared directly with pure tone thresholds.

speech sounds (though not within individual vibration periods of the vocal cords). The results of such measurements show a range of approximately 30 dB between the strongest sound / ɔ /, and the weakest sound /θ/. If filtering is also used, a measure of the intensity range within various frequency bands is obtained. In Figure 13 will be found an indication of the range of frequency and intensity covered by connected speech. This is again expressed with respect to the normal threshold of hearing (ISO 1964) and has been derived from data given by Wedenberg (1954) and attributed to Fant. Also shown on this diagram are the frequency ranges covered by the fundamental of voiced sounds, the first three formants, and the main spectral content of unvoiced fricatives.

2.6. Vowels and Vowel-like Consonants

Having discussed the gross acoustical features of speech, I shall now deal with the characteristics of various sound groups in the English language.

The vowels and vowel-like consonants are normally produced with vocal cord vibration and a raised soft palate. Thus only resonances of the pharyngeal and oral cavities are involved. The tongue is used to divide the vocal tract into two parts, the relative size of these parts and the length and size of the connecting passage being governed by the position and height of the raised portion of the tongue. Articulatory descriptions of the vowels are based on this position. For example, vowels may be front (e.g., /i, I/), central (/ ʌ /), or back (/ ɔ , u/). If the connecting space is narrow, the vowel is "close," but if the tongue is low in the mouth, the vowel is "open."

The size and shape of the lip opening is also variable, though in English it changes in a predictable manner with tongue positions, being small and rounded for back vowels and large and spread for front vowels. Lip movements contribute much less to the acoustical features of vowels than do tongue movements. It is possible to produce acceptable versions of all the vowels with the lips stationary and only the tongue moving, but not if the tongue is held stationary and only the lips are allowed to move.

The value of each formant is governed by every aspect of vocal tract configuration, but it is possible to identify the major influences of particular aspects of configuration. Thus the tongue height is reflected mainly in F_1, close vowels having low values while open vowels have high values. F_2, on the other hand, is influenced more by whether the tongue is in the front or back of the mouth, being high for front vowels and low for back vowels (Stevens and House, 1955). In fact, a two-dimensional plot of F_1 versus F_2 shows a close similarity to the phonetician's vowel quadrilateral based on tongue position (Peterson and Barney, 1952).

The effect of lip rounding or spreading is to accentuate some of the changes produced by tongue movement. I suspect that as the tongue approaches the limits of its movement toward the front or back of the mouth, it becomes easier to modify formant frequencies by moving the lips instead of the tongue. This would account for the association between tongue position and lip spreading found in the English language.

Research into vowel production and recognition has indicated that the different vowels of General American (G.A.) pronunciation have distinct combinations of values of F_1 and F_2. In addition, acceptable synthetic vowels can be produced in which only these two formants are present.

Fairbanks and Grubb (1961) measured the formant frequencies of vowels which were accepted by sophisticated listeners as being good examples of G.A. pronunciation. Their results are shown in Table II.

It will be seen from Table II that the frequency range covered by F_2 (800–2400 Hz) is greater than that of F_1 (250–800 Hz), although on a logarithmic scale (e.g., an audiogram form) they cover the same range (3:1). The range of F_3 is very limited (2400–3100 Hz), but Fant (1968) suggests that it may contribute significantly to the recognition of certain sounds. In fact, he suggests that when F_2 and F_3 have similar frequencies (as in /i/) they may be perceived as a single formant.

Table II. Mean Frequencies of the First Three Vowel Formants (Fairbanks and Grubb, 1961)

Vowel		i	I	ɛ	æ	ʌ	ɑ	ɔ	U	u
Frequency	F_1	263	387	493	733	588	775	600	392	279
in	F_2	2738	2038	1660	1654	1199	1064	846	1122	825
Hz	F_3	3099	2591	2444	2510	2623	2614	2636	2500	2496

The vowels /ɑ/ and /ɔ/ both have values of F_1 and F_2 which are very close to each other, and on a spectrogram they often appear as one single, though wide, formant.

Figure 14 illustrates some of the points made above with spectrograms of three sustained vowels, /i/, /u/ and /ɑ/. These show:

(a) The high value of F_2 and low value of F_1 for the close front vowel /i/.

(b) The marked difference between the value of F_2 in /i/ and that in /u/ as the tongue "hump" moves from the front to the back of the mouth.

(c) The similar values of F_1 for /u/ and /i/ (both are close vowels).

Diphthongs are characterized by a smooth transition between two vowel configurations and can be specified by the frequencies of F_1 and F_2 at beginning and end. Detailed information on the acoustical characteristics of diphthongs has been given by Lehiste and Peterson (1961) and Holbrook and Fairbanks (1962).

Vowel-like consonants are of short duration, but in other respects they are acoustically identical to vowels. The consonants /j/ and /w/ are

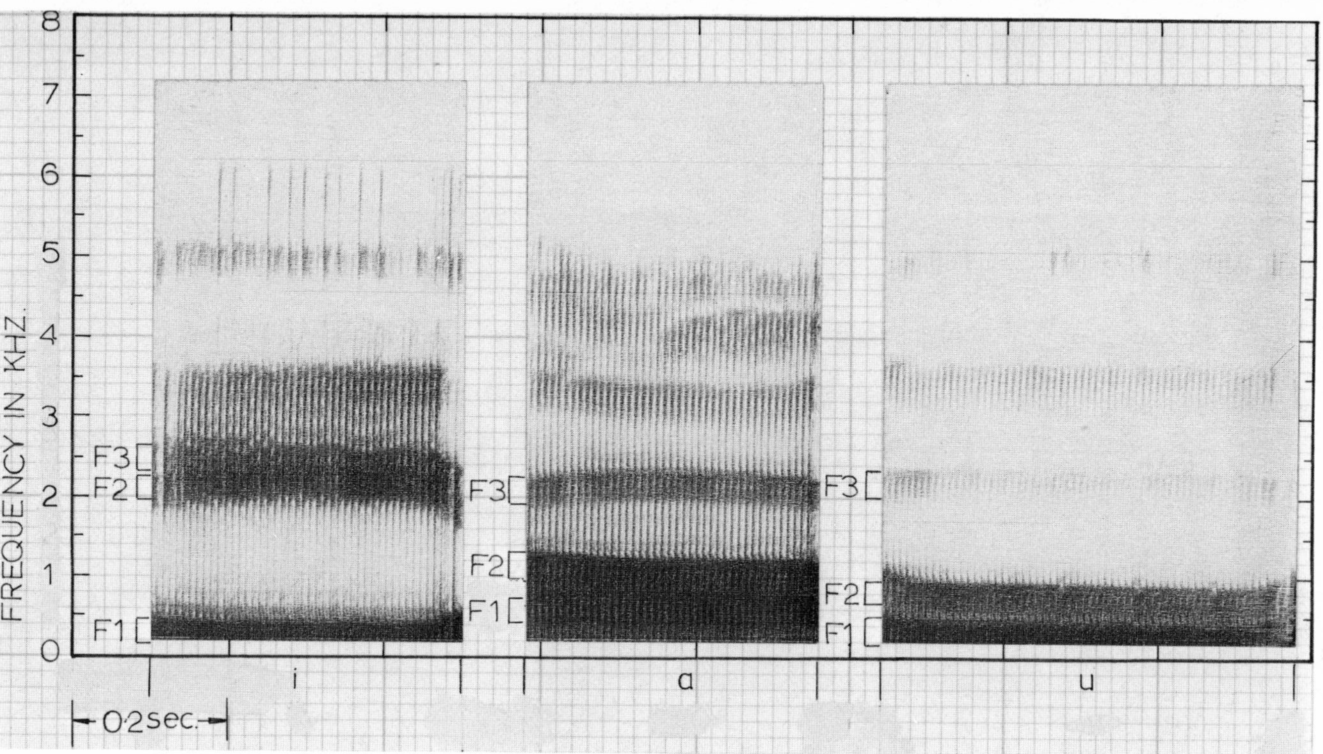

Figure 14. Spectrograms of three sustained vowels. Note that /i/ and /u/ have similar values of F_1 because they are both close vowels. They have very different values of F_2, however, since /i/ is a front vowel and /u/ is a back vowel. In /ɑ/, F_1 is higher than for /u/ or /i/, while F_2 has an intermediate value.

effectively short versions of /i/ and /u/ as is illustrated in Figure 15, by spectrograms of the words "you" and "we." The consonant /r/ is very similar to the vowel / ɝ /, but although /ℓ/ is vowel-like in terms of its acoustical properties it does not have a vowel equivalent.

The total picture of vowel production and recognition is more complicated than might be inferred from the foregoing. For example, the formant frequencies of women are some 20 percent higher than those of men for equivalent vowels, and eight-year-old children have formant frequencies which are higher still (Fant, 1968). This is believed to be due to the length of the vocal tract. In addition, the exact formant frequencies of the vowels spoken by an individual may differ considerably from those

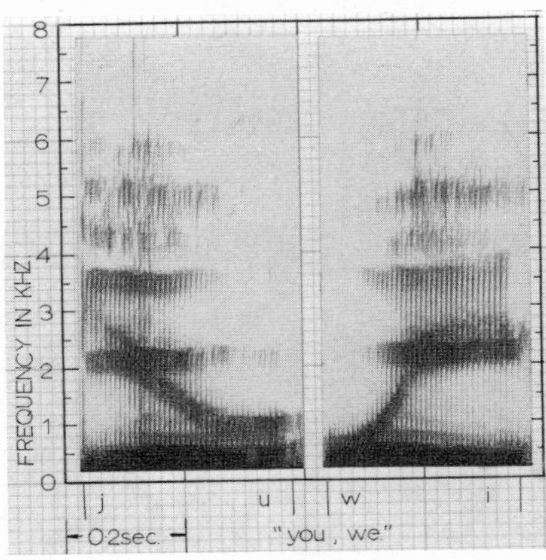

Figure 15. Spectrograms of the words "you" and "we." This illustrates that the vowel-like consonants are effectively short versions of vowels. The acoustic and articulatory changes in the word "we" are the reverse of those in the word "you."

given in Table I as a result of dialect (Peterson and Barney, 1952) or phonetic context (Lindblom and Studdert-Kennedy, 1967).

A further complication occurs when the factors affecting vowel recognition are considered. For instance, Laver (1965) has demonstrated that linguists and phoneticians vary, within their own performance, when making repeated judgments of vowel color, and Broadbent and Ladefoged (1960) have shown that vowel perception in context is based not on the absolute values of formant frequencies, but on their relation to the formant frequencies of other vowels. In other words, each speaker has a personal vowel system with certain frequency characteristics, and as we listen to his speech we learn this system and use it as a basis for making further vowel judgments.

2.7. Fricatives

The only sound source for voiceless fricatives is air turbulence at a constriction. When this constriction is at the glottis, the consonant produced is /h/, and its radiated spectrum carries a full formant pattern as a result of resonances of the vocal tract (see Figure 16). Since the vocal tract is free to move during the production of an /h/ it will normally take up a suitable position for the following vowel. In other words, there is no characteristic formant pattern for /h/, but instead it carries the formant pattern of the following vowel. This is an example of co-articulation.

The production of other fricatives is a little more complicated. For example, the spectral characteristics of the generated sound will be governed by the size, shape, and length of the constrictions. Thus the sound sources in /ʃ/, /s/, /θ/, and /f/ have different characteristics. Secondly, the modifications introduced by resonance will depend, not only on the characteristics of the vocal tract, but also on the position of the source within the tract. In general, the closer the source is to the front of the mouth, the less will be the effect of resonance, and resonances occurring behind the sound source may, in fact, subtract from the radiated energy at certain frequencies.

Data on the spectral characteristics of voiceless fricatives have been given by Hughes and Halle (1956) and Stevens (1960). In general, the main energy content of this class of sounds lies above 2000 Hz. Different fricatives have different resonant frequencies, and Heinz and Stevens (1961), using synthetic speech, have shown that the position of one major resonance is sufficient for making consistent distinctions. They found that fricative noises with a major resonance around 2000 Hz are recognized as /ʃ/ and that when the resonance is around 5000 Hz they are recognized as /s/. A very high frequency resonance, around 8000 Hz, resulted in the recognition of /f/ or /θ/, but no consistent separation of these two was found. These findings are in keeping with the data given by Fletcher (1953, chap. 18) on the low pass filtering of fricatives, which indicates that frequencies up to 2500 Hz must be present for 100 percent recognition of /ʃ/ and up to 5000 Hz for the recognition of /s/. Thus it appears that the recognition of voiceless fricatives in isolation can be based on the aperiodic nature of the sound source and the frequency of a prominent high frequency resonance. Two of the fricatives, /f/ and /θ/, are very difficult to distinguish on the basis of their acoustical features.

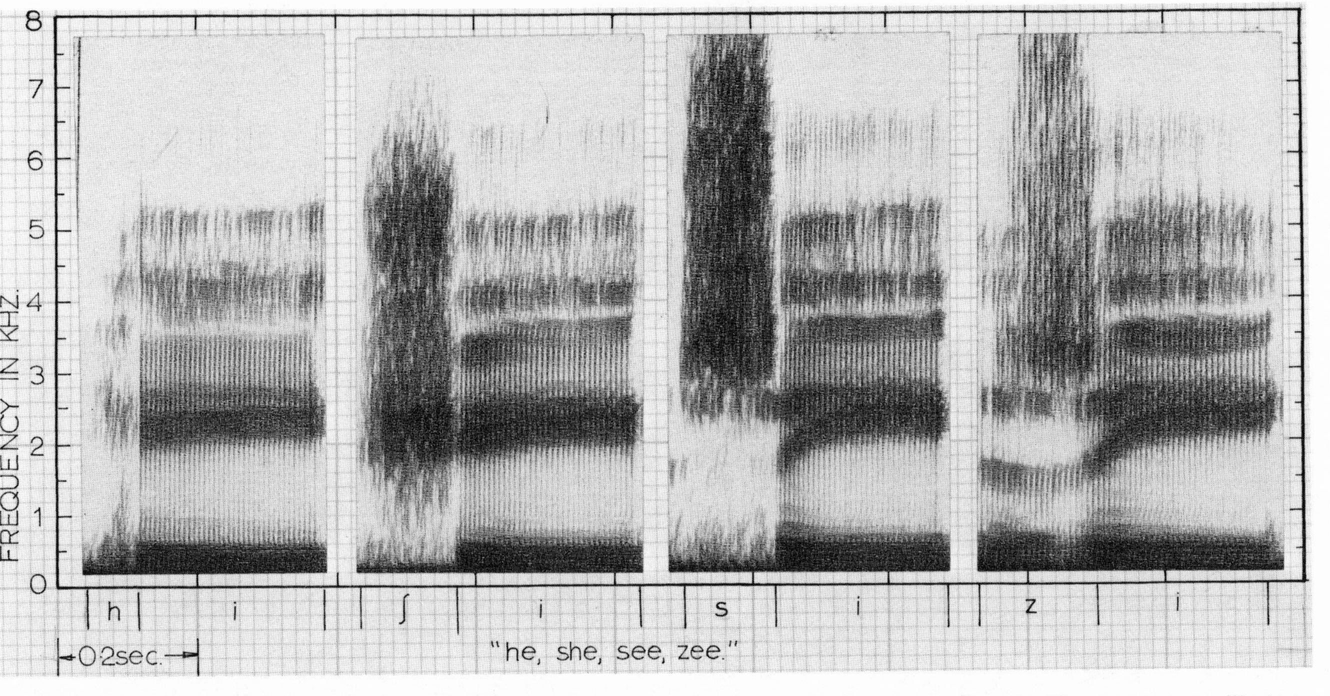

Figure 16. *Examples of fricative consonants. Four fricative consonants were spoken in the context of words. The spectrograms illustrate several important points:*

(i) *All are characterized by the presence of aperiodic noise.*

(ii) *The /h/ carries the formant pattern of the following vowel.*

(iii) */ʃ/ and /s/ are both very strong and have a lot of high frequency energy, but whereas the main resonance for /ʃ/ is around 2000 Hz, that for /s/ is around 3500 Hz.*

(iv) *The voicing of /z/ introduces a formant pattern at low frequencies in addition to the high frequency aperiodic sound found in the /s/. However, the aperiodic component of the /z/ is much weaker than that of the /s/.*

The voiced fricatives, /ʒ/, /z/, /ð/, and /v/, are similar to their unvoiced counterparts, but the presence of vocal cord vibrations gives them an additional harmonic structure. Also, the air flow interruptions due to voicing reduce the rate of flow in the constriction and hence the intensity of the aperiodic component. Note that the addition of vocal cord vibration will provide information on vocal tract configuration by resonance as in the case of vowels.

Figure 16 serves to illustrate some of the points discussed above. It shows spectrograms of the words *he, she, see,* and *zee.* Note the formant structure in /h/ corresponding with the following vowel, the difference in frequency range of /ʃ/ and /s/, and the difference in aperiodic component between /s/ and /z/ resulting from voicing.

2.8. Stops and Affricates

Voiceless stops (/k, t, p/) are produced by blocking the air flow in the vocal tract and allowing pressure to build up. When the pressure is released, the sudden disturbance causes the air in the tract to vibrate at its formant frequencies. At the same time, there is a short period during the release of the stop when turbulence occurs in the narrow space thus formed. The sound generated by this turbulence will be similar to that produced in a fricative articulated at the same place. For example, the spectral contents of /t/ and /s/ are almost identical. The turbulence can be deliberately extended by retaining a constriction after the stop has been released. This results in an affricate (e.g., /tʃ/).

When the stop is voiced, vocal cord vibration may begin before, or immediately after, the release of pressure. The restriction of air flow accompanying voicing reduces the aperiodic component of the sound as in voiced fricatives, and it may, in fact, become negligible. In addition, the pressure built up before release is less than in the unvoiced stops.

Basic information on the acoustical features will be found in papers by Fischer-Jorgensen (1954) and Halle and others (1957). An interesting feature of such data is the variability in characteristics of /k/ and /g/ depending upon the following vowel. This is due to a change of tongue position in anticipation of that required for the adjacent vowel—another instance of co-articulation.

The features necessary for recognizing stop consonants appear to be related to the period of silence immediately preceding the release, and the duration and spectral content of the aperiodic sound immediately following. In the voiced stops additional information is provided by the harmonic structure, the formant patterns during the release, and the relative weakness of the aperiodic component. These features are inherent in the acoustic properties of the consonant itself. However, many of the more important features used in recognition depend on the influences of the stop on adjacent speech sounds. In fact, it is not very meaningful to discuss stops as isolated acoustic elements. They really represent modifications of the beginnings and ends of continuous vowels or fricatives. This will be discussed in more detail later.

Figure 17 shows spectrograms of the words *key, pea,* and *bee.* They illustrate:

(a) the essential characteristic of a voiceless stop, i.e., the period of silence followed by a burst of aperiodic noise
(b) the difference in spectral characteristics of /k/ and /p/ resulting from different places of articulation
(c) the difference between /p/ and /b/ resulting from voicing of the latter. Note the almost complete absence of aperiodic sound in the /b/.

2.9. *Nasals*

By lowering the soft palate, resonances of the nasal cavity are added to those of the pharyngeal and oral cavity. The production of nasal consonants also involves blockage of the oral cavity at the lips (/m/), alveolar ridge (/n/), or at the rear of the hard palate (/ ŋ /). The oral cavity now becomes a side branch of the main resonant tube, and the size of this cavity depends on the place of articulation. One of its effects is to absorb or suppress certain harmonics of the vocal cord vibrations, thus creating an "antiformant." All nasal sounds are characterized by a well-defined low formant (around 300 Hz) and very little evidence of formant structure in higher frequencies. The quality of these sounds is often described as "nasal murmur." It is possible to distinguish between nasals on the basis of the antiformant produced by the vocal cavity, but they are easily confused (Fujimura, 1962). As with stops, it appears that a major source of information lies in the effects on adjacent sounds.

Spectrographic analysis shows marked discontinuities of the formants at the moment of closure or release of nasal consonants. This is illustrated in Figure 18 by spectrograms of the words *me* and *knee.*

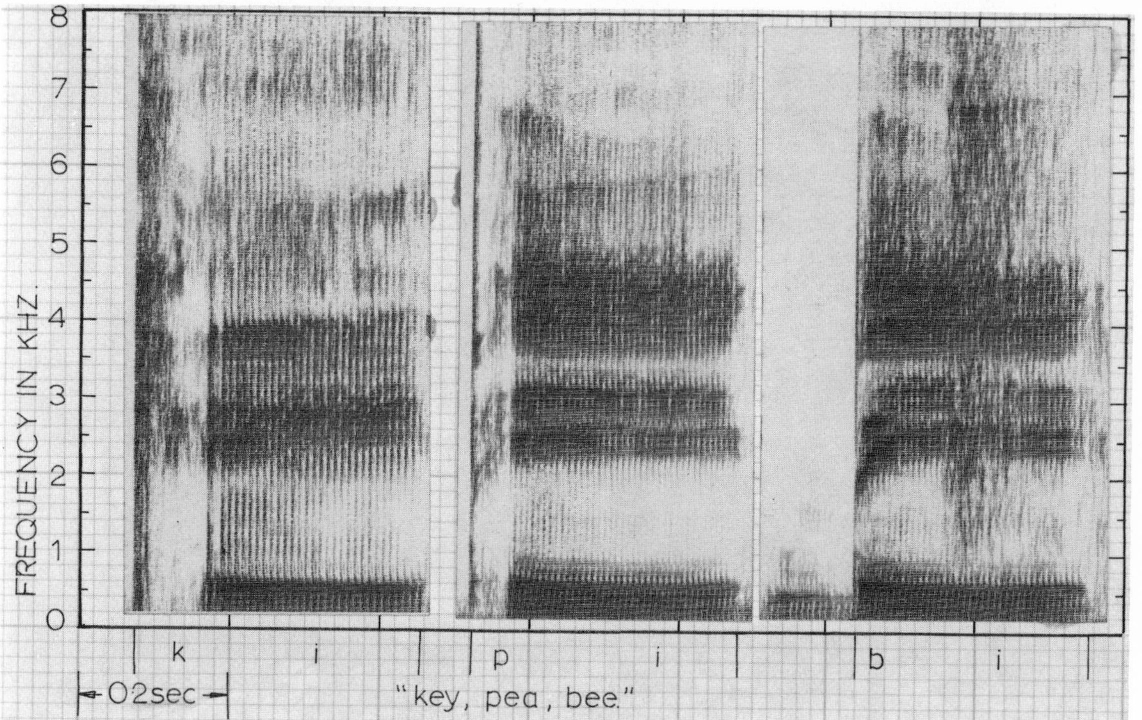

Figure 17. *Examples of stop consonants. These spectrograms are intended to illustrate the following points: (a) The voiceless stops are characterized by a period of silence followed by a sudden and transient burst of fricative noise. Voicing does not begin for some time after the release. (b) The voiced stop is similar except that the voicing begins before the release (with some speakers it may begin simultaneously with the release). (c) The /p/ and /k/ differ in terms of intensity and resonant characteristics. (d) The burst of fricative noise is much weaker in the /b/ than in the /p/.*

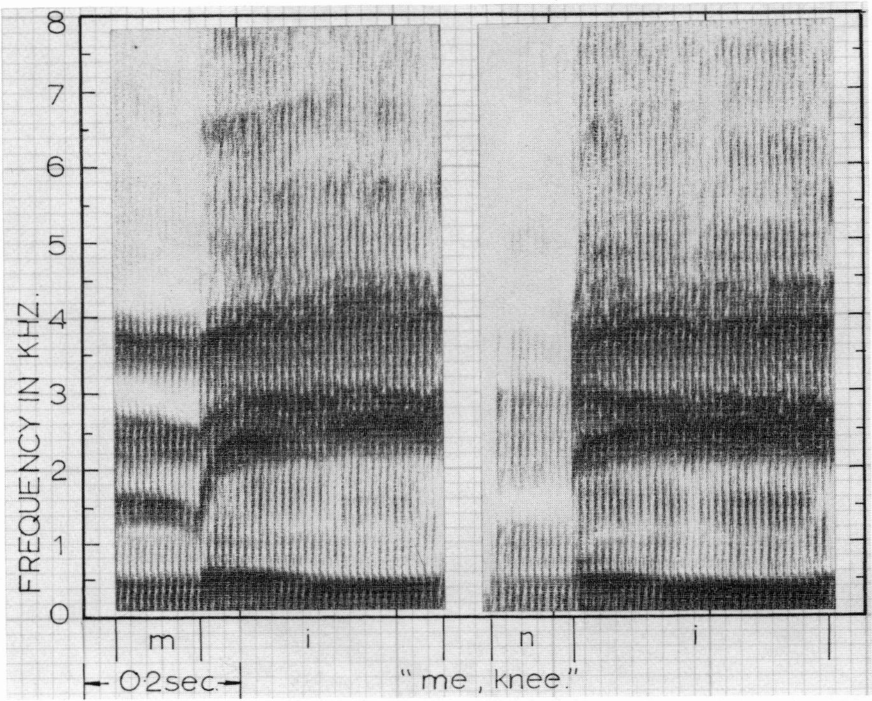

Figure 18. Examples of nasal consonants. Note the relative absence of high frequency energy as compared with the following vowel, and the sudden change of formant pattern accompanying the release of the oral closure.

2.10. Transitions and Connected Speech

So far, I have tried to limit discussion to the characteristics of isolated speech sounds, and to the features used for recognition of these sounds in isolation. When a sound is produced in connected speech, however, it may show the influence of the preceding or following sound. This occurs because the articulators cannot be in two places at once and must take a finite time to move from the configuration of one sound to the configuration of the next.

Examples of the mutual influence of adjacent sounds can be seen in many of the spectrograms illustrating this chapter. For example, in Figures 8 through 11, the initial consonant in *you* shows a lowering of F_3 as the lips come together to be ready for the vowel, and during the vowel the value of F_2 changes while the tongue is on its way to the back of the mouth. The reverse effect is shown in the *we* of Figure 15. In *he* (Figure 16) the consonant carries the formant structure of the following vowel, while in *see* and *zee* the vowel formants change as the tongue moves from the consonant to the vowel position. Changes in the consonant characteristics can be seen in the *pea* of Figure 17, while the *bee* shows the same changes during the initial part of the vowel. Figure 18 also shows the effect of the preceding consonant in the vowels of *me* and *knee*. These formant changes occuring during a sound are referred to as transitions. In general, changes of tongue height result in F_1 transitions while tongue position changes are reflected in F_2. When the size of the lip opening changes (as in *we* and *you* of Figure 15, *pea* of Figure 17, and *me* of Figure 18), F_3 transitions also occur.

Research with synthetic speech has shown that F_2 transitions in a vowel often give sufficient information for a listener to recognize the place of articulation of the preceding or following consonant (Liberman and others, 1959). Ainsworth (1968) has also demonstrated the importance of F_1 transitions in the synthesis of certain sounds.

Figure 19 is a spectrogram of an utterance of the word *two*. It illustrates two important features of transitions in formants.

(a) The voicing for the vowel starts almost immediately after the release of the /t/ and while the tongue is on its way to the back of the mouth. Thus, the initial value of F_2 indicates where the tongue has been.

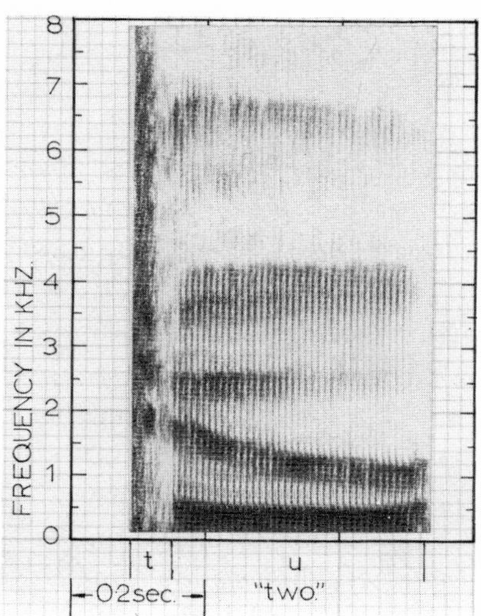

Figure 19. Spectrogram of the word two. *Note the continuous change of second formant frequency, caused by movement of the tongue from the /t/ position to the /u/ position. This change, or transition, gives information to the listener about where the tongue has been and where it is headed.*

(b) The value of F_2 spends most of its time between the /t/ value and the /u/ value and only reaches the latter when the word is almost over. Nevertheless, a listener has no difficulty in perceiving the utterance as a sequence of two sounds. What this implies is that the listener's perceptual system only needs to be informed of the "target" values of the formants, and once these have been reached, or even approximated, there is nothing to be gained by prolonging the utterance.

The second point is even more strikingly illustrated by the spectrogram of the phrase, *why are you where you are,* shown in Figure 20. Nowhere does the vocal tract assume a fixed position for a significant length of time except during the final vowel. Moreover, the formant frequencies for the first *are* only approach, but do not adopt the steady state values seen in the second *are*. This again shows that as soon as the listener has been informed about the intended position of the articulators they can move on to the next position (Lindblom and Studdert-Kennedy, 1967). Transitions can also be observed in fricative consonants (Uldall, 1964). For example, Figure 21 shows a spectrogram of the word *wasps*. During the first /s/ the lips are coming together to be ready for the following /p/ and there is a corresponding lowering of the resonant frequency of the cavity at the front of the mouth. Transitions can also be seen as the articulators relax at the end of the second /s/. Thus, the speech process does not involve a sequence of fixed articulatory configurations, but rather a sequence of movements, each movement conveying information about where the articulators have been and where they are headed.

2.11. Temporal Factors in Speech Sound Recognition

It is important to realize that time is a fundamental dimension in speech. The various speech sounds have typical durations, relative durations, and rates of change which we expect to hear. Moreover, these temporal factors may be basic to our perception of speech, providing a framework within which to assemble the perceived message (Boothroyd, 1967b).

An example of the significance of time patterns has already been given in connection with /s/ and /t/. These sounds differ basically in terms of their temporal features. In fact, if the /s/ at the beginning of a word is artificially shortened, a listener may perceive it as /t/.

Another example of the importance of temporal patterns is the effect of consonant voicing on duration of the preceding vowel. For example,

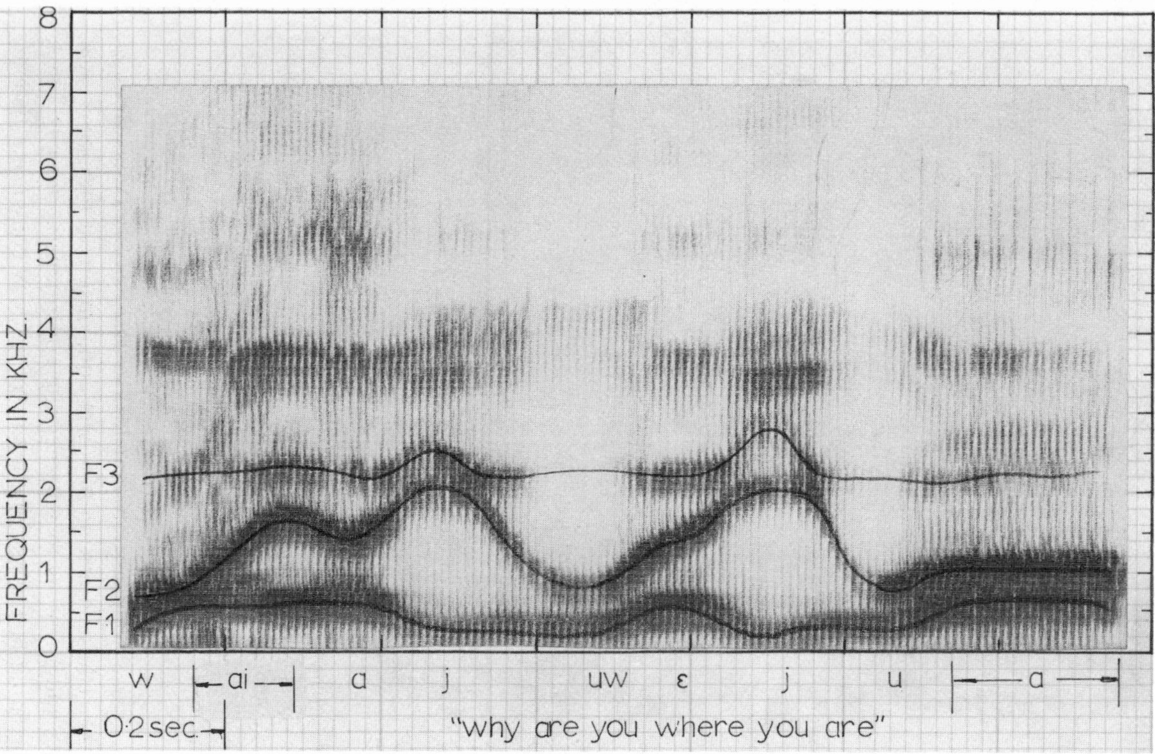

Figure 20. Spectrogram of a sentence containing only vowels and vowel-like consonants. With the exception of the final vowel, there is no steady state. The articulators, and hence the formants, are continually in transition from one "target" position to the next. Often they do not reach the target before moving on to the next, (e.g. the first / ɑ */), and sometimes the target is defined only by a slight hesitation (e.g. the /* ε */).*

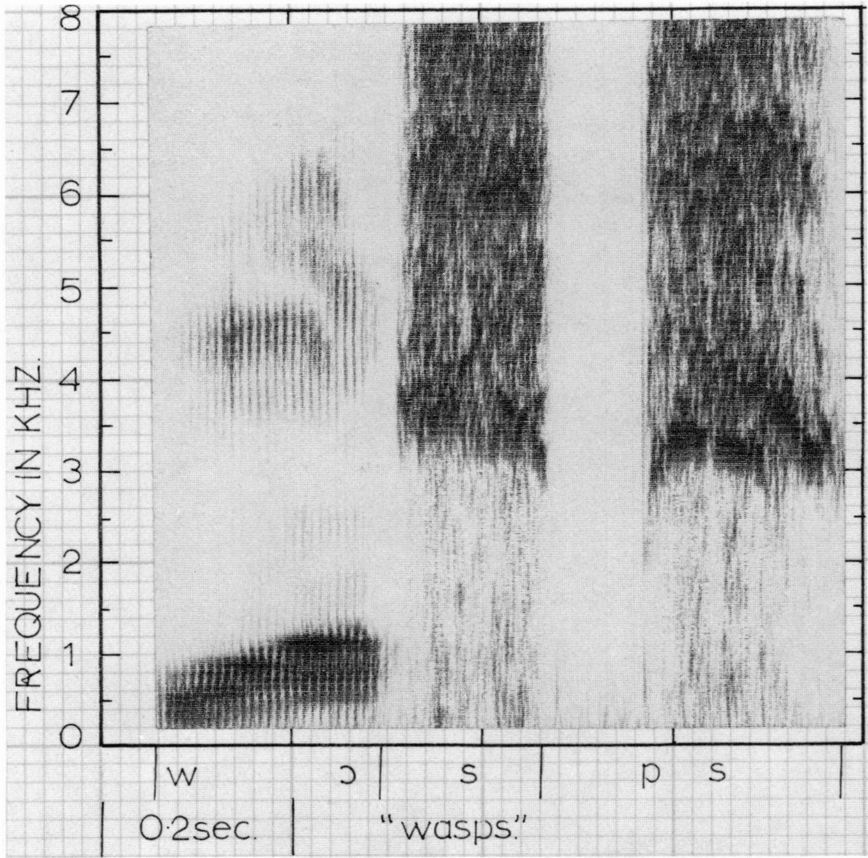

Figure 21. Transitions in fricative noise. During the first /s/ in wasps *the lips are coming together for the following /p/. This results in a lowering of the main resonant frequency for /s/. Similarly transitions can be seen in the final /s/ as the /p/ is released and as the articulators relax at the end of the word.*

the vowel in *eyes* is longer than that in *ice*. Denes (1955) has demonstrated that the relative duration of vowel and consonant may be critical in a listener's judgment as to whether the consonant is voiced. Thus, artificial shortening of the /s/ at the end of *ice* may convince a listener that he has heard a /z/.

The rate of change of formant frequencies is also of importance in speech recognition (Liberman and others, 1956).

2.12. Correlates of Stress

Information about the meaning and content of a spoken message can be carried in features which are not restricted to phonemic units. These features are intensity, fundamental frequency, and duration, and are referred to as prosodic features. Their importance in speech perception has been discussed at some length by Fry (1968).

A function of prosodic features is to provide stress patterns which may serve, for example, to distinguish statements and questions (Uldall, 1962) or to distinguish between certain word pairs such as *object* (noun) and *object* (verb) (Fry, 1955). It has been found that stress may be carried by pitch, duration, or intensity, but that intensity is the least effective feature. Changes of duration and pitch in stressed syllables are illustrated in Figure 22, which shows fundamental frequency as a function of time for the two words mentioned above.

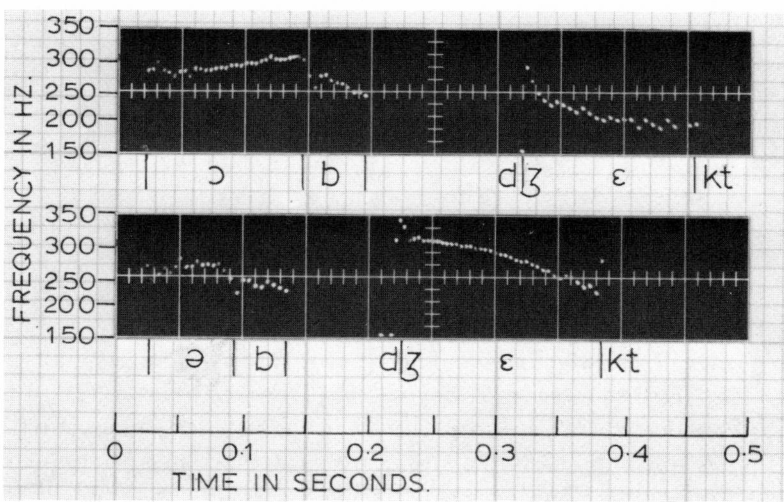

Figure 22. The contribution of pitch and duration to stress. This Figure shows fundamental voice frequency as a function of time for utterances of the words object *(noun) and* object *(verb). The change of stress needed to differentiate these two words is indicated by increased pitch and duration of the stressed syllable. This photograph was prepared with a visible pitch device developed for work with deaf children.*

2.13. Descriptive Features of Speech Sounds

Every speech sound can be specified by a suitable set of features describing the phonatory and articulatory activities involved in its production (voicing, nasality, place and manner of articulation, etc.). In the foregoing descriptions of the properties of speech sounds it has been shown that information about these features may be carried by different aspects of the acoustical structure, or even by acoustical or temporal features of adjacent sounds. When the acoustical characteristics convey to a listener the information for recognition of all the features which specify a particular sound, it can be said that the sound has been recognized. The removal of part of this information by distortion, masking, or a hearing loss may lead to a situation in which only some of the features are recognized. For example, one may decide that a particular sound was a voiceless stop without being able to say which one. In other words, speech sound recognition is not an all or none process, but a graduated process in which some, or all, of the phonatory and articulatory features needed to specify the sound may be recognized.

This approach to speech sound recognition has been adopted by Miller and Nicely (1955), who examined the consonant confusions resulting from masking and filtering. A binary system of distinctive features in which each descriptive feature can be specified as present or absent has been proposed by Jakobson and others (1952).

2.14. Linguistic Contextual Factors

It seldom occurs that a particular speech sound has to be recognized solelv on the basis of its acoustical features, since the listener receives a lot of information from its context. This information is in the form of statistical rules of phoneme and word sequence, vocabulary and word frequency, etc. (Miller and others, 1951; Rosenzweig and Postman, 1958; Broadbent, 1967). It forms part of the listener's linguistic background. A fuller discussion of the non-acoustic factors in speech sound recognition has been given elsewhere (Boothroyd, 1967b, 1968).

2.15. Section Summary

In this section I have described the production and acoustical features of various classes of speech sound and the intensity and frequency characteristics of speech as a whole. In addition, I have tried to explain how the acoustical features convey information about phonatory and articulatory activities.

The relevant acoustical features may be: harmonic structure, aperiodicity, duration, resonant frequencies, changes with time, fundamental frequency, etc. Information about a particular feature of articulation can be carried by more than one acoustical feature of a sound and also by features of adjacent sounds. In addition, the exact features of a sound may depend on its phonetic context and on the particular phonological system of the speaker. Recognition of speech is based partly on a recognition of acoustical features and partly on the linguistic knowledge of the listener.

3. SOME FACTORS OF RELEVANCE TO TEACHING SPEECH TO THE DEAF*

3. 1. Speech Input

Every deaf child is able to respond to sound—if it is sufficiently intense. In some cases these responses are an indication of auditory sensitivity, while in others they may be due to tactile sensitivity (Van Uden, 1958, Boothroyd and Cawkwell, 1970).

With suitable amplification equipment it is possible to provide a speech input for the deaf person, which in the most favorable instances will enable him to learn the recognition of speech sounds and in the least favorable will convey the temporal patterns of speech (Hudgins, 1951). This input is of potential value to the child in learning to speak, as it provides him with acoustic patterns on which to base his own efforts.

3. 2. Detection

An indication of the speech frequencies available to the deaf child can be obtained by examining his pure-tone threshold in relation to the speech spectrum as given in Figure 13. This has limited value, however, as it doesn't take into account the increased sensitivity of the child when he is wearing his amplification equipment. An additional drawback is that powerful hearing aids are capable of amplifying sounds to levels higher than the maximum levels normally used in pure-tone testing. For

*"Deaf" is used here to imply a hearing impairment without reference to severity.

example, over most of the frequency range, the output limit of a standard clinical audiometer is 110 dB above normal thresholds, while a high-power aid can give levels up to 125 or even 130 dB (i.e., 135 or 140 dB sound pressure level). Thus, the standard pure tone audiogram does not indicate the potential range of sound sensitivity possible with a hearing aid.

At Clarke School, we have found it useful to measure aided pure-tone thresholds, using the child's classroom equipment and to compare these with spectral analyses of the teacher's voice at her normal microphone distance. Thus we are able to ensure that her speech is available to each child and over an adequate frequency range.

3. 3. Discrimination

Children with similar sensitivity to sound may exhibit very different discrimination skills as a result of differences of pathology or auditory experience. However, the information available on speech recognition by the normally hearing gives an indication of the potential for children with limited sensitivity to sound. For example, even a child with only tactile sensitivity should be able to make judgments of duration or temporal patterns, and our experiences with tactile stimulation in the hand have indicated that the voiced-unvoiced discrimination is also possible. This is presumably based on the different sensations resulting from periodic and aperiodic sounds. Recent work by Risberg (1968) has indicated that the time taken to recognize such differences from tactile clues is greater than that needed with auditory clues and he has suggested that this could provide the basis for a differentiation of the two sensory modalities in the profoundly deaf.

A child with sensitivity up to 1,000 Hz can potentially detect changes in the first formant frequency. This will give information on tongue height and will differentiate between such vowel pairs as /u/ and /a/. There may also be sufficient information to determine the rate of onset of the sound and the presence of turbulence. For back vowels, the extent of lip rounding has a marked influence on F_1, but this articulatory information is much more effectively conveyed by the lipread pattern.

When hearing extends to 3,000 Hz, the second formant is audible. This can give not only a satisfactory differentiation between most vowels, including the /u/, /i/ discrimination, but will also provide the information on tongue position in consonant articulation which is often absent in the lipread information. It should be noted that many amplification systems do not provide amplification for frequencies above 3,000 Hz and that for the normally hearing the absence of higher frequencies has only a small effect on the recognition of speech sounds in phonetic context.

Inherent distortion in the child's auditory system may make it impossible for him to use the acoustic cues available. On the other hand, there is a possibility that some children may learn to use secondary cues which are not found to be of relevance to the normally hearing (Wedenberg, 1954). If sufficient information is available for differentiation and if it is made meaningful to the child, he may learn to use it in speech recognition. But perceptual learning relies on invariants in the stimulus, and the secondary features referred to by Wedenberg may be specific to a particular speaker or even a particular piece of amplification equipment. In such a case more demands will be made on the deaf child by changes of these factors than would be made of the normally hearing child.

3. 4. Environmental Noise

The speech input to the deaf person has to compete with environmental noise. This noise generally contains more energy at low frequencies than at high frequencies, and is particularly troublesome to an individual who hears only the low frequencies of speech (Boothroyd, 1967a). For such a person the speech and noise may be undifferentiated, and he may simply reject them both. The solution to this problem lies in keeping the noise level as low as possible and the speech level as high as possible. The former is accomplished by design and acoustic treatment of classrooms (sealed doors, double glazing, carpets, acoustic tiles, etc.), the latter by having the microphone of the hearing aid as close to the speech source as possible. The possible gains in speech level resulting from close microphone distance have been indicated in section 2. 2. It should be noted, however, that the microphone should not be in such a position as to receive the direct air stream from the lips. Blowing on the microphone in this way causes the generation of aperiodic noise.

3. 5. Importance of Low Fundamental Frequency

It will be recalled that vocal cord vibrations result in a complex sound with a harmonic structure and that the spacing of adjacent harmonics equals the fundamental frequency. Thus a high fundamental frequency will give widely spaced harmonics, and only a small number may fall within a formant. In contrast, a low fundamental will give closely spaced harmonics and will serve to more clearly define the formants. It has often been said that deaf people perceive low pitched voices better than high pitched voices, but this is due, not to the fundamental frequency as such, but to the closer harmonic spacing giving more information about formant patterns.

3. 6. Alternatives to Amplification

If a deaf child is unable to base speech recognition on the available acoustic information, there remains the possibility of artificially processing this information and presenting it in an alternative way. Examples of such procedures are the frequency transposer which takes high frequency information and presents it in the low frequencies, and the visual and tactile devices which have been built and used at various times. A conference on this subject was held in 1967, and the proceedings have been published in *The American Annals of the Deaf* (Vol. 13, March, 1968).

The major problems in designing and using such devices are not technical ones, but relate to an inadequate understanding of the processes of perception and perceptual learning. Research is currently under way in a variety of centers on the extraction of information from the speech signal, on the various ways of presenting this information to the deaf child, and on the ability of the various sensory modalities to handle this type of information. This work is discussed in more detail by Pickett in Chapter IV.

3. 7. Speech Production and Acoustic Feedback

It is often stated that the speech mechanisms of the deaf are intact. This is not strictly true as the hearing system is an integral part of our speech mechanism, and is by definition absent or defective in the deaf. Its function in speech is as a control system (Fairbanks, 1954), and to the extent that a deaf child can use hearing for this purpose he should be given the opportunity to do so (Hudgins and Numbers, 1942). The alternative control systems, kinesthetic, proprioceptive, and visual, may give inadequate or inappropriate information for the generation of the correct acoustical patterns.

All the comments made earlier about speech input apply equally well to input of the child's own voice. Thus: (a) the hearing aid can make possible the development of acoustic feedback control within the limits of the range and effectiveness of the child's hearing, (b) microphone distance is particularly important and should be as small as possible, and (c) the speech processing devices discussed earlier may be of value in teaching the child the appropriate control of his speech mechanisms. In fact, such devices have more application in speech teaching than as devices for the recognition of input signals.

3. 8. The Speech of the Deaf

The speech of a very severely or profoundly deaf person can differ in several respects from that of the normally hearing. Some of these differences are inherent in the absence of acoustic feedback and others may be the direct result of teaching methods. As mentioned in section 2. 6., the listener adapts to the phonological system of the speaker, and providing there is sufficient differentiation and consistency in a deaf person's speech it is possible to learn to recognize it. With continued exposure and familiarity the adaptation becomes partly unconscious, and the listener ceases to be aware of many of the defects. This situation arises with the teacher of the deaf, and reduces the apparent need and incentive for speech improvement. However, an awareness of the important acoustical features of normal speech might lead to a more objective assessment of speech. In this connection there is a potential for increased use of instrumental evaluation.

A severe detractor from intelligibility in the speech of the deaf is defective temporal pattern, and particular stress has been laid on its importance in section 2. The temporal pattern of speech is an integral part of its structure and unless it is correctly reproduced, the presence of perfectly articulated elements will not result in intelligible speech. In an examination of the speech of deaf children, Hudgins and Numbers (1942) reached the conclusion that errors of rhythm contributed as much to loss of intelligibility as errors of consonant articulation, and John and Howarth (1965) have shown that improved intelligibility can result from attention to temporal factors only.

3. 9. Section Summary

In this section, I have given a brief indication of some of the direct areas of relevance of acoustic phonetics to speech teaching. The areas discussed related to speech input, acoustic feedback, and the acoustical

Key to Phonetic Symbols

IPA Symbol	As in the word	Equivalent on Northampton Chart
/ i /	f*ee*t	ee
/ I /	*i*t	-i-
/ ε /	b*e*d	-e-
/ æ /	c*a*t	-a-
/ ʌ /	c*u*p	-u-
/ ɑ /	h*ear*t	a(r)
/ ɔ /	t*a*ll	aw
/ ʊ /	f*oo*t	o^{2}o
/ u /	sh*oo*t	o^{1}o
/ ɝ /	b*ir*d	ur
/ ə /	t*o*day	
/ j /	*y*ou	y-
/ ω /	*w*e	w-
/ r /	*r*un	r-
/ ℓ /	*l*eg	1
/ h /	*h*and	h-
/ ʃ /	*sh*ip	sh
/ s /	*s*it	$\overset{1}{s}$
/ θ /	*th*in	$\overset{1}{th}$
/ f /	*f*eet	f
/ ʒ /	mea*s*ure	zh
/ z /	plea*se*	$\overset{1}{z}$
/ ð /	*th*ese	$\overset{2}{th}$
/ v /	fi*v*e	v
/ k /	*c*at	k
/ t /	ca*t*	t
/ p /	*p*in	p
/ tʃ /	*ch*in	ch
/ g /	*g*un	$\overset{1}{g}$
/ b /	*b*ite	b
/ m /	*m*an	m
/ n /	ma*n*	n
/ ŋ /	si*ng*	ng

and temporal features of the speech output. These topics will be covered at greater length in later chapters of this book.

Conclusion

This chapter has been concerned primarily with one level in the process of verbal communication—namely the acoustical one. I have, however, tried to demonstrate the relationship between the acoustical features of speech sounds and the phonatory and articulatory activities which generate them. It has also been necessary to use phonemic classifications so as to limit the discussion to those factors of relevance to the English language, and to include semantic and perceptual factors. In fact, the communication of thoughts and ideas by spoken language is a process involving many levels of activity, and a full discussion of each level must include its relation to the complete process.

BIBLIOGRAPHY

Ainsworth, W. A. First formant transitions and the perception of synthetic semivowels. *Journal of the Acoustical Society of America,* 1968, **44,** 689.

Benson, R. W., and Hirsh, I. J. Some variables in audio spectrometry. *Journal of the Acoustical Society of America,* 1953, **25,** 499.

Boothroyd, A. The discrimination by partially hearing children of frequency distorted speech. *International audiology,* 1967, **6,** 136. (1967a)

Boothroyd, A. Theoretical aspects of auditory training. *Proceedings of International Conference on Oral Education of the Deaf.* Washington, D.C.: Alexander Graham Bell Association for the Deaf, 1967, 705–729. (1967b)

Boothroyd, A. Statistical theory of the speech discrimination score. *Journal of the Acoustical Society of America,* 1968, **43,** 362.

Boothroyd, A., and Cawkwell, S. Vibrotactile thresholds in pure tone audiometry. *Acta Oto-Laryngologica,* 1970.

British Standard No. 2497, The normal threshold of hearing for pure tones by earphone listening.

Broadbent, D. E., and Ladefoged, P. Vowel judgements and adaptation level. *Proceedings of the Royal Society,* 1960, **151,** 384.

Broadbent, D. E. Word-frequency effect and response bias. *Psychological review,* 1967, **74,** 1.

Denes, P. Effect of duration on the perception of voicing. *Journal of the Acoustical Society of America.* 1955, **27,** 761.

Dunn, H. K., and Farnsworth, D. W. Exploration of pressure field around human head during speech. *Journal of the Acoustical Society of America,* 1939, **10,** 184.

Dunn, H. K., and White, S. D. Statistical measurements on conversational speech. *Journal of the Acoustical Society of America,* 1940, **11,** 278.

Fairbanks, G. Systematic research in experimental phonetics: A theory of the speech mechanism as a servosystem. *Journal of speech and hearing disorders,* 1954, **19,** 133.

Fairbanks, G., and Grubb, P. A psychophysical investigation of vowel formants, *Journal of speech and hearing research,* 1961, **4,** 203.

Fant, G. Analysis and synthesis of speech processes. In B. Malmberg (Ed.), *Manual of phonetics.* Amsterdam: North Holland Publishing Co., 1968, Chapter 8, p. 173.

Fischer-Jorgensen, E. Acoustic analysis of stop consonants. *Misc. Phonetica.,* 1954, **2,** 42.

Fletcher, H. *Speech and hearing in communication.* New York: D. Van Nostrand, 1953.

Fry, D. B. Duration and intensity as physical correlates of linguistic stress. *Journal of the Acoustical Society of America,* 1955, **27,** 765.

Fry, D. B. Prosodic phenomena. In B. Malmberg (Ed.), *Manual of phonetics.* Amsterdam: North Holland Publishing Co., 1968, Chapter 12, p. 365.

Fujimura, O. Analysis of nasal consonants. *Journal of the Acoustical Society of America,* 1962, **34,** 1865.

Fujimura, O., and Lindqvist, J. Sweep tone measurements of vocal tract characteristics. *STL. QPSR,* 1/1965, p. 1.

Halle, M., Hughes, G. W., and Radley, J. P. A. *Acoustic properties of stop consonants.* 1957, **29,** 107.

Heinz, J. M., and Stevens, K. N. On the properties of voiceless fricative consonants. *Journal of the Acoustical Society of America,* 1961, **33,** 589.

Holbrook, A., and Fairbanks, G. Diphthong formants and their movements. *Journal of speech and hearing research,* 1962, **5,** 38.

Hudgins, C. V., and Numbers, F. C. An investigation of the intelligibility of the speech of the deaf. *Genetic psychology monographs,* 1942, **25,** 289.

Hudgins, C. V. Problems of speech comprehension in deaf children. *The nervous child,* 1951, **9,** 57.

Hughes, G. W., and Halle, M. Spectral properties of fricative consonants. *Journal of the Acoustical Society of America,* 1956, **28,** 303.

I. S. O., Technical Committee 43—Acoustics # 554. A standard reference zero for the calibration of pure-tone audiometers. *A.S.A.N.Y.,* 1964. (see, for example, Davis, H., and Kranz, F. W., *Journal of speech and hearing research,* 1964, **7,** 7)

Jakobson, R., Fant, G., and Halle, M. Preliminaries to speech analysis, M.I.T. *Acoust. Lab. Report,* 1952, p. 13.

John, J. E. J., and Howarth, J. N. The effect of time distortions on the intelligibility of deaf children's speech. *Language and speech,* 1965, **8,** 127.

Koenig, W., Dunn, H. K., and Lacy, L. Y. The sound spectrograph. *Journal of the Acoustical Society of America,* 1946, **17,** 19.

Laver, J. D. M. H. Variability in vowel perception. *Language and speech,* 1965, **8,** 95.

Lehiste, I., and Peterson, G. E. Transitions, glides and diphthongs. *Journal of the Acoustical Society of America,* 1961, **33,** 268.

Liberman, A. M., Delattre, P. C., Gerstman, L. J., Cooper, F. S. Tempo of frequency change as a cue for distinguishing classes of speech sounds. *Journal of experimental psychology,* 1956, **52,** 127.

Liberman, A. M., Ingemann, F., Lisker, L., Delattre, P., and Cooper, F. S. Minimal rules for synthesizing speech. *Journal of the Acoustical Society of America,* 1959, **31,** 1490.

Lindblom, B. E. F., and Studdert-Kennedy, M. On the role of formant transitions in vowel recognition. *Journal of the Acoustical Society of America,* 1967, **42,** 830.

Miller, G. A., Heise, C. A., and Lichten, D. The intelligibility of speech as a function of the context of the test material. *Journal of experimental psychology,* 1951, **41,** 329.

Miller, G. A., and Nicely, P. E. An analysis of perceptual confusions among some English consonants. *Journal of the Acoustical Society of America,* 1955, **27,** 338.

Peterson, G. E., and Barney, H. L. Control methods used in a study of the vowels. *Journal of the Acoustical Society of America,* 1952, **24,** 175.

Potter, R. K., Kopp, G. A., and Green, H. C. *Visible speech.* New York: D. Van Nostrand, 1947.

Risberg, A. Periodic-nonperiodic test of hearing capacity. *STL. QPSR.* 1968, 2–3, 19.

Rosenzweig, M. R., and Postman, L. Frequency of usage and the perception of words. *Science,* 1958, **127,** 263.

Sivian, L. J. Speech power and its measurement. *Bell System Technical Journal,* 1929, **8,** 646.

Stevens, K. N., and House, A. S. Development of a quantitative description of vowel articulation. *Journal of the Acoustical Society of America,* 1955, **27,** 484.

Stevens, K. N., and House, A. S. An acoustical theory of vowel production and some of its implications. *Journal of speech and hearing research,* 1961, **4,** 303.

Stevens, S. S., Egan, J. P., and Miller, G. A. Methods of measuring speech spectra. *Journal of the Acoustical Society of America,* 1947, **19,** 771.

Stevens, P. Spectra of fricative noise in human speech. *Language and speech,* 1960, **3,** 32.

Uldall, E. T. Ambiguity: Question or statement. *Proceedings of the 4th International Congress of Phonetic Sciences,* Helsinki. The Hague, The Netherlands: Mouton and Co., 1962.

Uldall, E. Transitions in fricative noise. *Language and speech,* 1964, **7,** 13.

Van Uden, A. A sound perceptive method. In A. W. Ewing (Ed.), *Modern educational treatment of deafness.* Manchester, England: Manchester University Press, 1958.

Wedenberg, E. Auditory training of severely hard of hearing preschool children. *Acta Oto-Laryngologica,* 1954, Supp. 110.

CHAPTER II

Linguistic Organization

JEAN UTLEY LEHMAN, Ph.D.

Communication and Language

Communication is language. Human knowledge is stored, and expressed in language. Our cultural patterns and social behavior involve communication, and language is the most distinctly expressed form of communication. Through communication the behavior of others is influenced, feelings are expressed, imagination is stimulated, and experiences are shared.

Language must be appreciated, and to be appreciated it must be understood. Whether language is a learned entity as the empiricist believes, or whether it is largely innate as the rationalist believes, is to be determined through the understanding of that language. Since so many of our thoughts assume linguistic form, and many of our concepts are identified by verbal labels, psycholinguistics is providing significant knowledge for our understanding of linguistic behavior and the psychological mechanisms responsible for it. Fundamental insights about language are essential for anyone studying or teaching the language.

The communication process encompasses the speaker's ability to string words together to form sentences which express his thoughts. The sentences are made up of words, each of which consists of meaning and pronunciation. The words are grouped according to linguistic rules which describe, rather than prescribe, their "combinability" (van Uden, 1968) in order to convey the desired meaning. Both the expression on the part of the speaker, and the reception by the listener, are made possible through the synchronization of the phonological and grammatical aspects of the language. Phonology represents the segmental phonemes composed of the acoustic/articulatory aspects, and the supra-segmental phonemes which make up the prosody of the language (intonation) —stress, juncture, and pitch. Grammar consists of morphology and syntax. The preceding description of the linguistic organization of American English, as it will be presented in this discussion, is diagramed in Figure 1.

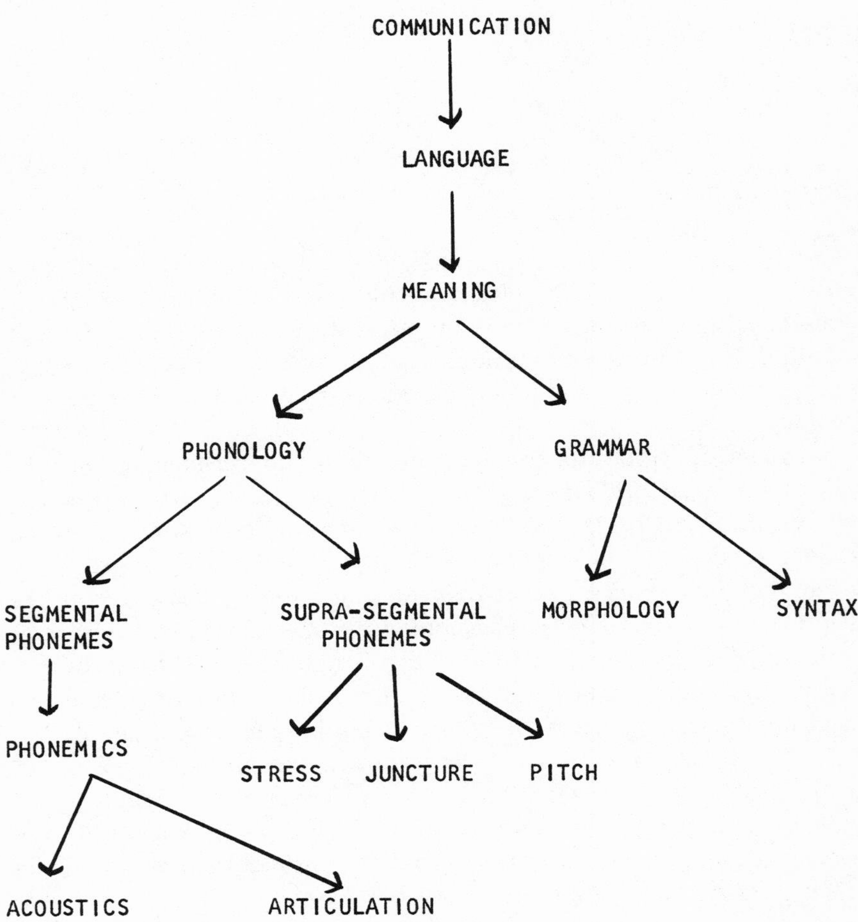

Figure 1. Linguistic Organization of American English (JUL)

Linguistics

Linguistics is the science of language—the study of language. How the language is learned is only partly dependent on the learning of words and their meanings. A full knowledge of the words in an American Language Dictionary would not ensure a person's ability to speak American English. The manner in which those words are combined into sentences and how the sentences are pronounced is a necessary underlying factor. Grammar enables us to do this.

A revolution in the teaching of grammar has taken place in the past few years. There seems to be no logical reason why the hearing impaired child should be exempt from taking advantage of what the new grammar has to offer.

Traditional grammarians based their description of English on inflected languages such as Latin and Greek, and their interpretations for "proper" usage. They failed to provide a simple, consistent, complete description of a useful language. They concerned themselves almost exclusively with the written language.

The new Transformation-Generative grammar is a device for producing or "generating" sentences and is concerned with the way in which language enables unlimited use of limited means (Chomsky, 1957). The grammar must describe the two levels of language—the underlying meaning of the sentence (deep structure) which exists in the mind but may perhaps not be directly expressed by the actual signal, and the surface structure of the sentence, which organizes the signal into words and phrases of particular length, sequence, and stress. The generative grammar refers to the system of rules governing the relationship between these two levels—between the semantic and the phonetic interpretations of the sentence, or between the meaning and the sound (Chomsky, 1966).

Generative or transformational grammar implies that the adult uses the relatively few kernel sentence patterns which consist of simple-declarative, affirmative sentences in active voice, together with the rules which make up the transformations, either single or double base. He makes changes on the structure of the kernel sentences to form transformations. Transformational grammar is said to offer a description, analysis, and set of definitions and formulas or rules, consistently and firmly based on form, the most objective aspect of language (Francis, 1964).

Since the spoken language is primary and since hearing impaired children will probably always write the language they speak; since language originates as speech; and since virtually all traditional grammar was based on the written language only, why shouldn't we as educators of the hearing impaired revise our teaching of grammar to parallel the modern structure proposed by the linguists?

Linguistics, however, is not a method. It is a growing body of knowledge about language. The linguists, whose major interest and contributions are in basic research and the building of theories, are not concerned with the *teaching* of grammar as it is involved in the expressive aspect (speaking and writing) or in the receptive aspect (reading and lipreading). Perhaps the largest contribution of the linguists to the classroom teacher is to affect the teacher's attitude toward language. The teacher must become informed about linguistic concepts and principles and fit his own applications to the linguistic needs of the individual child. He is cognizant of the children's accomplishments and contrives the experiences needed for oral language. The teacher must adapt the curriculum and content materials and methods to the learning processes of the individual children. The logical nature of the theory of generative grammar enables the teacher to see the grammar in terms of a developmental sequence. A thorough assimilation of the knowledge acquired through linguistic science should be utilized to shed new light upon whatever problems arise in respect to language (Fries, 1962).

Meaning

Semantics is the branch of linguistics concerned with the nature, structure, and especially with the development and changes, of the meanings of speech forms (Webster, 1959). Synchronic linguistic description minus phonology and grammar equals semantics. The speaker's ability to employ phonological and syntactic structure in expressing and understanding the language is dependent on semantics. Grammar provides identical structural descriptions for sentences that differ in meaning; different structural descriptions for sentences that are identical in meaning. Semantic ability eliminates potential ambiguities, detects semantic anomalies, and includes paraphrasing ability. Comprehension of a sentence is determined by its meaningful units (morphemes) and by the semantic relations among those meaningful units. A dictionary offers information about the morphological units (the lexicon of the language) of expressions of thought that the grammar does not explain. Yet, a dictionary together with the grammar of the language are not sufficient to match the speaker's interpretations of sentences. The grammar reveals a syntactic structure of a sentence which a semantic theory interprets. The meaning of the parts of a sentence determines the meaning of the whole (Katz and Fodor, 1967).

Phonology

The phonological system in the linguistic organization includes the segmental and supra-segmental phonemes. Speakers of a language communicate with each other by means of speech sounds or phonemes. A phoneme is the smallest unit in the language. The number of sounds that a speaker could produce or that a person with normal hearing could perceive is virtually unlimited. However, every language is composed of a limited number of sounds. Communication dictates this tenet. American English is a highly organized system of a limited number of phonemes. The combinability of these phonemes is characterized by the rules of the language. Speech is not an instinctive form of behavior; it is learned. The speaker learns to produce the sounds used by other speakers of the language in which he communicates. The sounds cannot be combined at random. The structure of the language is made up of the way in which the sounds are organized for purposes of communication. The individual phonemes are combined into meaningful units (morphemes) or words, which are then combined to form larger utterances or sentences. The elements (sounds, words, sentences) are inseparable and mutually dependent (Buchanan, 1963).

The supra-segmental phonemes which make up the prosody of the language assume equal importance to, and occur simultaneously with, the segmental phonemes. Stress, juncture, and pitch have linguistic reference. Each phoneme is relative in value.

Every utterance in American English has some degree of *stress*—primary (´), secondary (ˆ), tertiary (`), or weak/minimal (˘). The syllable marked as having primary stress is heard as the loudest syllable, relative to the other syllables. Ex.: Hôw's thĕ bábỳ? The placement of the stress determines the meaning of the utterance. Ex.: Î càn gó. Í càn ĝo. Î cán gò. Semantic differences are communicated by the change in supra-segmental phonemes, while the segmental phonemes remain the same (Buchanan, 1963).

Juncture is used to indicate the grammatical boundaries of the spoken language. The transition between speech sounds is made either by close (unbroken) transition/junctures, or by open (broken) transition/juncture, which is marked /+/. (Close juncture is left unmarked.) Ex.: close juncture, as in the word "nitrate," and open juncture, in the words "night rate." Sounds occurring before /+/ are in prejunctural position. Prejunctural means immediately preceding, or contiguous to, following open juncture. The type of open juncture which occurs at the end of utterances is called "external open juncture" or "terminal juncture." The rise/fall in the voice at the end of the final syllable is indicated / ↑ / ↓ / . /+/ does not involve a change of voice-pitch, nor does it occur before silence. The third variety of terminal juncture concerns a sustained pitch. Ex.: John went home.→Mary went to school. ↓ There are rules of juncture, also, characteristic of certain segmental phonemes/phoneme clusters (Buchanan, 1963).

There are four contrasting levels of pitch—low /1/, mid /2/, high /3/, and extra high /4/. The most common of the pitch phonemes is /2/. The pitch phonemes are placed immediately in front of the syllables which they mark, except in the case of the last syllable, which the phoneme follows. Ex.: ^{2}Aǹn + wènt + ^{3}shóppĭng! ↓

Every syllable in American English is uttered with some degree of stress and at some level of pitch, and terminal juncture ends every utterance. The meaning of a sentence can be changed by the supra-segmental phonemes.

Production of speech is inseparably connected with the reception of speech. Development of speech includes not only the learning of motor skills, the mastery of cues for recognition, but the constant storing of linguistic knowledge which forms the basis for both the production and reception of speech (Fry, 1966). The native sound system develops its acoustic and articulatory aspects as language units (Crocker, 1969). It has been said that intonation (the supra-segmental phonemes) may be the vehicle on which children arrive at the rudiments of syntax, since intonation is used for syntactic purposes and for discrimination between different emotional states (Pike, 1945). Another authority found that intonation contours were assignable only for the speech of a familiar language, which suggests that structure is an important source of information about intonation, but not vice versa. Hence, the encoding of the intonation contours structurally used in a language is dependent on knowledge of the sentence structure (Lieberman, 1965).

Some examples of Phonological Rules follow (Roberts, 1967):

1. Noun plurals—Regular

N + plural→N + /ə z/ when the N ends in /s/, /z/, /sh/, /zh/, /ch/, /j/*, **

2. Be + tense

   be + present→*am* when the subject is *I*

3. Present tense of verbs

   V + present→verb + s when subject is he, she, it, a proper noun, an indefinite pronoun, or a common noun not accompanied by plural

4. Past tense of verbs—Regular

   V + past→verb + /əd/ when the verb ends in a /t/ or /d/ sound

5. Intonation patterns in nonrestrictive relative clauses

   $$X + NP + Y + 2\text{-}3\text{-}1 \rightrightarrows NP + 2\text{-}3\text{-}2 \begin{Bmatrix} \text{who} \\ \text{which} \end{Bmatrix} + X + Y + 2\text{-}3\text{-}2$$

Grammar

Morphology. Grammar includes morphology and syntax. Morphology is the study of word forms and deals with the blending of phonemes into words and their parts, into the next larger units of structural meaning—the morphemes. A morpheme is the smallest meaningful unit in the language—i.e., it cannot be divided or shortened without resulting in a drastic change in the meaning (Gleason, 1955). Segmental phonemes provide segmental morphemes; supra-segmental phonemes provide supra-segmental morphemes. Ex.: Go→segmental material /gō/; stress; pitch /3-1/; juncture / ↓ / (Faust, 1958).

A morpheme meets three criteria:

1. It is a word, or a part of a word, that has meaning.
2. It cannot be divided into smaller meaningful parts without violation of its meaning or without meaningless remainders.
3. It recurs in differing verbal environments with a relatively stable meaning. (Stageberg, 1965)

The order of morphemes is basic to the language, and meaning depends on that order. There are three different kinds of morphemes:

1. Base words

   Ex.: boy, girl, book, word . . .

*All phonemic symbols are indicated in this discussion according to Thorndike markings.
See **Syntax, page 52

2. Inflectional affixes which express ideas like tense, number, or comparison

Ex.: plural, possessive, present, past, participle, -ing, comparative, superlative

3. Derivational affixes which change words from one word-class, or sub-class to another

Ex.: -ness, -ful, -ion, -ous, be-

Every simple (kernel) sentence contains at least one base word inflectional affix, and may or may not contain a derivational affix.

Syntax. An understanding of meaning and syntax is crucial if language is to be understood. The two components of a sentence—the surface structure (the actual organization of the physical signal, the shape and form of the utterance) and the deep structure (the determiner of semantic content) have been previously discussed.* Syntax is the set of rules or principles specifying the set of grammatical sentences and their structures; in other words, the string of morphemes, the meaningful minimal lexical units, constituting the sentence. Syntax is represented by the surface structure.

The syntactic component describes the parts of the sentence and the order in which they are arranged. There are rules of different types, and these are expressed algebraically using abbreviations. Phrase structure rules are applied consecutively and identify the elements of the sentence. Ex.: S→NP + VP (S stands for sentence; NP, for noun phrase; VP, for verb phrase;→, rewrite as, or consists of; +, plus, or followed by; or, A sentence consists of a noun phrase plus a verb phrase.) NP and VP are *structures,* and the use to which the individual structures are put is termed *function.* Thus, in the above example, NP is the *structure functioning* as the subject; VP is the *structure functioning* as the predicate (Roberts, 1967).

There are two types of sentences—kernel and transformation. A kernel sentence must be simple or declarative (not interrogative), affirmative (not negative), and in active voice (not passive). A transformation is a sentence that is not a kernel sentence, and is formed by making changes on the structures of the kernel sentence, either by reworking them, or by combining them.

According to Roberts (1967), the first rule of syntax is that a kernel sentence is made up of two main parts: the nucleus (a word or group of words) and an intonation pattern. Ex.: S→nucleus + 2-3-1. The second rule of the syntax defines the nucleus.

*See *Linguistics*, p. 47

$$\text{Ex.: nucleus} \rightarrow \left\{ \begin{matrix} \text{interjection} \\ \\ \text{NP + VP} \end{matrix} \right\}$$

Examples of other syntactic rules follow:

1. Noun Phrase

$$\text{NP} \rightarrow \left\{ \begin{matrix} \text{proper noun} \\ \text{personal pronoun} \\ \text{indefinite pronoun} \\ \text{determiner + noun} \end{matrix} \right\}$$

2. Verb Phrase

$$\text{VP} \rightarrow \text{AUX} + \left\{ \begin{matrix} \text{Be} + \left\{ \begin{matrix} \text{NP} \\ \text{Adj} \\ \text{Adv-P} \end{matrix} \right\} + \text{(Adv-F)} + \text{(Adv-T)} \\ \\ \text{Verbal} \end{matrix} \right\}$$

3. Auxiliary

$$\text{Aux} \rightarrow \text{tense} + \text{(M)} + \text{(have + part.)} + \text{(be + ing)}$$

4. Verbal

$$\text{Verbal} \rightarrow \left\{ \begin{matrix} \left\{ \begin{matrix} \text{VI} \\ \text{VT + NP} \end{matrix} \right\} + \text{(Adv-M)} \\ \left\{ \begin{matrix} \text{Vs + Adj} \\ \text{Vb} + \left\{ \begin{matrix} \text{NP} \\ \text{Adj} \end{matrix} \right\} \\ \text{Vmid + NP} \end{matrix} \right\} + \text{(Adv-P)} \end{matrix} \right\} + \text{(Adv-F)} + \text{(Adv-T)}$$

Syntactic rules are limited at first, and later are expanded to include more and more structures which, in turn, describe more and more functions.

Transformational rules apply to the phrase structure rules and account for additional words or structures in a kernel sentence; the parts of the sentence are rearranged or combined with parts of another kernel sentence, thus undergoing transformation. Examples of these would be the negative, the possessive, the adjective, the yes/no question, and so on. The transformational rules show that new sentences are formed by a regular pattern, which is used "unconsciously" after the "grammar" is learned and understood. The smallest element used to express a thought is a kernel sentence, which is the basis of any successfully formulated expression of cognitive information (Lee, 1969).

Linguistic Organization

A scheme of linguistic organization might be shown as Figure 2. In learning a language, a person must learn a set of lexical items (morphemes, and the manner in which they can be combined to form words) which could be called the lexicon of the language, a set of phonological rules, a set of syntactic rules, and a set of semantic rules. Each lexical item involves a phonological representation, a syntactic representation, and a semantic representation. A deep phrase structure is connected with a surface phrase structure by the choice of lexical items, whose semantic representations make them suitable to designate parts of the deep structure, and by syntactic rules. The output of the phonologic component feeds into the production component. The production component represents the person's ability to synchronize his total knowledge of the grammar, the social content, and the message set, and either produce speech by simplifying the articulatory control problem, or listen to speech by decoding the acoustic signal (Lieberman, 1967; Langacker, 1968).

Application to the Learning Problems of the Hearing Impaired Child

The hearing impaired child acquires language in the same developmental sequence as does the normally hearing child. If we are to assume that every individual, hearing or deaf, has a predisposition for language learning, application of linguistic knowledge to the educational procedures in our schools and programs for the hearing impaired is essential.

The language input must be structured according to the child's level of linguistic comprehension if his receptive language is to provide sufficient storage of patterns requisite to spontaneous oral expression.

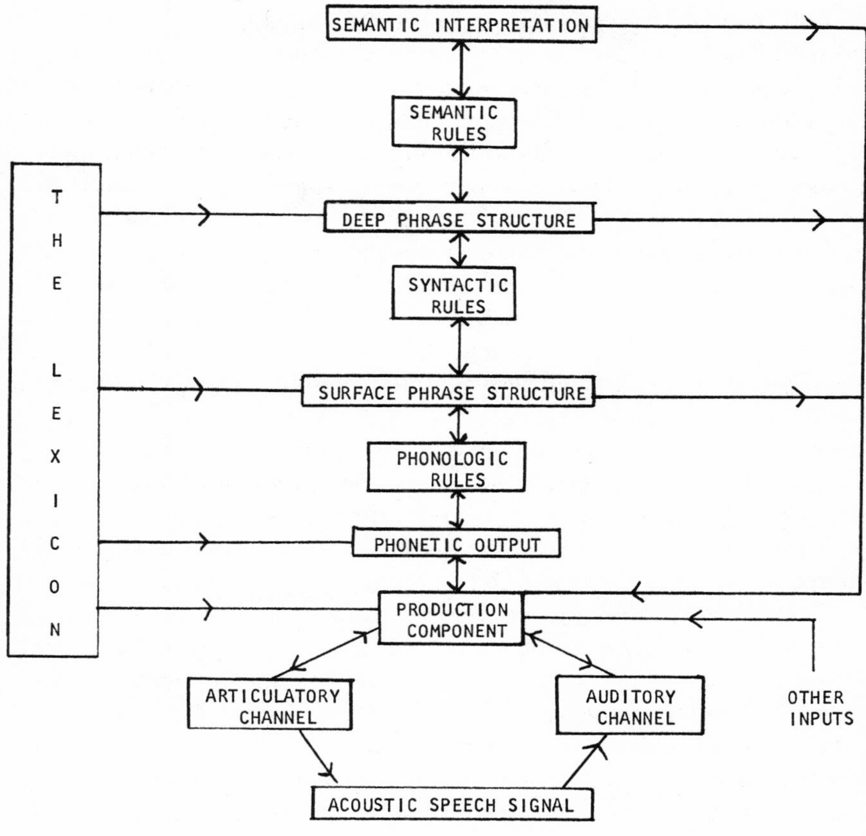

Figure 2

Relation to the Speech of the Hearing Impaired Child

Although speech and language cannot be separated, speech must be learned by any child. The instructional techniques involved in the learning of speech by the hearing impaired child are obviously more definitive than those used with the hearing child. Yet, if the hearing impaired child is provided with adequate amplification early in life, if the equipment is consistently used, and if his listening skills are perfected, there is every reason to believe that his speech and language development will parallel, sequentially if not chronologically, that of his normally hearing peers. Such growth is contingent, of course, on the assumption that his teachers are fully knowledgeable in the semantic, phonological, morphological, and syntactic aspects of the language. The emphasis on vocabulary which was so prevalent in previous years no longer maintains its prime spot in the curriculum. Initial teaching of the phrase structure, followed by the morphological phase, and leading to the transformational aspect of language is rapidly becoming the "core" of the teaching of speech and communication.

Instructional procedures found in the classes, programs, and schools for the hearing impaired are, for the most part, based on the child's linguistic competence. It is the teacher's prime responsibility to know each child's level of linguistic competence in order to structure his/her own language input for the purpose of intercommunication—a circuitous pattern which requires complete closure. Language and cognitive growth are interdependent and develop sequentially. Language/speech acquisition is a slow process which cannot be forced; no part of it can be bypassed. The teacher must be aware of the "steps" in language learning and must focus on the child's experiences necessary to this sequential pattern.

All approaches to linguistics are oral and auditory, enabling teachers to approach language learning at the basic levels of receptive and expressive speech rather than at the level of the more symbolic representation involved in reading and writing.

The child should be expected to combine intonation and structure. The structure consisting of phonemes, morphemes, syntax, and intonation provides the meaning in communication both receptively and expressively. The child who is afforded adequate meaningful linguistic stimulation necessary for storing linguistic knowledge for future use will be able to refine his linguistic approximations and develop oral communication commensurate with others in his speech community.

The teacher of the hearing impaired must (1) utilize and apply the psycholinguists' knowledge of the normally hearing child's language development, and be able to apply this knowledge in guiding the language behavior of the hearing impaired; (2) be able to describe the phonological, morphological, and syntactic level at which the child is functioning in order to plan, contrive, and make use of meaningful experiences sufficiently motivating to provide for the successive sequential steps adequate for linguistic input to elicit oral expression; and (3) modify and improve the child's language and speech in order to more nearly match that of his normally hearing peers.

Suggestions for Further Research in Relation to the Speech of the Hearing Impaired Child

Investigations should include development of more definitive measures for evaluation of spoken language through the use of visual acoustic instrumentation for the benefit of the child's voice quality, his use of the prosody of the language, as well as articulation of the phonemic aspect of phonology. The instrumentation should be simplified in operation in order to be used for self-help by the individual child. The development of an instrument, or "teaching machine" which would assist in the learning of language through the multisensory approach—lipreading, hearing, reading, and providing for the monitoring of the child's own voice, such as is implied in "lexical listening" procedures—would be helpful to teachers.

More comparative studies are needed involving normally hearing and hearing impaired children's acquisition of language from birth through early childhood in the areas of phonology, morphology, syntax, and semantics. Language acquisition of hearing impaired children in different types of educational programs would be of interest. For example, would the hearing impaired child acquire more natural language earlier if he were to participate in an "unlabeled" group and be educated in terms of his potentials rather than his deficits?

BIBLIOGRAPHY

Bruner, J. S. *Toward a theory of instruction.* New York: W. W. Norton and Co., 1968.

Buchanan, C. D. *A programmed introduction to linguistics: Phonetics and phonemics.* Boston: D. C. Heath and Co., 1963.

Chomsky, N. *Syntactic structures.* The Hague, The Netherlands: Mouton and Co., 1957.

Chomsky, N. The current scene in linguistics: Present directions. *College English,* 1966, **27,** 587–595.

Crocker, J. R. A phonological model of children's articulation competence. *Journal of speech and hearing disorders,* 1969, **34,** 3.

Faust, G. P. Something of morphemics. In H. B. Allen (Ed.), *Readings in applied English linguistics.* (1st ed.) New York: Appleton-Century-Crofts, 1958.

Francis, W. N. Revolution in grammar. In H. B. Allen (Ed.), *Readings in applied English linguistics.* (2nd ed.) New York: Appleton-Century-Crofts, 1964.

Fries, C. C. *Linguistics and reading.* New York: Holt, Rinehart and Winston, 1962.

Fry, D. B. The development of the phonological system in the normal and the deaf child. In F. Smith and G. A. Miller (Eds.), *The genesis of language.* Cambridge, Mass.: M.I.T. Press, 1966.

Gleason, H. A. *An introduction to descriptive linguistics.* New York: Holt, Rinehart and Winston, 1955.

Katz, J. J., and Fodor, J. A. The structure of a semantic theory. In J. D. DeCecco (Ed.), *The psychology of language, thought, and instruction.* New York: Holt, Rinehart and Winston, 1967.

Langacker, R. W. *Language and its structure.* New York: Harcourt, Brace and World, 1968.

Lee, L. L. Recent studies in language acquisition. *Journal of the American Speech and Hearing Association,* 1969, **11,** 6.

Lieberman, P. *Intonation, perception, and language.* M.I.T. Research Monograph No. 38. Cambridge, Mass.: M.I.T. Press, 1967.

Lieberman, P. On the acoustic basis of the perception of intonation by linguistics. *Word,* 1965, **21,** 1.

Pike, K. *The intonation of American English.* Ann Arbor: University of Michigan, 1945.

Roberts, P. *The Roberts English series: A linguistics program.* New York: Harcourt, Brace and World, 1967.

Stageberg, N. C. *An introductory English grammar.* New York: Holt, Rinehart and Winston, 1965.

van Uden, A. *A world of language for deaf children.* St. Michielsgestel, The Netherlands: The Institute for the Deaf, 1968.

Webster's new world dictionary of the American language. New York: World Publishing Co., 1959.

CHAPTER III

Speech Production and the Deaf Child

Harry Levitt, Ph.D.

The production of speech involves a complex interaction of acoustic, physiological, and perceptual mechanisms. Although there is much we do not understand about the speech process, we have at least some understanding of the basic mechanisms that are involved. It is the purpose of this chapter to review briefly and in simple terms the essential features of speech production and how deaf children differ from normal-hearing children in this regard.

It is important to bear in mind that speech production is only one part of a much larger process—that of speech communication. The process of speech communication consists of several interdependent links. These include: formulation of the speech message in the mind of the talker, generation of neural commands to the vocal mechanism, the acoustic production of speech sounds, transmission of these sounds through an intervening medium (e.g. air, telephone link), auditory encoding of these sounds in the ear of a listener and, finally, perception of the message by the listener. There are also additional links such as auditory and kinesthetic feedback of the speech production which is received by the talker and visual cues provided by lip movements, facial expressions, and bodily movements which are perceived by the listener.

Since the various stages of the speech process are highly interdependent, a breakdown or inefficient operation of one stage may greatly impair the operation or development of other stages. Thus, a congenitally deaf child usually has great difficulty in acquiring normal speech habits, although his speech apparatus may be perfectly normal. The difficulty is due to the inability of the deaf child to encode the rules system governing speech production, since his environment does not contain the auditory cues embodying these rules. The interdependence of the various stages of the speech communication process may, at the same time, help compensate for the inefficient operation of other stages. For example, the speech of a deaf child may be wholly unintelligible to a person who has had little contact with the deaf, yet to the child's parents and teachers, the speech may be quite intelligible. In this case, the perceptual mechanisms of the listeners have been attuned to the special characteristics of deaf speech (as well as the child's facial expressions), thereby compensating in part for the child's deficiencies in speech production. A good overall treatment of the separate stages of the speech communication process may be found in Denes and Pinson (1963).

SOME BASIC ACOUSTIC MECHANISMS

Typically, sound is produced by causing air particles to vibrate with sufficient intensity that these vibrations are transmitted to the eardrum of a listener, who in turn perceives an auditory sensation; that is, the listener *hears* the sound. There are at least three ways of producing sounds that are of particular interest in the study of speech production. One is the sound produced by causing air molecules to vibrate in a random or turbulent way, as occurs when we allow air to escape from an inflated balloon or when we blow out candles on a birthday cake. Sounds produced in this way have a characteristic hissing quality. Hissing sounds produced by different sources, however, do not necessarily sound the same. For example, the huffing and puffing of a child blowing out candles on a birthday cake sounds quite different from that of an adult doing the same thing. Even if the sources of sound are identical, it is possible to change the quality of one sound by forcing the sound waves to pass through a pipe or tube or other acoustic enclosure. For example, if we blow into an empty soda bottle, the sound that is produced has a tonal or resonant quality. If we change the size of the soda bottle, a resonant sound is again produced, but in this case the pitch of the sound is different. Although the source of the sound is the same, i.e., the turbulent flow of air into the neck of the bottle, the sound produced has a resonant quality determined by the size and shape of the bottle.

In technical terms, the turbulence of the air has caused the air particles to vibrate with a wide range of frequencies covering a large part, if not all, of the audible frequency range. This produces the hissing quality of the sound. The physical characteristics of the acoustic enclosure are such, however, that vibrations within a very limited range of frequencies are transmitted while vibrations at most other frequencies are effectively dampened out. The sound wave that reaches the ear thus has vibratory energy in a narrow frequency range. That is, the air molecules impinging on the eardrum and creating the auditory sensation vibrate randomly, but the frequencies of vibration cover a narrow range. The sound still has the characteristic hiss due to the randomness of the vibrations, but in addition there is a tonal quality to the sound due to the resonance characteristics of the acoustic enclosure. The frequency of vibration that is least reduced by the acoustic enclosure is known as the resonant frequency. For simplicity of description the discussion has been limited to an acoustic enclosure having only one resonant frequency. In practice, however, acoustic enclosures may have several resonant frequencies. Conceptually, it is convenient to think of such enclosures as being made up of a series of simple enclosures each having a single resonant frequency.

If there is no randomness in the vibrations produced by the sound source, then a distinctly different auditory sensation is obtained. For example, let us assume that we have air flowing smoothly through a pipe with virtually no turbulence so that there is no audible sound. The flow of air is then interrupted periodically by completely blocking the flow of air at regular intervals. The continuous flow is thus transformed into a periodic train of air puffs. If the frequency of interruption is on the order of 100 per second, then a distinct, audible buzz is produced where the pitch of the buzz is determined by the frequency of interruption. Whereas the turbulent air motion causes air particles to vibrate over a wide range of frequencies, the periodic interruptions cause the air particles to vibrate at only those frequencies "in tune" with the frequency of interruption. For example, if the frequency of interruption is 100 times per second, air particles vibrate at frequencies of 100, 200, 300, 400, . . . etc., cycles per second or hertz.* The lowest frequency of vibration, 100 Hz, is known as the *fundamental frequency*. The other frequencies, 200, 300, 400, . . ., Hz, which are exact multiples of the fundamental frequency, are known as *harmonics*.

Note that both the turbulent sound source and the buzz source have air particles vibrating at frequencies covering a wide range, including possibly frequencies beyond the normal range of hearing. The basic dif-

*The unit of frequency is hertz (abbreviated to Hz) where 1 cycle per second = 1 Hz.

ference between the two sources is that the buzz source has vibrations at only those frequencies that are exact multiples (i.e., harmonics) of the fundamental frequency. As with the turbulent sound, the buzz sound can be changed in quality by forcing the sound through a tube or other acoustic enclosure having one or more resonances. In this case, vibrational energy at the harmonic frequencies close to the acoustic enclosure's resonant frequencies is passed with little or no loss in intensity, but the vibrations at other frequencies are dampened out. The sounds produced in this way still have their buzz-like character, but in addition have a resonant quality. The result is a peculiar vowel-like sound, much like the vowels produced by the talking machines in science-fiction movies.

A third type of sound is that produced when air under pressure is suddenly released. An everyday example of such sounds is the pop produced by removing the cork from a tightly sealed bottle. The sound produced has a characteristic popping or plosive quality. As with the turbulent and buzz sounds, the quality of the plosive sound is dependent on the shape and size of the acoustic enclosure. The pop produced by opening a champagne bottle has a deeper, and, to some ears, a much more pleasant resonant quality than that produced by opening a soda bottle. When air under pressure is suddenly released from an acoustic enclosure, an acoustic shock wave is set up which causes the air particles in the immediate vicinity to vibrate. However, vibrations at frequencies other than the resonant frequencies die out rapidly. Vibrations at the resonant frequencies continue for some time after the initial shock, thereby giving a resonant quality to the plosive sound.

The Acoustics of Speech Production

The production of speech involves essentially the same acoustic mechanisms described in the preceding section. A sketch of the human vocal apparatus is shown in Figure 1. Speech is generally produced while exhaling. Air from the lungs is forced through the larynx, into the mouth and nose, then finally escaping into the surrounding acoustic medium. The vocal cords are situated roughly in the middle of the larynx. The region above the larynx consisting of the pharynx, nose, mouth, and lips is known as the *vocal tract.*

Voiced sounds are produced by a voluntary tightening of the vocal cords. When the cords are pulled taut, the flow of air through the larynx is blocked. This causes a build-up of air pressure behind the larynx

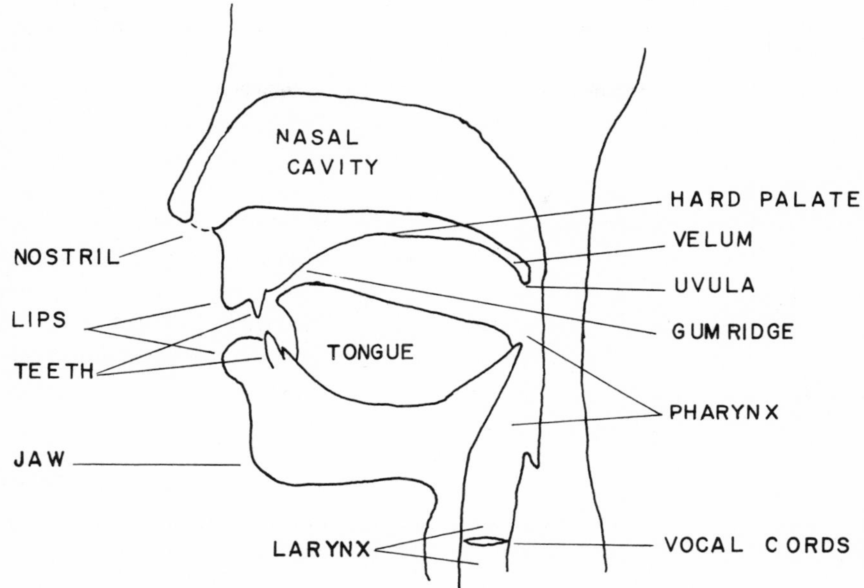

Figure 1. Schematic Diagram of the Speech Organs

which, after a short while, causes the vocal cords to fly apart, allowing some air to escape. With the release of air, the air pressure falls and the cords are pulled back together, blocking the larynx once again. This sequence of events is repeated cyclically as long as voicing continues. The opening and closing of the vocal cords is almost, but not quite, periodic in time. The result is a sequence of quasi-periodic air pulses flowing into the vocal tract.

The vocal tract is effectively an acoustic enclosure with distinct resonances. The shape of the tract is easily changed by movements of the *articulators,* i.e. the jaw, tongue, teeth, lips, and velum. The velum, as shown in Fig. 1, controls the entrance to the nasal cavity. By changing the shape of the vocal tract, the resonant frequencies are changed. For most practical purposes the vocal tract may be regarded as having three major resonances, or *formants,* as they are commonly known.

Voiceless sounds are produced by relaxing the vocal cord muscles so that there is no major obstruction to the air flow through the larynx. At some later point in the vocal tract, however, a constriction is introduced so as to cause turbulence in the air flow. Sounds produced in this way have a characteristic hiss, such as in the fricative sounds.

Speech sounds may be classified in many ways, and the voiced-voiceless distinction is only one of many features that can be used to categorize speech sounds. In this chapter we shall categorize sounds in terms of their minimum distinctive unit—the *phoneme.* A phoneme is the smallest possible grouping of sounds that operate analagously in a language. The word *tin,* for example, consists of three phonemes, /t/, /ɪ/, and /n/.* There are many possible pronunciations of this word, but if it is always heard as *tin,* then there has been no change in any of the phonemes. If, however, it is heard as *din,* then the first distinctive sound in the word, the phoneme /t/, has changed its identity to that of /d/. Phonemes may be subdivided into two broad categories, vowels and consonants. We shall consider each category separately.

The Production of Vowels

Vowels are generally voiced and are produced by tensing the vocal cords while exhaling. The vocal tract is shaped according to which vowel is produced. There are many possible configurations for the vocal tract and, hence, many variations of the vowel or vowel-like sound that can be produced. Each language has its own set of vowels. English, for example, has roughly a dozen distinct vowels. Variations of these vowels can be tolerated, provided the intended vowel is not lost or confused with another vowel. For example, when we speak with a blocked or stuffy nose the vowels we produce have a nasal quality, but they may still be identified as the intended vowels. The term "nasal" is used colloquially; the vowels are actually *denasalized* since there is no flow of air through the nasal cavity.

Associated with each vowel is a normative configuration for the vocal tract. Although slightly different configurations may produce essentially the same vowel, the normative positions are those most often used or aimed at by skilled speakers. Since movements of the articulators (i.e., tongue, jaw, teeth, lips) bring about extensive changes in the shape of the vocal tract, the normative positions are usually defined in terms of these manipulators, the tongue being the most important.

Of the 12 or so vowels in English, four are of particular interest since they correspond to extreme positions of the tongue. For the vowel /i/ as in *seen,* the arch of the tongue is placed high up and forward in the

*Phonetic symbols are used when referring to individual sounds. These symbols are always enclosed within two vertical slashes, e.g. /a/, /æ/. To simplify the text, however, we have attempted to minimize the use of phonetic symbols, and conventional English spelling is used when referring to words and phrases. A table of phonetic symbols appears in the Appendix at the end of this chapter.

mouth; that is, in the front of the mouth just behind the teeth and approaching the hard palate. For the vowel /u/ as in *soon,* the arch of the tongue is again placed toward the hard palate, but at the back of the mouth. For the vowel /æ/ as in *sat,* the tongue is placed at the front of the mouth, but is kept low behind the lower teeth. Finally, for the vowel /ɑ/ as in *father,* the blade of the tongue is placed at the back of the mouth and low down. The four vowels /i/, /u/, /æ/ and /ɑ/ are classified, respectively, as high front, high back, low front and low back, according to the position of the tongue. Other vowels may fit these same categories, such as /ɪ/ as in *bit,* which is also a high front vowel, or may involve intermediate categories such as /ʌ/ as in *up* which is a central vowel. When the tongue and other articulators are held in a relaxed position a neutral, *schwa* vowel is produced, such as the initial vowel of *above.* This vowel is the most commonly used vowel in speech and is frequently used in place of other vowels in unstressed syllables.

Although convenient for purposes of classification, the position of the tongue is not the only determinant of vowel type. There are important concomitant changes in lip and jaw positions, as well as changes in the shape of the pharynx cavity and other variables. For example, for the front vowels the lips tend to be spread out showing the teeth. For the back vowels the lips tend to be rounded. At the same time, the jaws are relatively close together for the high vowels and far apart for the low vowels.

Normative vowel tract configurations for the four vowels /i/, /u/, /æ/ and /ɑ/ are shown in Figure 2 together with typical *power spectrum diagrams.* A power spectrum diagram is a plot showing the intensity of vibration at different frequencies of vibration. In the case of vowels and other voiced sounds, the quasi-periodic train of air puffs produced by the vocal cords causes vibrations at only those frequencies that are harmonics of the average repetition rate of the air puffs. Each of the power spectrum diagrams of Figure 2 thus consists of a sequence of vertical bars, where each bar corresponds to a separate harmonic and the height of each bar represents the intensity of vibration for that harmonic. An identical repetition rate for the air puffs has been assumed for each vowel. The dashed line, or *envelope,* shows how the vocal tract configuration tends to emphasize certain harmonics and reduce the importance of others. The peaks of the envelope correspond to the resonances or formants of the vocal tract.

The shape of the vocal tract and the location of the formants are closely interrelated. Thus, for the vowel /i/, as in *beet,* the mouth open-

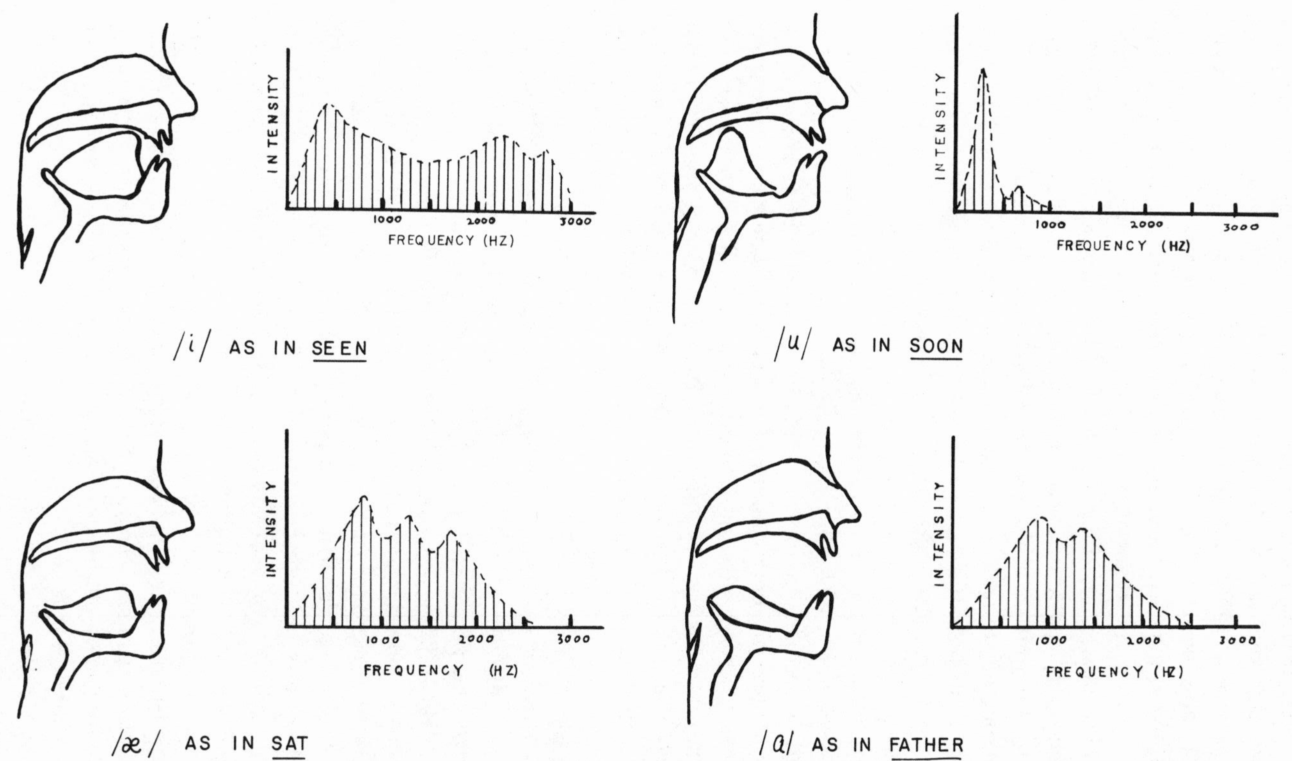

Figure 2. *Typical Vocal Tract Configurations and Power Spectrum Diagrams for Four Vowels. The vertical bars of the power spectrum diagram represent the harmonics of the voice frequency which is assumed to be 100 Hz. The peaks of the envelope correspond to the resonances or formants of the vocal tract.*

ing is relatively small and the arch of the tongue being up toward the hard palate, provides a further restriction to the air flow. The effect of the narrow constriction is to lower the first formant and raise the second formant. As may be seen in Figure 2, the lowest formant for /i/ is typically well below 500 Hz with second and third formants close to 3000 Hz. On the other hand, for the vowel / ɑ / as in *father,* the mouth is opened wide and the tongue restricts the air path as little as possible. In this case both the first and second formants are relatively low, as shown in Figure 2. Greater detail on the link between the shape of the vocal tract and the power spectrum diagram may be found in Ladefoged (1962) and Flanagan (1965). An excellent overall review of the acoustics of speech sounds will be found in the chapter by Dr. Arthur Boothroyd.

Another important classification of vowels is in terms of their duration. For example, the /ɪ/ in *bit* has almost the same tongue, lip, and jaw position as the /i/ in *beet.* The major articulatory difference between these two vowels is in their relative durations, the /i/ being longer than the /ɪ/. The terms *tense* and *lax* (referring to muscle activity) are sometimes used to describe these two vowel categories, but there is some controversy as to the accuracy of this description. The longer vowels tend to be less steady than the shorter and may drift into another vowel. For example, the vowel sound in *see* is commonly heard as two connected vowels, /ɪ/ and /i/. This process of gradually shifting from one vowel to another without abrupt change is known as diphthongization and the sound so produced is known as a diphthong. A typical example is the diphthong /ɑʊ/ which occurs in *town* and is an amalgam of the vowels /a/ and /u/.

Vowels that come at the end of a word, such as in *we* or *see,* are known as free vowels. Vowels that are terminated by a consonant, as in *wet* or *seat,* are known as checked vowels. The free vowels are invariably longer and are prone to a greater degree of diphthongization than checked vowels.

The Consonants

There are three major groups of consonants, plosives, fricatives, and the frictionless consonants. The last group, which are all voiced, may be further subdivided into nasals, glides, the lateral /ℓ/, and the rather special /r/ sound. Table 1 shows how the consonants of English may be classified.

Fricatives, as the name suggests, are produced by frication or turbulence in the air stream. Turbulence is caused by forcing the air to flow through a narrow constriction, and it is convenient to classify fricatives primarily in terms of the place where the constriction is narrowest. The fricative /θ/ as in *thumb* is produced by forming a constriction between the tongue and the upper front teeth. For the fricative /s/ as in *seen* the constriction is formed between the tongue and the gum ridge behind the upper front teeth. The /ʃ/ as in *ship* is produced by forming a constriction between the blade of the tongue and the mid-region of the mouth roof.

A second important classification is whether or not voicing occurs in addition to frication. The voiced fricatives / ð / as in *that,* /z/ as in *zoo,* and / ʒ / as in *treasure,* are produced in essentially the same way as their unvoiced counterparts /θ/, /s/ and / ʃ /, respectively, except that the speaker uses his vocal cords as well to provide a combination of voicing and frication.

The plosives, particularly those at the start of a word or phrase, are produced by blocking the flow of air through the vocal tract at some point and allowing pressure to build up and then, by a sudden movement of the articulators, unblocking the tract with sufficient speed to cause a minor acoustic shock wave—hence the name plosive. Plosives at the end of a word or phrase are produced by blocking the vocal tract, but not necessarily with the subsequent build-up and sudden release of air pressure. These plosives do not have the characteristic plosion of the initial plosives, but are nevertheless classified as plosives because of the similarity in vocal tract configuration.

The plosives may be classified according to the place at which the vocal tract is blocked. The plosives /p/, /t/ and /k/, as in *pot, tot,* and *cot,* for example, are produced by closure at the lips, upper palate, and soft palate, respectively. As with the fricatives, a second important variable is whether or not voicing occurs. The plosives /b/ as in *bash,* /d/ as in *dash,* and /g/ as in *gash,* are the voiced counterparts of /p/, /t/ and /k/, respectively. However, unlike the fricatives which are of relatively long duration, the plosives are produced by rapid movements of the articulators and are of very short duration. Voicing may not actually occur during the period in which the tract is blocked, but the timing of events, particularly the time taken before the onset of voicing, as well as the duration of the preceding vowel, play an important role in determining whether a plosive is heard as voiced or unvoiced. An unvoiced plosive will tend to have a longer release time* than its voiced counterpart and the duration of the preceding vowel will tend to be shorter.

Nasals are produced by blocking the air path through the mouth and allowing air to escape through the nose. For example, /m/ as in *mom,* is produced by blocking the vocal tract at the lips and lowering the velum to allow air to escape through the nasal cavity (see Fig. 1). The /n/ as in *nun* is produced by blocking the vocal tract with the tongue placed against the upper gum ridge. The nasal /ŋ / as in *sing,* is produced by blocking the vocal tract toward the rear of the hard palate.

The nasals, like the fricatives, can be produced continuously for as long as the lungs can maintain sufficient air pressure for exhalation. Consonants of this type are known as continuants.

The glides are produced by vocal tract movement from one articulatory position to the next. The glides generally precede a vowel and the resulting motion is from an initial vowel-like position to that of the intended vowel—for example, the word *we,* which starts with the glide /w/ is produced by initially holding the tongue and lips roughly in position for the vowel /u/ as in *boot,* and moving tongue, jaw, and lips to the position for the /i/ as sound is produced. Similarly, the word *you,* which starts with the glide /j/ is produced by starting from the position for the vowel /i/ as in *deed* and gliding into the /u/ position. There are various modifications to the production of glides, depending on which sounds precede and follow the glide. If, for example, a voiceless consonant precedes a glide, as in the words *sweet, twenty,* and *tune* (when the latter is pronounced /tjun/), then the onset of voicing is delayed and the glide is heard as devoiced.

The affricates are a rather special group in that they are a combination of a plosive and fricative pronounced as one sound. This occurs when a stop is released relatively slowly into a fricative that is produced in the same area of the mouth. Although there are several such combinations, only two are recognized in American English. These are /tʃ/ as in *chin,* and /d ʒ / as in *gin.* Other combinations, such as in the words *hats* and *bids,* are recognized as two distinct sounds in sequence since the plosives may be separated from the following fricatives.

The lateral /l/ is produced by placing the tip of the tongue against the upper gumridge with the sides of the tongue free from contact with

*The period of time during which the build-up of air pressure resulting from the blockage in the vocal tract is released.

other parts of the mouth so that air can flow out laterally. The /ℓ/ is a voiced sound similar to a glide and is partially devoiced when following a voiceless plosive in a stressed syllable, (e.g., *play, clean*) or when following a voiceless fricative (e.g., *flew, sly*).

There are two important variations of the /ℓ/ sound. A "light" /ℓ/ occurs before a voiced sound, as in *like,* and a "dark" /ℓ/ occurs after a voiced sound as in *fool.* The "light" /ℓ/ is made with the tongue forward in the mouth, the tongue blade touching the upper gumridge. The "dark" /ℓ/ is made with the tongue farther back in the mouth with the body of the tongue being raised toward the velum.

The consonant /r/ is perhaps the most complicated of the speech sounds. It has a number of different forms which vary with dialect and pronunciation. Two important cases for General American English are the glide /r/ and the vowel-like /r/. The glide /r/ generally occurs before a vowel, e.g., as in the word *red,* and is produced like a glide with an initial position similar to that for the vowel /ɜ/ as in *turn.* The vowel-like /r/ may precede a consonant or occur at the end of a word or phrase, as in *bird* or *mother.* It is produced in a manner similar to a vowel with the tongue pulled back slightly towards the center of the mouth. In some parts of the country, the /r/ sound is dropped altogether and the preceding vowel is lengthened, sometimes forming a diphthong. Space does not allow for a detailed discussion of the various forms of /r/, and the reader is referred to Bronstein (1960, pages 114–122) for further details.

THE PRODUCTION OF SPEECH SOUNDS IN CONTEXT

Although the sounds of speech may be classified into minimum distinctive units known as phonemes, the flow of speech involves more than simply articulating a sequence of such units. There are important variations in how a phoneme is produced, depending on interactions with neighboring phonemes as well as on the overall structure of the utterance. In this section we shall review briefly the overall structure of speech and then discuss variations in the production of sounds in context.

Speech has both a segmental and suprasegmental structure. The segmental structure refers to the features and characteristics of individual phonemes. The suprasegmental structure refers to those features and characteristics that do not relate to specific phonemes, but to entire phrases or sentences. There are two basic groups of suprasegmental features—those that directly affect the meaning of what is said, and those that have little effect on meaning but relate primarily to that elusive property known as speech or voice quality.

The key suprasegmental characteristics which affect meaning directly are *intonation, stress, rhythm,* and *phrasing.* By intonation is meant the modulation of voice pitch. The pitch* of the voice is determined by the frequency of vibration of the vocal cords which in turn is controlled by the tension on the vocal cords and the air pressure developed by the lungs. Rhythm refers to the pattern in which certain syllables are stressed and others are left unstressed. A stressed syllable is one that is spoken in such a way as to make it perceptually more prominent. This may be done by raising the pitch of the voice or by increasing the duration or loudness of the syllable. Usually some combination of these factors is used.

Phrasing refers to the process whereby words are grouped together according to the linguistic structure of the utterance. A basic unit in phrasing is the *sense group* which is a group of one or more words forming a distinct linguistic entity such as a phrase or clause. Sense groups are bounded by breaks in the flow of speech. Several sense groups may be linked together before the speaker finds it necessary or convenient to pause for breath. The portion of an utterance between pauses for taking breath is known as a *breath group.*

Intonation is perhaps the most important variable used by a speaker to link the separate sounds of speech into a unified whole. Even with voiceless sounds the orderly change in pitch before and after the sound compensates for any short-term variations in the overall pattern. Since the mechanics of voicing require a flow of air through the larynx, the basic unit for characterizing intonation contours is the breath group. At the start of a breath group air pressure in the lungs is high and typically the voice frequency increases rapidly to reach a comfortable pitch and, as in the case of simple declarative statements, the voice frequency remains roughly steady until the last portion of the breath group when the voice frequency begins to fall, ending in a downward glide. In the case of a question, the voice frequency rises and may end in an upward glide. There are important modifications to these basic contour shapes, depending on the linguistic structure and meaning of what is said.

Superimposed on the basic contour for an utterance are prominences

*The distinction between frequency and pitch should be noted. Frequency is a physical variable whereas pitch is a subjective auditory percept. Typically, when frequency of vibration is increased, an increase in pitch is perceived. Similarly, loudness is the perceptual correlate of intensity.

and valleys which reflect the pattern of stressed and unstressed syllables. There are also breaks in voicing due to short pauses or voiceless consonants. The contour follows its overall characteristic pattern by means of inflections and glides during the voiced portions and by means of jumps between breaks in voicing.

Space does not allow for a detailed examination of how a speaker modulates his voice frequency in keeping with the phonemic and linguistic constraints set by a given utterance. There is also some divergence of opinion as to the interpretation of intonation contours. The reader is referred to Bronstein and Jacoby (1967) for an excellent introduction to the subject, and to Pike (1946) for a classic study on the intonation of American English. For two important new developments see Bolinger (1958) and Lieberman (1967).

Having briefly reviewed the most important variables governing the suprasegmental structure of speech, we can now return to consideration of how the production of individual phonemes is affected by neighboring phonemes. Generally, phonemes within a sense group interact, but there is little, if any, interaction between adjacent phonemes belonging to separate sense groups.

One of the major causes of interaction between phonemes is that the required movements of the articulators for each sound are not initiated at the same time. Some articulators are moved earlier than others in anticipation of the phoneme to follow. The effect is to change the quality of the ongoing phoneme as well as that of the following phoneme. The effects are also most pronounced if the same articulator plays a major role in both sounds. For example, in the word *plan* the release of air for the plosive /p/ occurs laterally, since the tongue is already in position for the /ℓ/ by the time the release occurs. This effect is common to all the plosives when followed by an /ℓ/. Some illustrative examples are *pan - plan, bud - blood, care - Clare, gory - glory.*

A similar anticipatory interaction occurs when nasals follow a plosive. In this case the air is released nasally. Several examples occur in the sentence "A*gn*es woul*d n*ot ru*b m*y *hot n*ose." If the entire sentence is spoken as a single sense group, the plosive-nasal interaction occurs between the *italicized* pairs. If, however, the speaker introduces a break between a pair, such as between the words *would* and *not* so as to emphasize the word *not,* then the /d/ and /n/ belong to separate sense groups and are articulated separately.

Another common anticipatory interaction occurs when a plosive leads into a vowel. Typically, those articulators which are not required for the plosive move toward the vowel target positions well before the plosive is actually released. To demonstrate the effect, the reader may articulate the syllables *dee* and *doo* in front of a mirror. The lip positions should be quite different for *dee* and *doo* even before the /d/ is produced.

In the case of the plosives /k/ and /g/, the place of articulation can be varied over a fairly wide range and the effect of the following vowel is to move the place of articulation to a location more in keeping with the target position of the vowel. The effect is demonstrated in the words *keep, cope,* and *coop.* In *keep* the transition is to a high front vowel and the /k/ is produced by placing the hump of the tongue in a fairly high position behind the hard palate. In *cope* the transition is to a mid-back vowel, and the place of articulation for the /k/ is moved down toward the velum. In *coop* the transition is to a back vowel, and a low velar position is used in articulating the /k/.

Anticipatory movements are very pronounced when an /ℓ/ or /n/ precedes either of the dental fricatives /θ/ or /ð/. In this case the /ℓ/ or /n/ is produced with the tongue tip placed against the upper teeth which is the characteristic position for the fricative. The following pairs demonstrate the changes in tongue position during /ℓ/ and /n/; *on a day—on the day, Anthony—Antony, all at—all that, will throw—will row.* The articulation of /ℓ/ is also affected by its position relative to adjoining vowels, as evidenced by the distinction between the "light" /ℓ/ and "dark" /ℓ/ discussed in the preceding section.

Interactions tend to increase when sounds using the same mechanisms follow each other. Plosives, especially voiceless plosives, are marked by aspiration (i.e., a turbulent outward flow of air) after their release. If the following sound is a fricative, which requires aspiration for its production, then much of the plosive release is absorbed by the fricative. For example, compare the following pairs: *hippy - hipsy, tar - tsar, big ape - big shape.* Even if the fricative precedes the voiceless plosive, the aspiration during the release is greatly reduced, such as in *tar - star, par - spar.* Plosives leading into plosives also have marked interactions. Generally, the release of the first plosive is absorbed into the release of the second plosive. Several illustrative examples are *topcat, topdog,* and *topboy.* The effect is most marked when the two plosives use the same articulators, as in *topboy.*

Not all articulatory interactions result in the reduction or absorption of one sound into another. Sometimes an additional, unintentional sound is introduced. This effect usually occurs when the articulators, in moving from their positions for one sound to the next, pass through the characteristic positions of a third sound which may be produced unintentionally. Thus, *sense* may be produced as *scents, prince* as *prints, do in* as *do win* and *see am* as *see yam.* The inverse also happens in that the intermediate sound may be intended but is not produced, such as the /d/ in *hindsight.* It should be noted that the paired examples cited above are perceptually very similar and it is frequently difficult even for a trained listener to determine which phoneme sequence was produced.

Another form of interaction results from poor timing in the control of voicing. The facility with which we can control the movement of our articulators greatly exceeds that with which we control the onset and termination of voicing. Thus it is to be expected that when voiced and voiceless sounds are produced in sequence, a voiceless sound will occasionally be voiced and voiced sounds occasionally devoiced. The voiced-voiceless confusion frequently occurs when a voiceless sound of brief duration, such as a plosive, is surrounded by strongly voiced sounds. Typical examples are *bicker* pronounced as *bigger, batter* as *badder,* and *beetle* as *beadle.* The voiceless fricative /h/ is also frequently voiced when in the intervocalic position, such as in the word *mayhem.*

A typical speaker usually provides additional cues as to whether a consonant is intended as voiced or voiceless. Subtle changes in timing play a key role. The duration of a vowel is longer before a voiced consonant than before a voiceless one. Also, voiceless plosives are strongly aspirated when leading to a stressed vowel. These subtle changes in timing and manner of production are lost, however, when both syllables surrounding the consonant are unstressed. Voiced-voiceless confusions are most marked during the unstressed portions of speech.

Devoicing, or partial devoicing, of voiced sounds tends to occur before pauses such as at the end of sense groups or breath groups. The voiced fricative is a common candidate for devoicing when in this position, or when preceding a voiceless consonant. Typical examples are the /v/, /ð/ and /z/ in the sentence "I lo*ve* *s*moo*th* *s*eas and mountai*ns*." If the speaker pauses between *seas* and *and* the /z/ in seas may also be partially devoiced.

Many of the preceding examples showed how phonemes in context are affected by the suprasegmental structure of the utterance. By far the most dominant effect, however, is the subordination of articulatory behavior to maintaining the natural rhythm of speech. Stressed syllables are generally of fairly long duration, and in order to maintain a smooth, rhythmic flow, the unstressed syllables tend to be very short in duration. A common effect in unstressed syllables is that of vowel reduction in which the articulators do not have the time to reach their characteristic positions resulting in an indistinct schwa-like vowel. In addition to severely curtailing the durations of vowels and other continuants, it is also not unusual in casual speech to omit certain sounds. A common example is the omission of /v/ when preceding a consonant in an unstressed location, e.g., *cuppa coffee* instead of *cup of coffee.*

It is beyond the scope of this chapter to engage in a detailed discussion of all the phonemic interactions that occur in speech. This section has been concerned primarily with representative examples of the major types of interaction in General American English. Interactions that are heavily dialect-oriented have not been discussed and the reader is referred to Gimson (1962), McDavid (1958), and references cited therein, for a detailed treatment of dialectal differences.

Almost all interactions between phonemes spoken in context involve subtle variations in articulatory movements, and most talkers are quite unaware of these variations when speaking. Their main concern is that the sounds produced should be heard as the intended sounds. Variations and adjustments in articulatory movements that produce distorted or erroneous sounds are corrected with time, but articulatory adjustments that do not cause noticeable or unacceptable changes gradually become part of the speaker's speech habits. Deaf children, unfortunately, are unable to monitor their own speech production adequately. As a result, their speech development follows a markedly different pattern from that of normally hearing children. In the next section it will be shown that one of the major problems in the speech of the deaf is the poor linking together of speech sounds to form an evenly flowing, intelligible sequence.

Speech Production by Deaf Children

Errors or deficiences in the production of speech by deaf children can be divided into two major categories: errors affecting intelligibility and errors or deficiences affecting voice quality. Our main concern is with errors affecting intelligibility. These errors can in turn be subdivided into two further categories: errors of articulation involving individual phonemes and errors involving suprasegmental features, such as intonation, rhythm, and phrasing.

An analysis of the articulatory errors produced by deaf children (Hudgins and Numbers, 1942) showed that most common consonant errors were:

i) Non-function of initial consonants. Typically, the proper degree of closure is not made, thus preventing air pressure from producing the consonantal effect. The perceived effect is that of dropping the consonant.

ii) Voiced-voiceless confusions. Typical examples are /p/ for /b/, /t/ for /d/, /k/ for /g/, /f/ for /v/, and /θ/ for /ð/, and vice versa.

iii) Errors in clustered consonants. These errors may take one of two forms: a) one or more of the members making up a cluster may be dropped; b) the members of the cluster are spoken too slowly, with the result that adventitious syllables are added to the word. Typical examples are *sunow* for *snow* and *sulamuz* for *slams*.

The following errors were also found to be important, although they occurred less frequently:

iv) Errors involving abutting consonants. For two adjacent syllables with abutting consonants, an adventitious syllable is added between the final consonant of the first syllable and the initial consonant of the second syllable, e.g., *flag-u-pole* for *flagpole*.

v) Errors of nasality. Consonants may be nasalized, leading to substitutions, such as /m/ for /p/ or /b/, /n/ for /t/ or /d/, and /ŋ/ for /k/ or /g/.

vi) Substitution of one consonant for another, such as /w/ for /r/, /l/ for /r/, /t/ or /θ/ for /s/. This category accounts for substitutions other than those already considered in (ii) and (v) above.

vii) Non-function of final consonants. The consonantal movement is too slow, incomplete, or dropped entirely. The effect is that the syllable is not arrested and the vowel trails off slowly.

Hudgins and Numbers also found that the most common vowel errors were:

i) Substitution of one vowel for another, e.g., *tin* for *ten*.

ii) Errors involving diphthongs. These may take one of two forms: a) the diphthong is split, making two distinct vowels, e.g. *da-ee* for *day;* b) one of the components of the diphthong, usually the final member, is dropped, e.g., *found* becomes *fond*.

iii) Neutralization of simple vowels. The vowel loses its distinctive quality and becomes more like the neutral vowel /ə/. The syllables are usually shortened and are not given their expected degree of stress. This type of error may be classified as both segmental and suprasegmental because, although a specific phoneme is misarticulated, the error is primarily due to incorrect rhythm.

iv) Diphthongization of pure vowels. A diphthong is made out of a simple vowel; e.g., *ha* becomes *how*.

Most of the errors listed above involve incorrect movements of the articulators. The linking together of successive phonemes is particularly prone to error, whether it be in consonant clusters, abutting consonants between syllables, consonant-vowel or vowel-consonant transitions, or the components of a diphthong. The plosives, which require careful timing and skillful manipulation in moving from one set of articulatory positions to another, are a frequent source of error. A detailed study by Calvert (1961) of voiced and voiceless consonants in the intervocalic position (i.e., between two voiced sounds) showed that voiced-voiceless errors by deaf speakers correlated very closely with systematic differences in the release period of the plosives. Shorter release periods were associated with the voiced plosives. The deaf speakers generally tended to distort the durational characteristics of phonemes. In particular, the systematic differences in duration as a function of phonetic environment that are characteristic of normal speech were greatly distorted by the deaf speakers.

Even with continuous sounds, the lack of synchrony between articulation and voicing is an important source of error. Thus, for example, Mártony (1966), in a study on the speech of three deaf boys, found prominent errors in synchronization of voicing when linking fricatives, vowels, and nasals. Improper control of the velum is another source of error and leads to abnormal nasalization of vowels and continuants in addition to the errors of nasality cited by Hudgins and Numbers.

Those errors of articulation that do not involve movement of the articulators also tend to be less severe in that they lead primarily to substitutions rather than unidentifiable, inarticulate sounds. In a study of vowel production by young deaf boys, Angelocci, Kopp, and Holbrook (1964) found that the formants of the vowels produced by the deaf children tended to group together, approaching the pattern for the neutral / ə / vowel. This is in keeping with the finding in the Hudgins and Numbers study that many of the vowel substitutions were towards the neutral vowel. Angelocci, Kopp, and Holbrook also observed that the deaf children tended to use a higher voice frequency than the normal-hearing children. They suggest that the deaf children are raising their voice frequency in order to produce a vowel which, according to their limited means of monitoring their own speech, may tend to "sound" like the intended vowel.

If the articulatory errors involving vowels are primarily errors of substitution, it may be wondered whether a listener, not knowing which vowels are intended, can tell the difference between speech produced by deaf and normal-hearing speakers. Calvert (1961) found that recordings of sustained vowels by deaf and normal-hearing speakers provided insufficient cues for reliable identification of the deaf speakers. If the recordings contained at least a diphthong or a consonant-vowel-consonant syllable, then listeners could reliably identify which recordings were of deaf speakers. Thus it would seem that movements of the articulators are not only a major source of the most severe errors of articulation, but also produce errors which clearly distinguish the speech of the deaf from normal speech.

Perhaps the most noticeable feature of deaf speech is the severity of suprasegmental errors. Intonation is frequently flat and monotonous, rhythm is either lacking or incorrect, and phrasing can be completely inaccurate. Deaf speakers as a rule produce sounds inefficiently and have to pause for breath more frequently. They also tend to speak more slowly and the combined effect is to have short breath groups encompassing only a few words at a time. Short breath groups need not be too severe a handicap in speaking provided the pauses for breath are properly located, such as between sense groups. The importance of good respiratory control was emphasized by Hudgins (1946), who found a marked reduction in intelligibility due to poor breathing habits. Hudgins, in his pioneering study on the speech of the deaf, found that his deaf speakers used short, irregular breath groups of only one or two words in length, and that pauses for breath interrupted the flow of speech at improper points. A common source of difficulty was excessive expenditure of breath on single syllables.

Closely allied to the problem of breath control, which affects phrasing directly, is that of proper rhythm. Thus, Hudgins found that poor respiratory control leads not only to incorrect groupings of syllables, but also to improper placing of stress. Errors of rhythm may be categorized into two basic groups: lack of rhythm, as occurs when all syllables are equally stressed, and incorrect rhythm, as occurs when the wrong stress pattern is used. In both cases the reduction in intelligibility can be substantial. Hudgins and Numbers (1942), in a study on the speech of 192 deaf children, found a high correlation between rhythmic errors and poor intelligibility. Sentences which were either arhythmic or had incorrect rhythm were also the least intelligible of the sentences studied.

An important variable controlling the placing of stress is the relative durations of stressed and unstressed syllables. Many deaf speakers, in producing speech on a phoneme by phoneme basis, tend to extend the durations of vowels and continuants. The result is usually a severe, if not complete, distortion of the stress pattern. The prolongation of vowels and continuants, moreover, can sometimes be so exaggerated as to obliterate any semblance of suprasegmental structure. Under these conditions, even if all the phonemes are correctly identified, the listener may still not understand what has been said. The effect is much like reading on a letter-to-letter basis; the symbols are there but the message is lost.

The importance of correct timing has been demonstrated by Johns and Howarth (1965), who concentrated on the temporal patterns rather than articulatory features in training a group of 29 children. The children had hearing losses ranging from severe to profound. The results showed significant increases in speech intelligibility for both the moderately and profoundly deaf children.

Intonation is perhaps the most complex of the suprasegmental characteristics. The modulation of voice frequency is the key element in the control of intonation, yet at the same time, voicing plays an important role in the production of individual phonemes. The extent of this interaction may not be quite as obvious in normal speech as it is in the speech of the deaf. Aside from the basic voiced-voiceless distinction, there are also variations in voice frequency depending on which vowel or voiced continuant is being produced. Different sounds require different amounts of subglottal air pressure for their production and, since a change in subglottal air pressure on the vocal cords affects their frequency of vibration, some form of interaction between sound type and voice frequency is to be expected. Normal-hearing speakers tend to adjust vocal cord tension so as to compensate in part for changes in subglottal air pressure, so that there are only secondary interactions between voice frequency and sound type. Since deaf speakers are not able to monitor and control their voice frequency with the same degree of precision, there can be wide variations in voice frequency depending on which vowel or voiced continuant is produced. Data reported by Mártony (1968) show variations in voice frequency between different vowels of as much as 50 percent for deaf children. The corresponding figure for normal-hearing children is close to 15 percent. Large interactions of this type may possibly be explained in part by the theory mentioned earlier that deaf children attempt to compensate for poor control of the formants by varying their voice frequency (Angelocci, Kopp, and Holbrook, 1964). The control of intonation is further complicated by the fact that some deaf speakers produce sudden and uncontrolled changes in voice pitch, particularly with vowels of long duration.

One of the great difficulties facing the deaf speaker is that by the time he has learned to control his voice frequency adequately, he has then to learn the rules governing intonation. Most normal-hearing children learn the rules of intonation by ear without quite knowing what these rules are. Many deaf children tend to avoid any attempt at controlling intonation by speaking in a flat, monotonous voice. Others resort to the simple device of using a "favorite intonation contour" (Stewart, 1968), whether or not it fits the meaning of the sentence. The difficulty of learning the rules of intonation is underscored by the fact that there is still much ongoing research aimed at elucidating the basic structure of intonation contours (Lieberman, 1967; Levitt and Rabiner, 1971).

In addition to problems of phrasing, rhythm, stress, and intonation, deaf speakers also tend to have difficulties with voice quality. Although voice quality may have a secondary effect on meaning, an unpleasant or abnormal-sounding voice may nevertheless be an important psychological impediment to communication. One of the most commonly noticed qualities in the speech of many deaf children is the high average pitch. Measurements by Green (1956), Angelocci, Kopp, and Holbrook (1964), Mártony (1968), and others show that a large proportion of deaf children have a significantly higher average voice frequency than normal-hearing children. The range of average frequencies for deaf children is also greater.

The tendency of many deaf children to put undue effort into producing speech leads to a quality known as *overfortis* which is characterized by excessive breath pressure, over-emphasis in articulation and sometimes fluctuating pitch. Other common problems of voice quality include: breathiness, due to improper closing of the vocal cords leading to a continuous turbulent flow of air during voicing; nasality, due to improper control of the velum; and stridency, due to improper control of intensity. Greater detail on the topic of voice quality may be found in Travis (1957) and Ogilvie and Rees (1970).

In order to develop better techniques and instruments for improving the speech of deaf children, it is necessary to have a basic understanding of the mechanisms of speech production as well as a knowledge of how deaf children tend to deviate from normal-hearing children. This chapter has attempted to provide a capsule summary of how speech is pro-

Table I.

ARTICULATORS USED	STOPS		AFFRICATES		FRICATIVES		FRICTIONLESS CONSONANTS		
	Voiced	Voiceless	Voiced	Voiceless	Voiced	Voiceless	Nasals	Glides	Laterals
Lips	b	p				ʍ	m	w	
Lips and Teeth					v	f			
Tongue and Teeth					ð	θ			
Upper Gumridge	d	t			z	s	n		ℓ
Upper Gumridge & Hard Palate			dʒ	tʃ	ʒ	ʃ		(Retroflex) r	
Hard Palate								j	
Velum	g	k				ʍ	ŋ	w	
Glottis						h			

duced and the major differences between deaf and normal-hearing children in the production of speech. Although our knowledge of the deaf speaker is far from complete, we can at least point to several major distinctive characteristics. There is still much we need to know, such as, how consistent is the deaf speaker in his articulatory habits? To what extent are there consistent error patterns in the speech of the deaf, and how are these related to degree of hearing loss? Which errors are deeply ingrained and which are most amenable to correction? Research on the speech of the deaf is growing, and with time we may be able to answer some of these questions. Of greater importance, the acquisition of new knowledge may yet spawn novel and better techniques for improving the speech of the deaf.

BIBLIOGRAPHY

Angelocci, A., Kopp, G., and Holbrook, A. The vowel formants of deaf and normal hearing 11 to 14 year old boys. *Journal of speech and hearing disorders,* 1964, **29,** 156–170.

Bolinger, D. L. A theory of pitch accent. *Word,* 1958, **14,** 109–49.

Bronstein, A. J. *The pronunciation of American English.* New York: Appleton-Century-Crofts, 1960.

Bronstein, A. J., and Jacoby, B. F. *Your speech and voice.* New York: Random House, 1967.

Calvert, D. R. *Some acoustic characteristics of the speech of profoundly deaf individuals.* Doctoral dissertation, Stanford University, 1961.

Denes, P. B., and Pinson, E. N. *The speech chain; the physics and biology of spoken language.* Baltimore: Williams and Wilkins, 1963.

Flanagan, J. L. *Speech analysis, synthesis and perception.* New York: Academic Press, 1965.

Fry, D. B. The development of the phonological system in the normal and the deaf child. In F. Smith and G. A. Miller (Eds.), *The genesis of language.* Cambridge, Mass.: M.I.T. Press, 1966.

Gimson, A. C. *An introduction to the pronunciation of English.* London: Edward Arnold, Ltd., 1962.

Green, D. S. *Fundamental frequency characteristics of the speech of profoundly deaf individuals.* Doctoral dissertation, Purdue University, 1956.

Hirsh, I. J. Teaching the deaf child to speak. In F. Smith and G. A. Miller (Eds.), *The genesis of language.* Cambridge, Mass.: M.I.T. Press, 1966.

Hudgins, C. V., and Numbers, F. C. An investigation of the intelligibility of the speech of the deaf. *Genetic psychology monographs,* 1942, **25,** 289–392.

Hudgins, C. V. Speech breathing and speech intelligibility. *Volta review,* 1946, **48,** 642.

John, J. E. J., and Howarth, J. N. The effect of time distortions on the intelligibility of deaf children's speech. *Language and speech,* 1965, **8,** 127.

Ladefoged, P. *Elements of acoustic phonetics.* Chicago: The University of Chicago Press, 1962.

Lieberman, P. *Intonation, perception, and language.* M.I.T. Research Monograph No. 38. Cambridge, Mass.: M.I.T. Press, 1967.

Levitt, H., and Rabiner, L. R. An analysis of fundamental frequency contours in speech. *Journal of the Acoustical Society of America,* 1971, **49,** 569–582.

Mártony, J. Studies on the speech of the deaf. *Quarterly Progress and Status Report,* Speech Trans. Lab., Royal Inst. of Tech., Stockholm, January 1966.

Mártony, J. On the correction of voice pitch level for severely hard of hearing subjects. *American annals of the deaf,* 1968, **113,** 195.

McDavid, R. I., Jr. The dialects of American English. In W. N. Francis (Ed.), *The structure of American English.* New York: Ronald Press, 1958.

Ogilvie, M., and Rees, N. S. *Communication skills, voice and pronunciation.* New York: McGraw-Hill, 1970.

Pike, K. L. *The intonation of American English.* Ann Arbor: The University of Michigan Press, 1946.

Stewart, R. B. By ear alone. *American annals of the deaf,* 1968, **113,** 147.

Travis, L. E. (Ed.) *Handbook of speech pathology.* New York: Appleton-Century-Crofts, 1957.

Acknowledgements

I would like to thank Doctors Katherine Harris, Arthur J. Bronstein, Laurence R. Rabiner and Mrs. Clarissa Smith for their helpful comments and criticism.

The preparation of this chapter was supported in part by NIH research grant # NS 09252-01.

APPENDIX I

THE PHONEMES OF AMERICAN ENGLISH

Consonants

/p/ as in pen

/b/ as in bend

/m/ as in men

/w/ as in win

/f/ as in fine

/v/ as in vine

/θ/ as in thin

/ð/ as in then

/r/ as in red

/s/ as in said

/z/ as in zero

/ʃ/ as in shed

/ʒ/ as in measure

/tʃ/ as in child

/dʒ/ as in jump

/j/ as in yes

/k/ as in call

/t/ as in ten

/d/ as in den

/n/ as in no

/l/ as in low

/g/ as in gate

/ŋ/ as in sing

/h/ as in home

Vowels

/i/ as in seat

/ɪ/ as in sit

/ɛ/ as in set

/æ/ as in sat

/a/ as in half

/ɑ/ as in calm

/ɔ/ as in sought

/ʊ/ as in foot

/u/ as in food

/ə/ as in alone

/ʌ/ as in shut

/ɚ/ as in mother

/ɝ/ as in third

Diphthongs

/eɪ/ as in safe

/aɪ/ as in sigh

/aʊ/ as in now

/oʊ/ as in soap

/ɔɪ/ as in toy

/ju/ as in few

CHAPTER IV

Speech Science Research and Speech Communication for the Deaf

J. M. PICKETT, PH.D.

I believe that large improvements in the lives of deaf persons depend on making large improvements in their speech communication. There are current developments in speech science that have high potential for leading to this goal. I review these developments here and suggest ways in which they might, with further research, contribute a great deal to improved speech communication.

Today's possibilities for speech for the deaf are based on groundwork which began 100 years ago: in the first modern acoustic research on hearing and speech by Helmholtz, and in applications of acoustic science to the training of deaf pupils by Alexander Melville Bell. His son, Alexander Graham Bell, carried on this tradition; he continued and expanded the scientific approach to speech for the deaf, and he excited the interest of many other phoneticians and communication scientists. At Bell Telephone Laboratories the earliest of modern methods for measuring hearing loss and its effects on speech communication, and the first electronic aids for the deaf, were developed beginning about 1920. In the 1930's certain scientists began to devote most of their research to speech communication in deafness, notably, in the United States, R. H. Gault at Northwestern University, C. V. Hudgins and Louis DiCarlo at Clarke School for the Deaf. Recently, speech research at Bell Laboratories and at the Swedish Royal Institute of Technology has led to new ideas for electronic aids for the deaf (Dudley, 1936; Potter, Kopp, and Green, 1947; Risberg, 1968). Many of these new aids are now manufactured for use or are available in prototype form.

It is extremely important to maintain the closest possible relations between speech science and deaf educators. I am happy to say that today such relations are stronger than ever before and that they extend even into such esoteric fields as psycholinguistics and theoretical linguistics.*

In my survey, below, of speech-science research on deafness, I first describe new ideas for aids for the deaf that attempt to re-code speech for visual presentation, or for tactual or auditory presentation. Then I discuss the use of synthetic speech sounds for investigating hearing capacity and for auditory training. Finally I note future research needs for maximizing the applications of speech science to language acquisition by the deaf child.

Visual Speech Aids

The history of visual displays of speech for the deaf goes back to A. G. Bell. In 1874 he attempted to use an instantaneous visual display for the feedback of the pupil's speech waves in training deaf speakers. One aspect of his thinking on visual feedback for speech training helped him to solve a basic problem in the invention of the telephone in 1876 (Rhodes, 1929). Today visual displays of speech sound patterns are still considered primarily as aids to speech-teaching or speech correction. Quite a few visual speech trainers have been designed and I will now describe briefly the major types that employ principles of speech analysis. Further details may be found in the Proceedings of a recent conference on speech-analyzing aids (Pickett, 1968).

There has been a strong interest in visual aids for training speech production, because visual aids may be particularly well suited to certain aspects of speech training. First of all, a model or desired pattern can be presented to the pupil, and the model pattern can be stored for comparison with the pupil's own pattern. Secondly, a stored visual pattern is easy for the teacher to point to, for the purpose of indicating some part of the desired pattern; this may be very difficult, or even impossible, with auditory or tactual patterns.

In present methods for developing speech in deaf children and for correcting speech in deaf adults a teacher listens and informs the pupil as to the correctness of his articulation and how to improve it. One problem

*Recently two special committees of scientists were formed, in engineering circles, to promote research on new speech communication aids for the deaf: The Subcommittee on Sensory Aids of the National Academy of Engineering, and the Subcommittee on Speech-Coding Aids for the Deaf of the Institute of Electrical and Electronics Engineers.

with this procedure may be the lack of immediate feedback that is closely related to speech articulation. Recent developments in electronic speech analysis provide ways to derive instantaneous indications of selected speech characteristics. Some of these indications are closely related to the basic articulatory activity, and thus they may be useful as visual speech feedback in a trainer.

The current era of visual speech for the deaf began in 1944 at Bell Telephone Laboratories with the marriage of a sound analyzer to instantaneous phosphorescent screens, similar to television screens, to display the speech sound patterns. This device is called the Visible Speech Translator (VST). Some displays of speech on the VST screen are shown in Figure 1. The frequency patterns are analyzed and painted in time from left to right on the screen. The vertical dimension of the screen shows a range of frequencies from low to high, and the presence of sound energy at each frequency is represented by lighting the screen. Two examples of speech are shown, for utterance of the word *clap*. The utterance on the left is from a deaf talker and, for comparison, the one on the right is from a normal talker. You will note that the utterance of the deaf talker is longer than normal in the initial

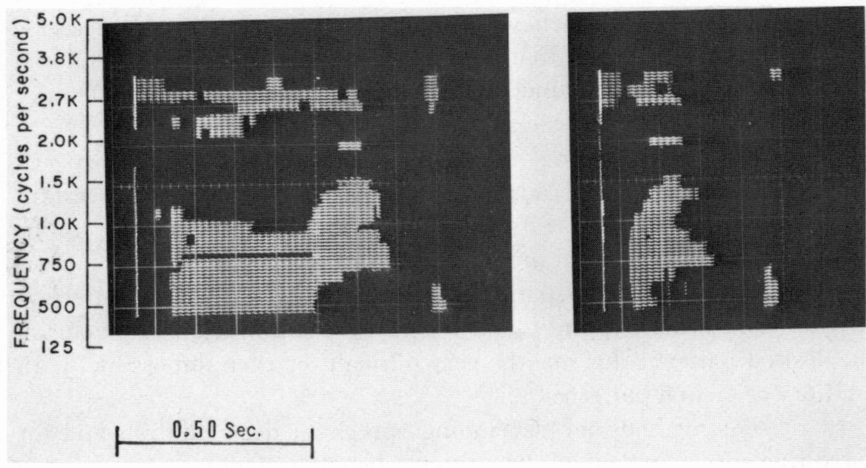

Figure 1. Visual displays on the Bell Telephone Laboratories' Visible Speech Translator. Displays are shown for two utterances of the word "clap," on the left by a deaf boy, and on the right by a normal-hearing boy. The deaf boy's utterance is much longer than normal and the frequency pattern is more poorly defined in the last phase of the word (from Stark, et al, *1968).*

low-frequency phase, the l-sound. The abnormally slow and uncoordinated speech of a deaf person may be correctable, using a display of this type as a training device.

You will also note in Figure 1 that the frequency concentrations or bands toward the end of the vowel are better defined in the normal speech.

These bands are the formants, and they vary in their frequency positions in response to the articulatory movements of speech; their normal course and positions are fairly well known (see Chapters 1 and 3 above, and Fant, 1960). Thus the VST may provide a feedback of speech patterns that can be related to speech movements, insofar as the movements are reflected in the apparent formant patterns.

The first results of research on speech training of deaf speakers, with visual feedback from the original VST, have been mildly encouraging (Kopp and Kopp, 1963). A new version of the VST with a storage screen, as seen in Figure 1, was described by Stark, Cullen, and Chase (1968). The storage screen will hold and display the pattern as long as desired; the teacher can point to features of the pattern and then erase it for a new trial by pushing an "erase" button. The storage screen can also display both a model pattern and the pupil's pattern and the patterns can be separately erased.

Stark has recently reported some preliminary research on speech training of deaf children using the VST patterns (Stark, 1970a and 1970b). She trained eight deaf children, 7–12 years old, to improve their production of the syllable *pa* by observing their syllables on the VST screen and comparing them with a model. A control group of deaf children were trained by a conventional tactile method and they showed significantly less improvement, in the post-training test, than did the group trained on the VST. Figure 2 shows the VST patterns corresponding to a deaf child's pronunciation of *ba* and *pa*. These patterns were successfully discriminated by the children.

Visual speech aids may also be valuable for improving speech reception. The first training experiments with a visual aid for speech reception were carried out at Bell Telephone Laboratories with the first models of the VST. After systematic training, viewers were able to read a large number of words, and to converse in simple phrases if the phrases were carefully pronounced (Potter, Kopp, and Green, 1947). However, the VST patterns for fluent phrases are very complex and it would probably never be possible to communicate solely in this way at a speed approaching that of fluent speech.

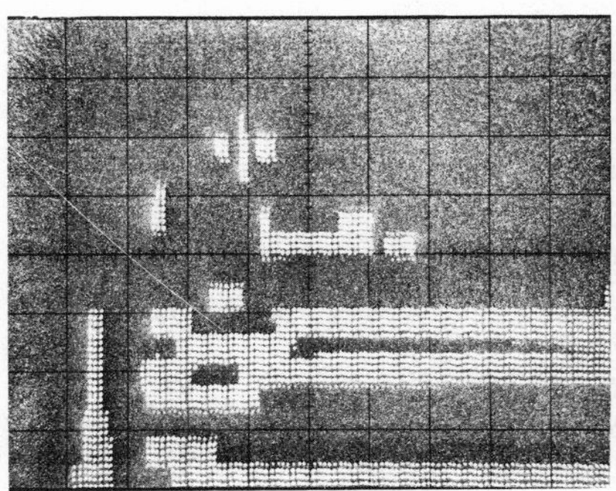
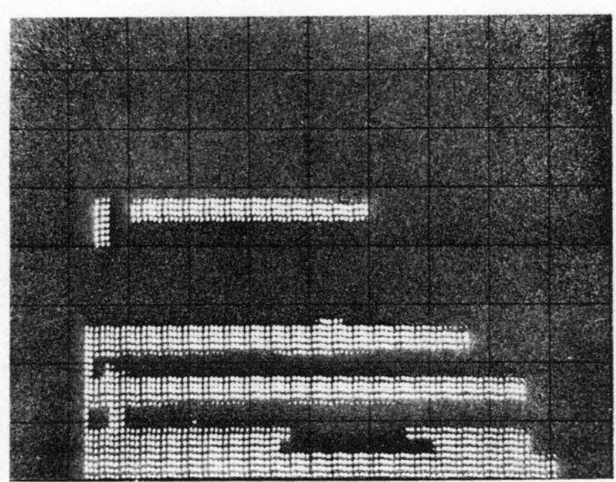

0 seconds .25

Figure 2. Pupil's patterns of pa *and* ba *on the Visible Speech Translator.* Pa *is on the left and shows first a burst of sound as the lips open, followed by a short gap before the vowel begins; for* ba *the vowel begins immediately after the lips open. Frequency scale same as Fig. 1, but expanded time scale.*

One visual speech display has been especially designed to be worn as an aid to speech reception by deaf persons, to supplement the hearing aid and lipreading (Upton, 1968). The indications of speech sounds are presented on miniature electric lamps mounted on eyeglasses so as to flash speech-derived signals to the wearer while he watches the person talking to him. The display is shown in Figure 3. You will see there are five lamps. The lighting of each lamp is controlled by circuits that react to features of frequency and duration in the speech received by a special analyzer worn like a large hearing aid. The lamp flashes are roughly related to the presence of certain sound categories which are noted for each lamp in the figure. A prototype model of this aid has been built and used by its inventor, Hubert Upton. Evaluations with a sample of deaf persons are needed, but have not yet been carried out.

Some workers have developed visual speech trainers that are more simple than the VST in their indications of various speech features. The exact shapes of formant patterns are not clearly depicted by the VST but they can be shown using a rearrangement in the display of the frequency analysis. The first such trainer, called LUCIA, was built and tested briefly at the Speech Transmission Laboratory in 1957–1959 (Lövgren

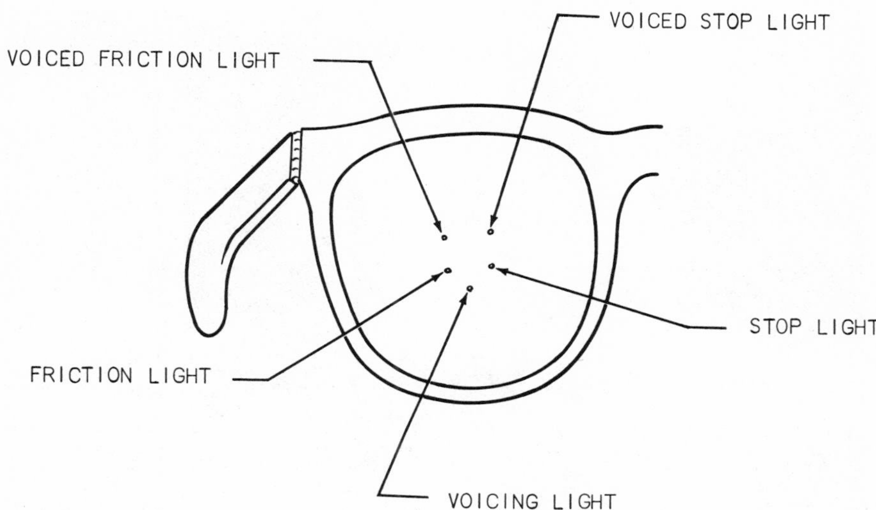

Figure 3. Eyeglass speechreading aid. Five miniature lamps are mounted behind the lens so as to flash light signals to the wearer. The light signals are controlled by a small analyzer which derives speech sound information that is partially correlated with the five categories of speech sound noted, one for each light (from Upton, 1968).

and Nykvist, 1959). A current version of LUCIA is shown in Figure 4 (Risberg, 1968). The display screen is a matrix of blocks, 10 × 20 blocks, which can be lighted individually from behind, according to the speech frequency patterns of the pupil. The horizontal dimension of the display represents frequency, which is divided into 20 frequency bands. The vertical blocks of light represent sound intensity in 10 steps (blocks) of 3 dB each. Thus an intensity range of 30 dB is available; this range is necessary to differentiate many important speech sounds, and to indicate voice quality.

Normally, with fluent speech spoken into LUCIA, the pattern of lights changes very rapidly. For some purposes, such as training of coarticulation, this may be desirable; but for early articulatory positioning, without encouraging prolonged utterance to observe the pattern, a momentary pattern can be frozen to permit examination. Whenever delayed feedback seems desirable, the display can be switched off, but a sample pattern can be taken and displayed afterwards. Display patterns of several speech sounds are shown in Figure 5.

A number of speech experimenters, feeling that display of complete frequency patterns might be too complex for some training situations

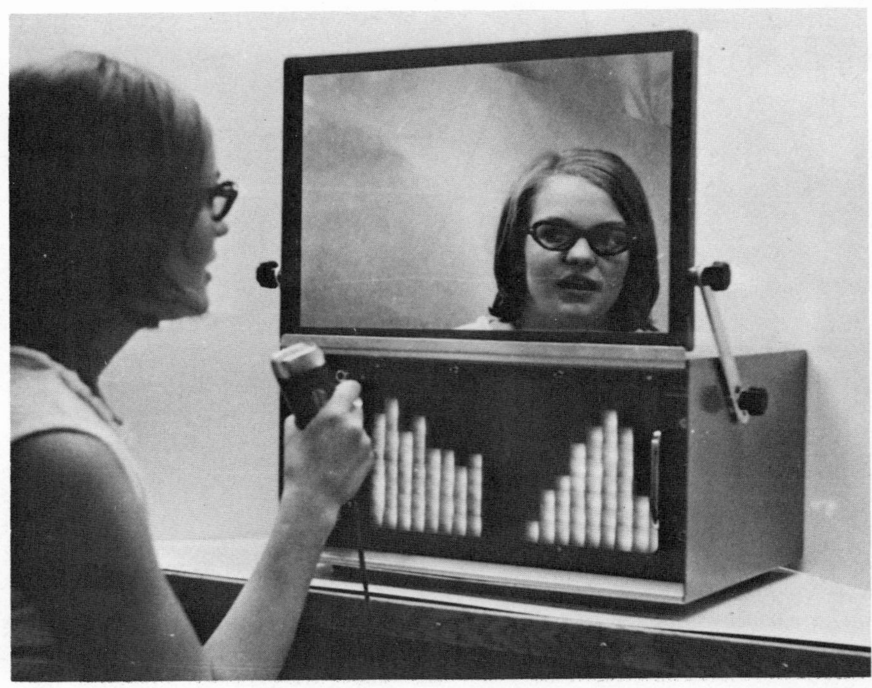

Figure 4. Swedish LUCIA speech indicator. Each column of lights represents a frequency band of speech. There are 20 bands from low frequencies on the left to high frequencies on the right (from Risberg, 1968).

and too expensive for widespread adoption, have built more simple indicators of frequency patterns. Probably the first of these was a device built and used by Pronovost and Lerner, called the Voice Visualizer (Pronovost, Yenkin, Anderson, and Lerner, 1968). Differences between broad classes of sounds are seen in this display, e.g., between front vowels, back vowels, and noise-like sounds.

A common defect of deaf speech stems from the difficulty of obtaining the proper tongue positions in forming the different vowels. The result is a distribution of vowel formant frequency positions that are often closer to those of a neutral vowel than to those of the intended vowel (Angelocci, Kopp and Holbrook, 1964).

I built a two-dimensional display using a single spot on the screen to roughly represent tongue articulation during vowels, glides, and semivowels (Pickett and Constam, 1968). Figure 6 shows some of the spot

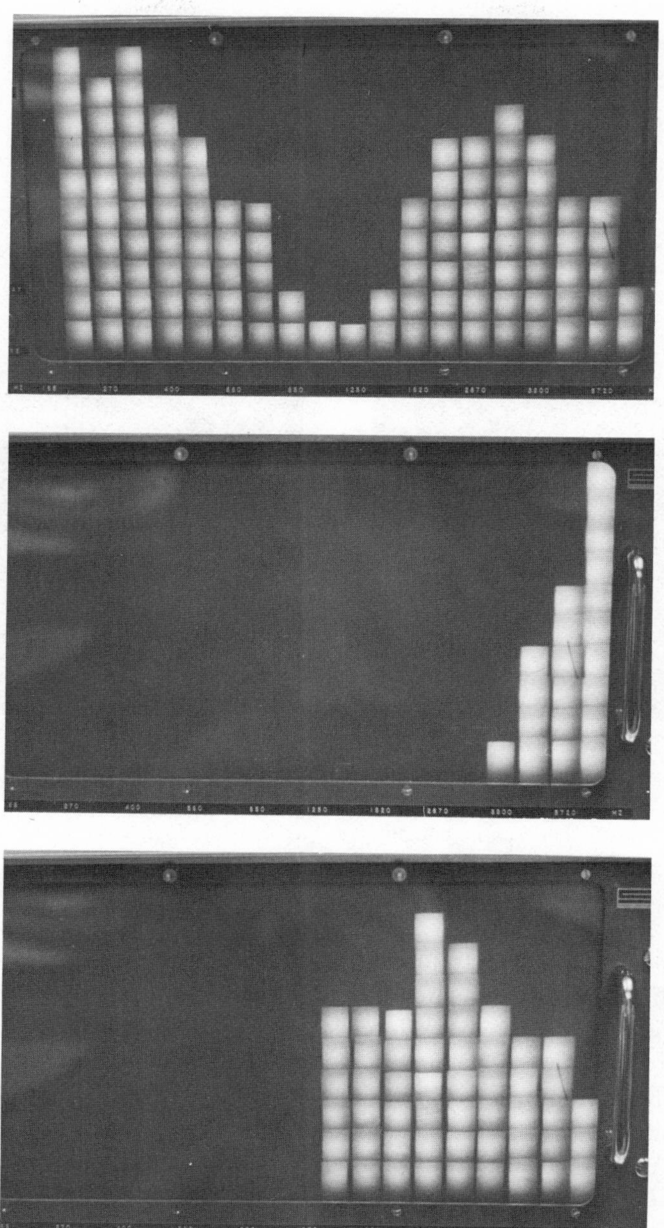

Figure 5. Speech sounds displayed on the Swedish LUCIA. Three sounds are shown: top, the vowel "ee"; middle, the consonant "s"; bottom, the consonant "sh."

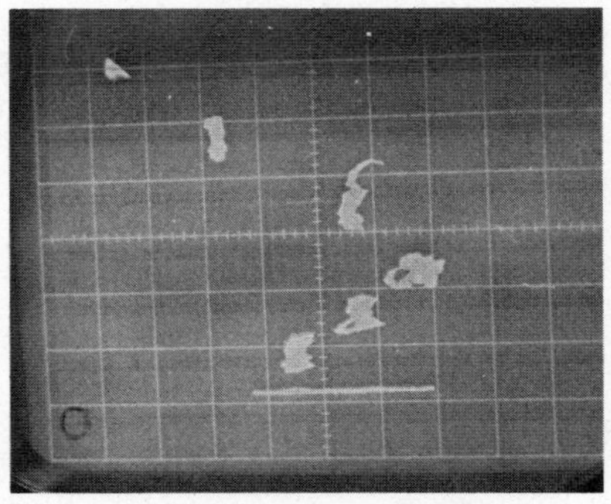

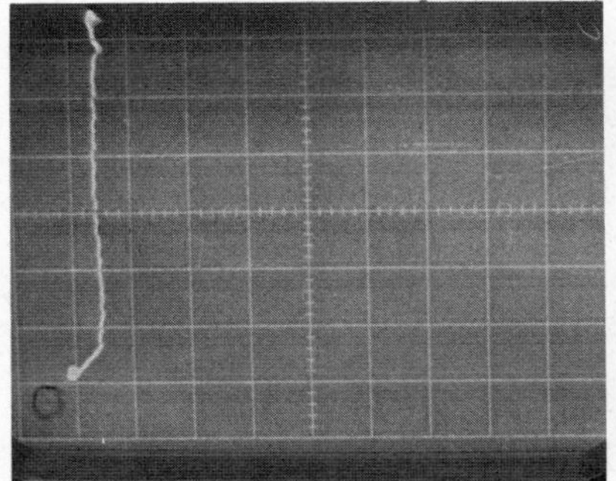

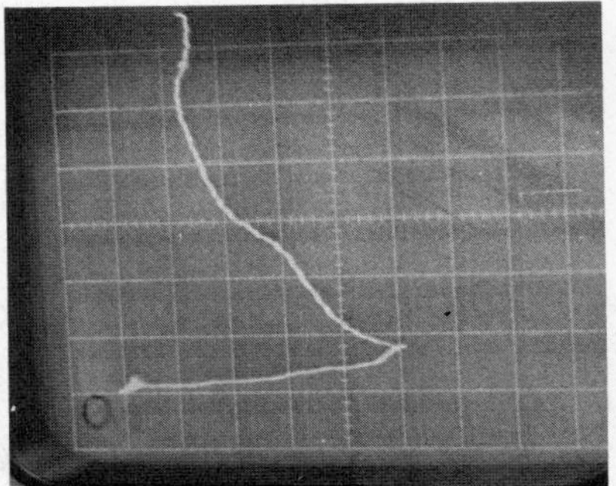

Figure 6. Displays of speech sounds on the Gallaudet visual speech trainer. Top, sustained vowel sounds, from above "ee" as in beet, *"ay" as in* bay, *"eh" as in* bet, *"ah" as in* box, *"awe" as in* bought, *"oh" as in* boat. *Left, trace of the word* bee. *Right, trace of the word* we.

locations for vowels, and patterns of glides. The horizontal position of the spot on the screen is related roughly to the articulatory position of the tongue in the mouth as to its closeness to the palate; the vertical position of the spot is somewhat related to the front-to-back location in the mouth of the tongue hump. These relations between articulatory position and spot position are far from being perfectly correlated but I feel that, together with a teacher, the display may be of considerable value, at least in loosening up tongue movement.

Besides the sound patterns of speech that reflect tongue and lip movements there are important patterns that depend on vocal factors operating at the basic level of the sound source. These are the voice pitch patterns and the rhythmic coordination. The duration patterns of different rhythms can be seen in the display on the VST. Also a single scanning beam on a storage oscilloscope can provide an obvious display of voice pitch variations, combined with the rhythmic patterns. An example is shown in Figure 7. The beam traces time horizontally and voice pitch vertically.

Mártony (1968) and Phillips, *et al* (1968), have reported research results on changing the levels of voice pitch used by deaf trainees who watched their pitch patterns in a display like that of Figure 7.

A very simple and inexpensive display can be provided by the movement of a needle on a meter. Meter displays have been built for voice pitch and for indicating the quality of sounds like *s* and *sh*. These sounds cannot be heard by most deaf persons, so they do not speak them correctly, but it is easy electronically to derive a quality measure of these sounds and present the measure as a needle deflection on a meter. A recent version of an *s*-indicator is shown in Figure 8.

Simple meter-needle indications of *s*-sound, of voice pitch level, and of voice volume have been built and used by Bøorrild (1968) and Risberg (1968). These may be useful at certain stages of training, and they are much less expensive than the oscilloscope indicators. An important feature of Risberg's indicator is the provision, in addition to the meter reading, of a "yes-no" light operated from a criterion-setting circuit that is adjustable by the teacher. In initial stages of training, the original *s*-sound may deteriorate as the pupil attempts to readjust his *s* according to the teacher's instruction. At this point, the teacher can lower the criterion so that the light will come on for a sound that is closer to an *s* than

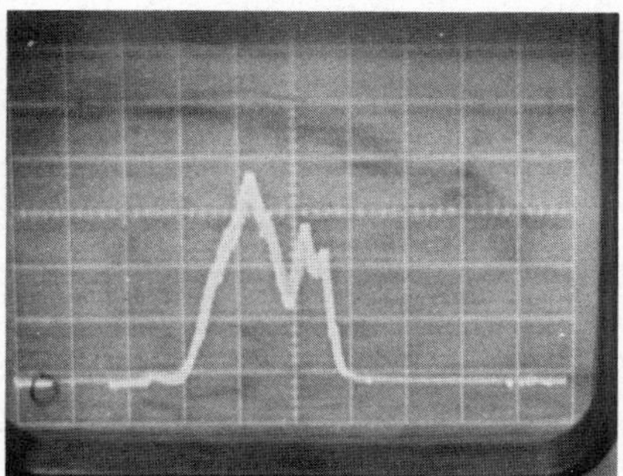

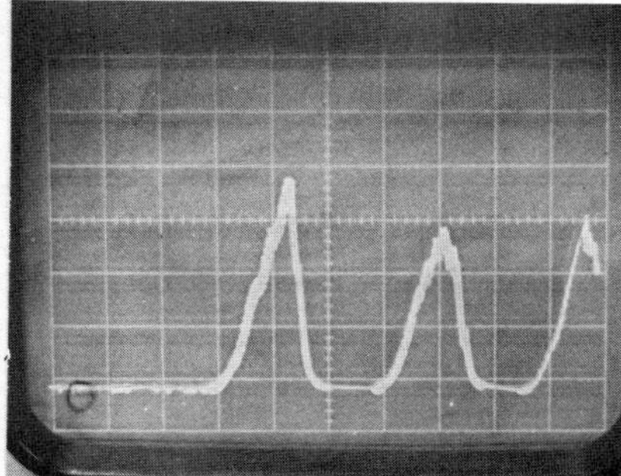

Figure 7. Displays of a voice pitch indicator. Pitch is traced upward and time from left to right. Display on the left shows a trace of the phrase How are you? *with accent on the last syllable. On the right is the same phrase spoken with separated syllables.*

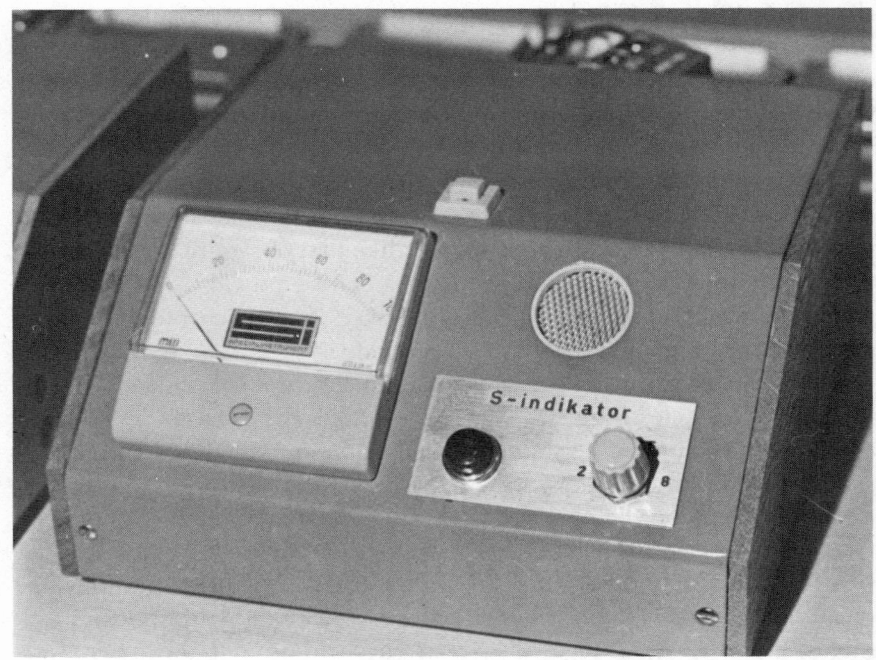

Figure 8. S-indicator. This indicator is small and self-contained. The microphone is behind the round grill. A good s-sound moves the needle of the meter to the upper part of the scale. A poor s-sound is indicated in the low part of the scale. The criterion light and setting knob are just below the microphone.

were the examples produced just previously by the pupil, thus rewarding him for changing his *s*-sound in the desired direction.

A nasal indicator has been designed by Risberg (1968) which measures nasality through a vibration pickup applied to the side of the nose. The indications are similar to those of the *s*-indicator. Both nasal consonants and nasalized vowels are well discriminated from normal non-nasal sounds, which have a very weak vibration level at the nose. This is an electronic version of the older method of feeling for nose-vibrations with the finger.

Voiced speech sounds are fairly easy to discriminate from unvoiced ones by electronic comparison of the balance between high and low frequencies. If the balance is displayed by a trace in time on a screen, a type of consonant-vowel training aid is available for improving speech coordination, for detecting "extra" sounds, and for seeing gaps in phonation.

This type of display has been used in the Bell VST, and by Risberg (1968). In Risberg's indicator, three trace movements are used, corresponding to 1) consonant noise intensity (trace deflects downward), 2) silence (trace stays in middle), and 3) voiced sound intensity (trace deflects upward).

Tactual Speech Aids

It is possible to give a deaf person tactual representations of speech sound patterns. Research work on this idea began in the 1920's, with the many studies of Gault and his students at Northwestern University (Gault and Crane, 1928). It was found, fairly early, that direct skin reception of speech vibrations would be of very limited value compared with the normal ear or even with the severely hard-of-hearing ear. The main difficulty is the limited capacity of the skin for frequency analysis. In addition, tactual speech must contend with the wide spatial spread of stimulation across the skin (Rösler, 1957; Sherrick, 1964). The spatial spread of tactual stimulation makes it hard to substitute spatial patterns for the speech frequency patterns, because the frequency bands may merge together when they are converted to tactual locations.

Nevertheless, various tactual speech coders have recently been built that analyze the frequency patterns of speech and re-code these patterns in a tactual form. Many workers are confident that some form of tactual aid will be useful for those people who are so profoundly deaf that little or no auditory information can be received.

Another reason for interest in tactual speech coding is that the perception of time patterns and rhythms through the skin appears to be similar to hearing. This does not seem to be true for the sense of vision, although I don't know of evidence on this point. Also, some types of visual speech display might interfere with lipreading, but this probably would not occur with tactual displays.

Two tactual speech-coding aids have been systematically tested on deaf children. Both of these attempt to represent the frequency patterns of the incoming speech by means of spatial patterns of vibration applied to the skin.

The first aid tested was a tactual "vocoder" built in 1957 at the Speech Transmission Laboratory in Stockholm (Lövgren and Nykvist, 1959). Basically, this aid attempted to represent the frequency-amplitude patterns of sound using ten vibrators applied to the ten finger tips. Each vibrator represented a different frequency region in the speech.

Tests with deaf children measured improvements in speech sound discrimination relative to lipreading alone; the tests covered all the major phonetic distinctions. It turned out that this tactual device was fairly helpful on some of the speech distinctions that are extremely difficult to lipread, such as voicing, nasality, and affrication. Discrimination of these features through the tactual vocoder was not perfect, but it was much better than the chance scores obtained with lipreading alone (Pickett, 1963; Pickett and Pickett, 1963).

A unique and much simplified tactual vocoder was designed and tested by Kringlebotn (1968). This vocoder employs only five vibrators applied to one hand. Training tests of this system were carried out with deaf children. The results were much better than those previously obtained with the vocoder having ten channels.

Research on tactual coding of speech has thus far been limited to discrimination tasks and to identification of isolated words from small sets. The results show that certain important speech discriminations can be conveyed tactually. It still remains to develop and test portable or wearable tactual aids for everyday use.

Frequency Transposition for Hearing Aids

It is now easy electronically to transpose sound patterns instantaneously down to lower frequency ranges. Thus, the dense regions of speech information, especially between 1.0 and 3.0 KHz, might be brought within the range of the low-frequency hearing capacity which many deaf persons possess. A number of scientists have suggested that a hearing aid using this principle might provide improved speech communication for those with severe hearing loss (Denes, 1967; Johansson, 1966; Oeken, 1963; Piminow, 1962; Raymond and Proud, 1962; Tiffany and Bennett, 1961).

The first transposer hearing aid was developed and tested by Johansson in 1954–1955. This transposer leaves the vowel sounds unchanged, and transposes only the high frequency sounds, such as unvoiced fricatives, like *s, sh,* and *f,* and the noise bursts of stops like *p, t,* and *k.* Tests with this transposer showed dramatic improvements in discrimination of certain fricative and stop consonants by profoundly deaf children. After transposer training, discrimination using a conventional amplifier showed no improvement over the previous low performance (Johansson, 1966).

Transposition by a partial re-coding method has been tested in training of word reception by deaf children (Ling, 1968; Ling and Doehring, 1969). For the partial re-coding, speech sounds occurring in the range of frequency between 2.0 and 3.0 KHz were separated out and re-coded to be special sounds in the range 0.7 to 1.0 KHz; then the re-coded sounds were added to the original speech in a "hole" formed by rejecting the original band of 0.7 to 1.0 KHz. In training and testing with deaf children, this method was compared with the Johansson method and with conventional amplification. The results were generally disappointing; both methods of transposing produced only small positive effects, if any, on word reception, and they were not found to be significantly superior to reception through the conventional amplifier.

Very serious retraining problems arise when we attempt to develop a radically new auditory code for speech, for example, by merely dividing all the frequencies in the original speech. The frequency-divided sounds still sound very much like speech, and many of them are similar to back vowels, such as /u/, / ɔ /, and /o/ and to low-frequency consonants, such as /w/ and /r/, and they are so interpreted by a listener. Retraining the listener to interpret these sounds as front vowels or as high-frequency consonants may be very difficult, or even impossible.

Can we justify attempting to train deaf infants to perceive speech through a radical re-coding system? This might solve the re-learning problem. However, we would need in addition to train the infants with conventional hearing aids because we probably could not guarantee that the same re-coding system would be available to the children during all situations in later life. In this case, the children would have to learn speech communication based on two different systems of sound patterns.

Some re-coding devices attempt to form new sound patterns that are not speech-like, and then add them to the original speech, as did the coder used by Ling; this coder used a set of low pure tones to represent the speech at the higher frequencies. So far, however, the auditory training of deaf children with this device has not been particularly successful, as we noted above. One problem may be that interpretation of a mixture of speech and non-speech sounds, *both as representing speech,* is inherently very difficult for a listener who has already learned to perceive some of the speech sounds. There is evidence that, normally, speech sounds are treated separately from non-speech, in their processing by the nervous system at the higher levels (Liberman, *et al,* 1967; Shankweiler and Studdert-Kennedy, 1967). Risberg has written a review of similar problems in transposing (Risberg, 1969).

It appears from the present test results with transposers that considerably more research will be necessary before we know how best to design transposer hearing aids. It will be necessary to solve some very difficult problems, as discussed above. It will probably also be necessary to take into account different individual hearing capacities at various frequencies, and for different time patterns.

Research on Hearing Capacity for Speech

We now consider how speech science may lead to a better understanding of residual hearing for speech sounds. How does speech sound to deaf persons? In what ways does impaired hearing interfere with discriminating the sound patterns of speech? We are now in a position to seek detailed scientific answers to such questions.

Recent research on normal speech perception has developed a large body of knowledge about the sound cues in speech, for example, the formants that listeners use to tell what a speaker is saying. For deaf persons, however, there is little knowledge of this process. We know that the deaf population includes persons ranging very widely in their general capacity for understanding speech; even when the sound is amplified to their best listening level, some deaf persons have little or no success in discriminating the different speech sounds while others can do rather well. Yet we know very little about the details of these capacities; that is to say, we do not know much about which speech cues are correctly perceived by various types of deaf persons and which are not.

There is a great need for complete and systematic knowledge of how speech cues are perceived by deaf persons. Such knowledge might tell us what speech sounds to use in initial auditory training, to try to ensure that we use discriminable inputs to the deaf child. The teacher, too, might better be able to choose speech material for the classroom. Designers of hearing aids and other amplifying devices also need to know what speech cues deaf persons can already perceive so that these cues are retained in the amplified sound.

There are three major ways to investigate the problem of how speech cues are perceived by hearing impaired persons: (1) examine and analyze word reception to determine patterns of sound confusions, (2) study auditory discrimination for different cues in speech-like sound patterns, and (3) study the perceptual similarities of speech sounds, using ratings or other similarity judgments. A beginning has been made on sound confusions and speech cue discrimination by deaf listeners.

In my laboratory we have just completed a study of the perception of certain speech features in words heard by deaf listeners (Pickett, *et al,* 1970). The listeners were grouped into classes according to their overall success in speech reception. Our aim was to see how the reception of consonants might vary over a population of deaf persons having different capacities for speech perception. The consonant sounds perceived by the listeners were analyzed according to their phonetic features of voicing, place of articulation, and low-frequency continuance. Each consonant perceived was scored separately as to whether its phonetic features corresponded to those in the test word. If all these features were heard correctly, the response consonant was correct, but there were many wrong responses which were correct as to voicing but wrong as to place of articulation. For example, if the test word were *mad* and the listener responded with *lad,* this was scored as correct for voicing, but wrong for place of articulation. This response would also be scored correct as to low-frequency continuance, in that both *m* and *l* are strong low-frequency consonants; if the response had been *pad,* it would have been wrong as to low continuance and voicing, but correct as to place of articulation in that both *m* and *p* are produced by closure of the mouth at the same place.

The test population consisted of those students admitted to Gallaudet College in 1967 and 1968 who had *any* speech discrimination ability at all for common "spondee" words like *baseball, mousetrap, cowboy,* etc. This population consisted of about one-fourth of the entering students.

The results are shown in Figure 9. It will be seen in the figure that the features of voicing and low continuance are perceived much better than the feature of place of articulation.* This is generally true for all levels of discrimination in this population, and for initial consonants as well as final consonants. It is interesting to note that normal listeners also show better perception of the voicing feature when receiving only the low frequencies of speech (Miller and Nicely, 1955). Thus the well-known fact that deaf persons often appear to have good low-frequency hearing is also reflected in their speech perception.

More research of this type is needed to develop a complete picture of speech perception in the deaf population. However, from the few results we now have, educators and therapists will note that speech features that are sometimes easy to lipread, i.e., place features, are hard to hear and some features that are hard to lipread, voicing and low continuance, are

*Two unpublished investigations also support this result (Rosen, 1962; Cox, 1969); an analysis of the data of Schultz (1964) is also consistent with this conclusion.

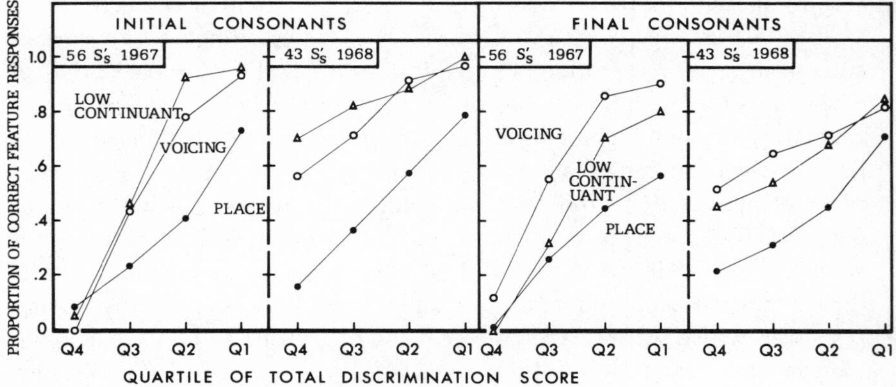

Figure 9. Perception of the different sound features of consonants by deaf listeners in word-reception tests. The proportion heard correctly for each feature is plotted vertically, and separately for four groups of the listeners (Q4, Q3, Q2, Q1) according to their rank in test score in the year of testing. Note especially that the voicing feature and the low continuant feature are perceived better than the feature of place of articulation. *Perception of voicing and low continuance probably depend on hearing low-frequency sound while perception of place depends on hearing the vowel formant transitions and the high-frequency bursts; see text for examples of the features. The data are for one-syllable words spoken by a single talker and each point plotted gives the results from the responses of one-quarter of the listeners in each year to a total of 20 spoken consonants.*

easier to hear. It is fortunate, too, that the voicing and other low-frequency features of speech carry a higher information load in speech communication than do the place features (Denes, 1963).

The study of auditory discrimination for small changes in speech sounds, our second major method, has been greatly facilitated by the recent development of synthetic speech that is produced electronically.

The idea of synthetic speech production is not new; Helmholtz and A. G. Bell did mechanical experiments to synthesize speech sounds in the 1860's. Recently, electronic speech synthesis has been used very successfully in the research leading to our current knowledge of the perception of speech cues: electronic synthesis makes it possible to produce any sound cue we desire and to test for its effect on perception.

We have just begun to use tests with synthetic speech sounds in order to describe the hearing capacity of deaf persons. Synthetic sounds have many advantages for this purpose: they can be produced and controlled at will; the composition of the sounds can be controlled as we see fit, i.e., one aspect of the sound pattern can easily be changed by a known amount. For example, the frequency of a formant, and its loudness, can be changed independently for experimental purposes to see what effect these changes might have on formant discrimination by a deaf listener. Later we will see how this might lead to new methods of auditory training.

In research on hearing capacity, we used synthetic vowels where a resonance or formant in the spectrum of the vowel was manipulated for a test of vowel sound discrimination by deaf listeners (Pickett and Mártony, 1970). We found that low-frequency formants around 100 Hz and 200 Hz were easier to distinguish than formants around 400 Hz and 800 Hz. Nevertheless, improvement in discrimination occurred at 400 and 800 Hz over several months of practice, for some of the listeners. Other listeners, however, showed very poor discrimination and little improvement with practice.

These experiments employed formants that were steady in frequency for the duration of each sound. However, during actual speech the vowel formants have rapid transitions in the vicinity of consonants, and these formant transitions are important cues to identification of the consonants, especially as to their place of articulation, and partially as to their manner of articulation. We have carried out some preliminary tests of capacity to hear formant transitions with six listeners having moderately severe sensorineural hearing losses (Pickett and Martin, 1970). The tests were carried out to measure the discriminability of transitions through low, middle, and high frequency regions (respectively to end-frequencies of 1.2, 2.0, and 3.0 KHz). The transitions were easier to hear when they were large. The size of transition that was necessary to make it just discriminable, from the same sound with no transition, was the index used for describing the hearing capacity for these transitions. If the size of transition is large, capacity is poor. Slower transitions were easier to hear than faster ones, so this factor was also varied from test to test. The results are shown in Figure 10.

We see in Figure 10 that the transition-detecting capacity of the hearing impaired listeners was worse for high frequencies than for lower frequencies. For brief transitions of 50 and 100 msec, which are like those of stop and glide consonants, the listeners with hearing losses always had larger thresholds than normal listeners. Only for low, long transitions, similar to those occurring in diphthongs, does the group with flat hearing loss become equal to the normal group.

To discriminate the various consonants of natural speech, as to place

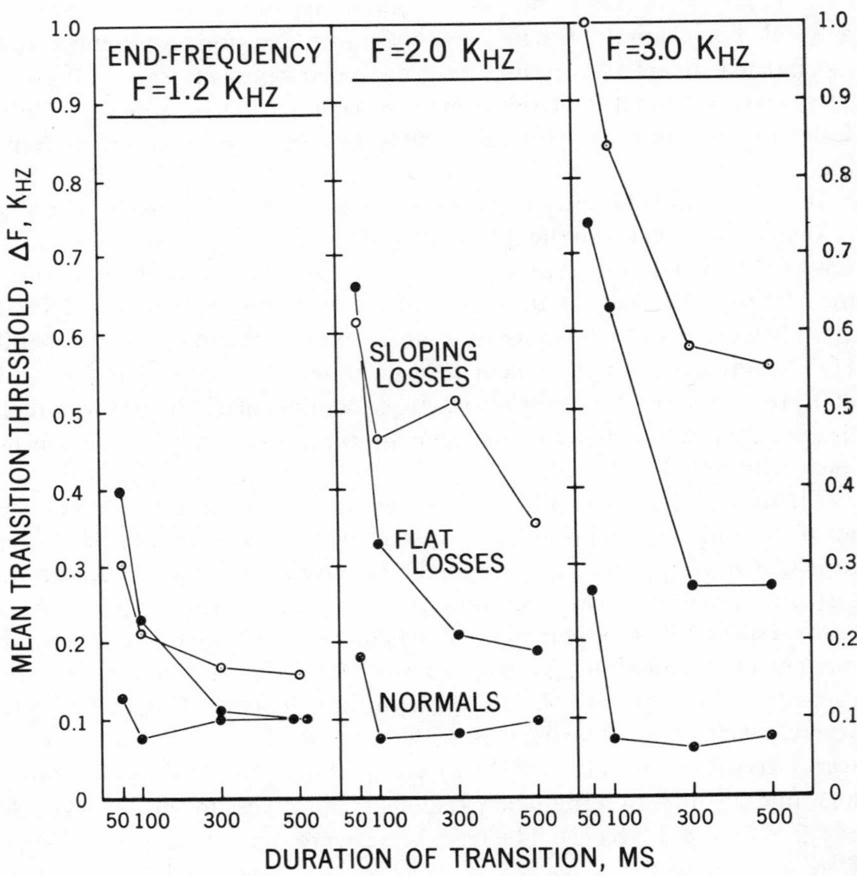

Figure 10. Experimental results showing deficient auditory detection, by deaf listeners, of the occurrence of a formant transition in synthetic vowel sounds. The results that are higher in the graph show the more deficient detection, in that a larger amount of transition is necessary for the listener to detect it. Tests were made at low, middle, and high frequencies, respectively labeled as end-frequencies of 1.2, 2.0, and 3.0 KHz, and with short, medium, and long durations of transitions. The deaf listener's results are shown separately according to whether their hearing losses were about equal at all frequencies (FLAT losses) or whether there was a relatively steep increase in hearing loss going from low to high frequencies (SLOPING losses). Results from normal listeners are the lowest points in each graph. There were three listeners in each group. Note that the listeners with sloping losses are the most deficient compared with normal, and the listeners with flat losses are generally less deficient than those with sloping losses. See text for explanation of the effects of the duration of transition.

of articulation, a listener must detect a transition of about 0.4 KHz or less occurring over 50 to 100 msec, somewhere in the frequency range 1.0 KHz to 3.0 KHz. It will be seen that the listeners with hearing losses would rarely be able to hear these transitions. This finding is quite consistent with our results in analyzing the perception of the phonetic features of consonants in a population of deaf listeners, using natural speech (see above Figure 9).

The third method for the study of auditory perception is to provide ways for a listener to compare different sound patterns and make a judgment as to their similarity. This method is now highly developed for perceptual studies and is especially good for perceptual systems where we have poor insight and no prior information as to the pattern dimensions that are perceived. In studying the speech perception of deaf persons, similarity judgments might reveal to us any special dimensions that are due to the distorting effects of deafness on the auditory patterns. Speech sound patterns are constructed along dimensions determined by the language and the common constraints of the nerves, muscles, and organs that produce the speech sounds. Thus we look for these same dimensions in investigating the auditory dimensions of normal speech perception. However, auditory distortions in deafness may have great effects on how the articulatory dimensions are realized in perceiving speech, and we probably will not be able to describe such effects without using direct judgment techniques.

These have not been used, as yet, to study speech perception by the deaf. Considerable complexity is encountered in programming the comparison tests, especially with stimuli of many dimensions, and the analysis methods are also very complex and time-consuming. However, the use of computers for controlling and analyzing judgment experiments has recently been developed, and I expect such experiments to be carried out soon when computerized auditory research on deafness has begun.

Speech Sciences and Auditory Training

Speech science can now provide a great deal of basic data, technique, and instrumentation for auditory training; thus close cooperation should be maintained with speech scientists. They can provide special synthetic speech sounds with artificially enhanced cues; these might be used in early stages of training to provide very obvious cues to listen for; the enhanced cues could then be gradually made closer to normal. In this way a deaf person might be trained to hear a normal cue which he formerly overlooked because his hearing loss had reduced the salience of the cue. In addition, speech science can provide automatic programming of auditory training sounds, either natural ones, stored in a computer memory, or synthetic ones generated by the computer during the training sessions. Needless to say, all the possible benefits of computer-aided instruction can be expected to apply to the improvement of auditory perception of speech by deaf persons, once we have developed effective training materials and methods.

Needs in Basic Research

In emphasizing, as I have above, the developments in speech science that appear to be of value for improving oral language acquisition by hearing impaired persons, I do not want to leave you with the impression that large improvements are imminent. There are certain gaps in basic knowledge which will probably need to be filled in before we will be able to put speech science to optimum use for the deaf.

First of all, there are limitations in our understanding of the relations between speech articulatory patterns and the resulting sound patterns. Thus we cannot at present build an acoustic analyzer that will derive and display the articulatory events at work. In fact it may be that this is impossible because a given acoustic pattern can be produced by more than one articulatory position. Thus, Liberman, *et al* (1968), have suggested that the most useful display might be a representation of the motor nerve action patterns that produce the articulations. As might be expected, we are a long way from knowing how to derive motor nerve patterns for display in a trainer.

The normal process of language acquisition is only partially understood. Current work on this problem is progressing under the impetus of new linguistic theories of language structure. It is apparent that the normal child acquires a very large amount of language competence during the first five years of life. The ways in which development of complex language rules, and their use in speech communication, can occur so rapidly are only now being discerned. Needless to say, the course of language acquisition in deaf children is little understood. Even the extent to which it can lag normal acquisition, at various ages, and still achieve given levels of development is not known. It is highly probable that critical age-marks exist, after which certain levels or types of language achievement are impossible. It is important when designing and using new speech aids for the deaf that the levels of achievable performance be known. As such knowledge becomes available through research on speech acquisition, it can be used to improve training with special aids. Until such knowledge is available, these aids will necessarily be less effective than they could be.

In addition, we know relatively little about the physiological and motor conditions of speech acquisition and how it depends on feedback conditions, such as auditory self-monitoring, approval or correction by a teacher, and other types of feedback. These are critical factors in the design and use of a speech training display, and yet almost nothing is known about the normal operation of these factors. Risberg has proposed an interesting model as a tentative basis for speech acquisition (Risberg, 1968).

Finally, we need to know more about the inherent conditions of perception through all the senses. It has sometimes been assumed by the designers of new aids that, to circumvent deafness, all that is necessary is to give some representations of sound patterns to another sense. Visual display of speech frequency patterns to the deaf is an example, where it is hoped that visual dimensions can be substituted for the auditory dimensions of frequency, loudness, and time. It is assumed that the speed of visual perception can keep pace with auditory pattern analysis. Furthermore, it implies that the speech communication chain, from articulation to sound to auditory perception, involves the same transformations as would the conversion to visual frequency patterns. Much more basic knowledge is necessary about the differences between visual and auditory perception before we can confidently make assumptions like those behind the notion of visual speech. Analogously, we need to know more about tactual perception in comparison with auditory perception of speech, before we will be able to design and use tactual speech aids with maximum effectiveness.

New Aids and Future Deaf Education

We have seen from our survey that there is quite a variety of special speech-analyzing aids for the deaf. In the future, speech "technology" will continue to suggest many new devices for this purpose. However, in my opinion, we need now to test extensively the new aids already available from small manufacturers.* We have very little information on how well these aids can substitute for the normal auditory control and reception of speech and how they might be used in deaf education. The new aids look promising, but we will need considerable experience with them, and controlled evaluation of results, before we will know what the aids can and cannot accomplish in deaf education.

One problem in educational use of some of the new aids may be that they must be employed in rather artificial training situations. Some of the aids are not designed for use in actual communication situations where the child can learn spoken language in a natural way. This is how the normal child learns language, and natural communication probably provides the most efficient, highly motivated conditions for learning. The developers of future aids for speech communication should be constantly reminded that the more compatible are their aids with natural communication, the more effective they will be. Parents and classroom teachers are the best sources of information to guide the designer of new aids as to the natural conditions of speech communication.

BIBLIOGRAPHY

Angelocci, A., Kopp, G., & Holbrook, A. The vowel formants of deaf and normal hearing 11-to 14-year-old boys. *Journal of speech and hearing disorders,* 1964, **29,** 156–170.

Børrild, K. Experiences with the design and use of technical aids for the training of deaf and hard of hearing children. *American annals of the deaf,* 1968, **113,** 168–177.

Cox, B. P. The identification of unfiltered and filtered consonant-vowel-consonant stimuli by sensori-neural hearing-impaired persons. Unpublished doctoral dissertation, University of Pittsburgh, 1969.

Denes, P. On the statistics of spoken English. *Journal of the Acoustical Society of America,* 1963, **35,** 892–904.

Denes, P. On the motor theory of speech perception. *Proceedings, Symposium on models for the perception of speech and visual form* (Air Force Cambridge Res. Labs., Boston, Mass., Nov. 11–14, 1964). Cambridge, Mass.: M.I.T. Press, 1967.

Dudley, H. Synthesizing speech. *Bell Labs Rec.,* 1936, **15,** 98–102.

Fant, G. *Acoustic theory of speech production.* S'Gravenhage, The Netherlands: Mouton and Co., 1960.

Gault, R. H., and Crane, G. W. Tactual patterns from certain vowel qualities instrumentally communicated from a speaker to a subject's fingers. *Journal of general psychology,* 1928, **1,** 353–359.

Johansson, B. The use of the transposer for the management of the deaf child. *International audiology,* 1966, **5,** 362–372.

Kopp, G. A., and Kopp, H. G. Visible speech for the deaf: an investigation to evaluate the usefulness of the visible speech cathode ray tube translator as a supplement to the oral method of teaching speech to deaf and severely deafened children. Wayne State University Speech and Hearing Clinic, Detroit, Mich., Final Report. Grant RD-526, Vocational Rehabilitation Administration, 1963.

*Special Instrument AB, Apothekshuset, Djurgardsbrunn, Stockholm NO, Sweden; and Precision Acoustics, 55 West 42nd Street, New York, New York 10036.

Kringlebotn, M. Experiments with some vibratactile and visual aids for the deaf. *American annals of the deaf,* 1968, **113,** 311–317.

Liberman, A. M., Cooper, F. S., Shankweiler, D. P., & Studdert-Kennedy, M. Perception of the speech code. *Psychological review,* 1967, **74,** 431–461.

Liberman, A. M., Cooper, F. S., Shankweiler, D. P., & Studdert-Kennedy, M. Why are speech spectrograms hard to read? *American annals of the deaf,* 1968, **113,** 127–133.

Ling, D. Three experiments on frequency transposition. *American annals of the deaf,* 1968, **113,** 283–294.

Ling, D., and Doehring, D. G. Learning limits of deaf children for coded speech. *Journal of speech and hearing research,* 1969, **12,** 83–94.

Lövgren, A., and Nykvist, O. Talöverforïng och talträning med döva barn pa visuell och taktil vag under utnyttjande av speciell apparatur. *Nord. tidskr. dövundervisn.,* 1959, 122–143.

Mártony, J. On the correction of the voice pitch level for severely hard of hearing subjects. *American annals of the deaf,* 1968, **113,** 195–202.

Miller, G. A., and Nicely, P. An analysis of perceptual confusions among some English consonants. *Journal of the Acoustical Society of America,* 1955, **27,** 338–352.

Oeken, F. W. Frequenztransposition zur horverbesserung bei innerohrschwerhorigkeit. *Archiv ohren usw. heilk u. z. hals usw. heilk,* 1963, **181,** 418–425.

Phillips, N., Remillard, W., Pronovost, W., and Bass, S. Teaching of intonation to the deaf by visual pattern matching. *American annals of the deaf,* 1968, **113,** 239–246.

Pickett, J. M. Tactual communication of speech sounds to the deaf: Comparison with lipreading. *Journal of speech and hearing disorders,* 1963, **28,** 315–330.

Pickett, J. M. (Ed.) Proceedings of the conference on speech-analyzing aids for the deaf. *American annals of the deaf,* 1968, **113,** 116–330.

Pickett, J. M., and Constam, A. A. visual speech trainer with simplified indication of vowel spectrum. *American annals of the deaf,* 1968, **113,** 253–258.

Martin, E. S., Pickett, J. M., and Colten, S. Discrimination of vowel formant transitions by listeners with severe sensorineural hearing loss, *Proc. Symposium of Speech Communication Ability and Profound Deafness. Stockholm, 1970.* In press, Alexander Graham Bell Association for the Deaf, Washington.

Pickett, J. M., and Martony, J. Low-frequency vowel formant discrimination in deaf listeners. *Journal of speech and hearing research,* 1970, **13,** 347–359.

Pickett, J. M., and Pickett, B. H. Communications of speech sounds by a tactual vocder. *Journal of speech and hearing research,* 1963, **6,** 207–222.

Pickett, J. M., Martin, E. S., Johnson, D., Smith, S. B., Daniel, Z., Willis, D., and Otis W., On patterns of speech feature reception by deaf listeners, *Proc. Symposium of Speech Communication Ability and Profound Deafness, Stockholm, 1970.* In press, Alexander Graham Bell Association for the Deaf.

Piminow, L. L'Application de la parole synthetique dans la correction auditive. *Acustica,* 1962, **12,** 285–290.

Potter, R. G., Kopp, G. A., and Green, H. C. *Visible speech.* New York: D. Van Nostrand, 1947.

Pronovost, W., Yenkin, L., Anderson, D. C., and Lerner, R. The voice visualizer. *American annals of the deaf,* 1968, **113,** 230–238.

Raymond, T. H., and Proud, G. O. Audiofrequency conversion. *Archives of Otolaryngology,* 1962, **76,** 436–446.

Risberg, A. Visual aids for speech correction. *American annals of the deaf,* 1968, **113,** 178–194.

Risberg, A. A critical review of work on speech analyzing hearing aids. *Trans. I.E.E.E.,* 1969, AU-17, 290–297.

Rhodes, F. L. *Beginnings of telephony.* New York: Harper Bros., 1929.

Rosen, J. *Phoneme identification in sensorineural deafness.* Doctoral dissertation, Stanford University, Palo Alto, Calif., 1962.

Rösler, G. Uber die vibrationsempfindung. *Z. esp. angew. psychol.,* 1957, **4,** 549–602.

Schultz, M. C. Suggested improvements in speech discrimination testing. *Journal of auditory research,* 1964, **4,** 1–14.

Shankweiler, D., and Studdert-Kennedy, M. Identification of consonants and vowels presented to left and right ears. *Quarterly journal of experimental psychology,* 1967, **19,** 59–63.

Shepard, R. N. The analysis of proximities: Multidimensional scaling with an unknown distance function. I. *Psychometrika,* 1962, **27,** 125–140; II. Ibid., 219–246.

Stark, R. A. Teaching /ba/ and /pa/ to deaf children using real-time spectral displays. (Submitted to *Language and speech,* 1970) 1970a.

Stark, R. A. The use of real-time visual displays of speech in the training of a profoundly deaf, non-speaking child: A case report. (Submitted to *Journal of speech and hearing disorders,* 1970) 1970b.

Stark, R., Cullen, J., and Chase, R. Preliminary work with the new Bell Telephone visible speech translator. *American annals of the deaf,* 1968, **113,** 205–214.

Tiffany, W. R., and Bennett, D. N. Intelligibility of slow-played speech. *Journal of speech and hearing research,* 1961, **4,** 248–258.

Upton, H. Wearable eyeglass speechreading aid. *American annals of the deaf,* 1968, **113,** 222–229.

The original research data reported in this chapter were gathered with the support of Gallaudet College, the U.S. Office of Education, and the U.S. Public Health Service.

Part II. Speech Development and Disorders

CHAPTER V
The Development of Speech

Boyd V. Sheets, Ph.D.

The average child, despite parents unskilled in the language arts, despite unfortunate and uncomfortable childhood illnesses, and despite a social environment which may discourage a pleasurable speech experience, is still able to marshal his natural strengths and achieve speech. Under most circumstances, children do learn to talk.

The speech life of an individual begins in its most meager forms shortly after birth. It grows and becomes increasingly complex—even as the physical habitus in which it dwells grows and develops—and passes through various overlapping stages. But in the final analysis speech never becomes completely mastered, even though physical and mental maturity are reached.

It is difficult to separate the speech function in man from the man himself—as a total organism—or from the environment in which he functions. Goldstein (1948) applies an "organismic" approach to language development and considers that each speech act must reflect its relation to the total individual.

Speech per se is a fairly vapid human accomplishment unless it is used as a tool. Dynamically utilized it serves as an extremely powerful linkage between individuals, and can act as a most effective carrier wave in the interchange of ideas. Carhart et al (1969, p. 82) feel that man's ability to communicate with verbal symbols is probably his most distinctive characteristic.

Oldfield and Marshall (1968) have noted that speech and verbal language have become so much a part of our everyday life, and so characteristically a prerogative of man that it was largely taken for granted until recently, when scientific curiosity has been brought to bear on the phenomenon. Here one could point to what often appear to be contradictory attitudes. The fact that the average child *does* learn to speak with little or no teaching effort has frequently caused us to take this unique ability for granted, and has allowed us to accept the notion that speech is basically simple—in some inexplicable way.

In contrast to this attitude we have another which looks at the phenomenon of speech as impossibly complex to the finite mind. For instance, Cherry (1957, p. 12) points out that it is impressive that human communication is even possible when so many things seem to be against it.

While it is perfectly appropriate for lay persons to set up attitudes oriented toward a simplistic explanation of the speech and language process, it is a luxury not given to professional workers who deal with the developmental, clinical, habilitative, or research aspects of verbal communication. Such an extended attitude becomes all the more essential in a period when clinicians, teachers, and investigators have moved beyond peripheral manifestations of the speech process—a description of infant cry, babbling, lallation, first words, and the chronology of sentence development—to encompass all elements of the total verbal communication cycle, which includes the, as yet, unexplained area of central language processing.

Of necessity, only an abbreviated view can be given to many of the elements which are important in the normal development of speech. However, a serious attempt will be made to cover the basic scope of this rather remarkable childhood acquisition called "speech." In considering the different arbitrary parameters of speech development, it is important to keep closely in mind the global aspects of the speech and language process—man as an organized, functional unity, of which speech is only a part; man, organized to become a part of his physical and social environment, with speech serving as a vital, binding force; man's speech and language mechanism per se, a functioning unity in its own right, as mediated by the nervous system.

TERMINOLOGY OF SPEECH AND LANGUAGE DEVELOPMENT

As is true of all professional fields, the area of speech and language has developed a vocabulary which allows workers within the field to communicate with each other. As is also true of other fields there is, unfortunately, not always complete concurrence in the verbal symbols attached to elements of the developing manifestations of speech.

For purposes of more effective communication, some of the terms which will be used in this chapter are described briefly:

Speech. The use of systemized vocalizations to express verbal symbols or words (Sheridan, 1964).

Language. The symbolization of thought; in verbal language, it is often seen as evocation of a broader act of communication. Warfel (1962) describes it as a structural system of overt, voluntary human vocal sounds which are learned (noninstinctive), are produced in sequence, and carry symbols so that communication can be carried on between two or more individuals.

Communication. The act of communication is described with three elements, *reception,* which begins in a sensory stimulus; *interpretation,* an intellectual process; and *expression,* terminal motor activity (Fry, 1957).

Linguistics. The discipline which is concerned with the study of language.

Decoding. The cerebral act of comprehending the meaning of an incoming language pattern.

Encoding. The cerebral act of formulating a language response for motor implementation.

Central Language Processor. The brain centers active in all elements of speech and language processing, e.g., auditory, visual perceptions; memory banks; syntactical centers; language formulation areas.

The Parameters of Language Development

Emphasis has already been placed upon the fact that even a quasi-substantial study of speech and language development is a complex and challenging undertaking. It leads through many areas of man-related specialties—child development, anatomy, physiology, neurology, speech pathology, audiology, psycholinguistics, and others. Ultimately, the quest leads to some level of personal frustration, since many of the most basic dynamics of spoken language are still not known. Beyond this point one can only speculate.

An effort is made in this section to present briefly some of the more obvious elements of speech development which will reflect, not only the great mass of knowledge currently available, but point the direction which future investigations must take.

The Basic Unity of the Human Body

Mention has earlier been made of the need to contemplate the speech mechanism as being housed in a body concerned with other activities and other behaviors. There is much to be said in favor of underlining this concept of physiological unity. Lewis (1963) has pointed to the ever-changing patterns within the child. He states that as we learn more about the gradual everyday changes in the language, speech, feeling, thought, and social behavior of children it becomes evident that there is a continuous process taking place by which the child becomes a person, as his innate possibilities and potentialities are being developed and realized within the conditions of his environment. As he grows, his speech develops into language, his language affects his feeling and thought, and his feeling and thought in turn influence his language and speech.

McCarthy (1966, p. 498), in her monumental study of language development in children, notes that many of the child developmental studies which were carried out in recent decades have included all aspects of linguistic development as parts of the broader studies. While it has often been difficult to separate out from accumulated data those having specifically to do with speech and language, the point is made very strongly that investigators have recognized the importance of studying all possible aspects of child behavior simultaneously to yield the most meaningful data.

The clinician, who frequently sees children referred for a delay in speech and language development, must be constantly alert to the many factors which—singly or in combination—could bring about speech retardation. The writer recently saw a five-year-old boy who was reported to have little or no spoken language. The accompanying medical report did not yield any clues which were helpful. An extensive speech and hearing evaluation revealed nothing more than had been reported in advance—the youngster presented an impoverished language capability for his age level. It was only as a conference was held with the mother that some important clues were uncovered.

The product of a broken home, the boy was, in effect, living the life of a social and emotional isolate. The mother worked nights, during which time the boy was cared for by a relative who did little more than put him to bed. During the day the mother was at home, but asleep for the most part. There were no other children in the family and thus the boy was alone in the small apartment all day. When he became hungry he had to feed himself from the refrigerator. He was left totally to his own devices. Even when the mother was awake it appeared that her own feelings of frustration and unhappiness did not allow her to contribute significantly to the boy's pleasurable speech experience. Seemingly, this unfortunate combination of familial-social experiences did not encourage the normal development of speech and language.

The Backgrounds of Work in Speech Development

In presenting the background picture of speech and language development, Oldfield and Marshall (1968) point out that little organized research was carried out in this area before the eighteenth century. However, language development in the child did become a subject of observation after the end of the 18th century through the influences of the naturalism of the Romantic movement, of the Darwinian revolution, and of the growing concern with education of the handicapped. At the end of the 19th century, Wilhelm Stern made the first systematic observation and recording of child speech. Soon after World War I, Jean Piaget of Switzerland and Lev Semonovich Vygotsky of Russia developed hypotheses and gathered a significant amount of valuable material. Between World War I and World War II, the acquisition of vocabulary and the emergence of correct use of the parts of speech were the main areas of study in the development of children's language.

Oldfield and Marshall (1968) also point out that with the development of great interest in linguistic factors in speech development, investigators such as Brown and his group have been recently working to analyze the child's speech in terms of its own proper structure, and not as if it were a poor approximation of the adult pattern.

When McCarthy (1966, p. 494) undertook a review of pertinent literature in language development she found that, although a substantial number of child language studies had been done, they were of little scientific significance. The studies were generally of a one-child observation nature, and the study designs were sufficiently dissimilar that it was very difficult to make a meaningful comparison of data.

However, McCarthy (1966, p. 494) notes that two significant types of studies have emerged since the 1940's, one which emphasizes the genetic approach to language disorders, and one which deals with infant vocalizations and utilizes phonetics and recording devices. The clinical and genetic points of view are apparently merging. Studies of deviations in language have become more concerned with total syndromes and the search for causes than with symptoms. The studies of language disorder, reports McCarthy, now take into consideration the dynamics of the disorder and the total personality of the individual.

McCarthy stresses the increased growth of interest among psychologists in the phenomenon of speech and language development, and points out that nearly every textbook in child psychology which has appeared since 1930 includes a significant portion on speech and language development, while, before this time, it was difficult to find more than a paragraph or two on this subject in psychology textbooks.

Often, in the history of speech development, a great interest generated with abnormal manifestations of language has sparked investigations into normal patterns. Typical of this pattern is the problem of aphasia. The investigations and hypotheses of such men as Carl Wernicke, Hughlings Jackson, Paul Broca, Marc Dax, and Bastian in the mid-nineteenth century sparked controversies which still have not been entirely resolved. In the meantime, the language problems of the aphasic adult have been studied and then related to symptoms of an aphasoid character sometimes seen in children. These children characteristically have difficulty in handling the symbolic functions of language. Having identified this problem area in children, we have now moved to probe further into the substrata of normal language development. Roberts, Lenneberg, and Ajuriaguerra are among those who have moved in this direction.

We noted earlier that McCarthy has pointed out the important historical trend extending from the treatment of peripheral symptoms to a searching for syndromes and for causes. In the past decade the profession of speech pathology has also made significant moves, reflecting modified and more sophisticated attitudes toward speech and language development, as well as some of the related disorders. Following the lead of the psycholinguist and the neurophysiologist, lines of investigation are extending beyond the end-organs—ears and peripheral speech mechanism—and moving centrally to establish new horizons of knowledge. Wepman (1966, p. 141) and the study he has given to the total problem of aphasia has been notable in this expanded range of interest.

Child-Parent Relationships in Speech Development

In a series of publications Lilly (1961, 1967, 1967) has written at length concerning his experiences in attempting to set up communication systems with dolphins. A strong basic premise appears in Lilly's reports—the factor of affection which is a prime requisite between man-and-dolphin if inter-communication of any order is to be achieved. Negative behavior or reprimands on the part of the trainer results in a withdrawal of the dolphin and a refusal of any further interaction.

Lilly has found that dolphins seem to require a close and warm response pattern from the trainer, even as he is quite ready to reciprocate the same fondness. Indeed, if he is to be successful, the prospective dolphin trainer requires a very strict set of personality credentials, which include, according to Lilly (1967, p. 44), dedication, personal involvement, flexibility, curiosity, sensitivity, and training.

One feels moved to wonder if infants and little children are less worthy of these personality benefits in parents and teachers if they, too, are to prosper. Little can be done by way of setting up criteria for prospective parents, but it sometimes becomes discouraging—from this frame of reference—to note the type of persons entering the teaching profession.

With regard to the impact of the parent—and, particularly, the mother—upon the child and his emerging speech patterns, Abercrombie (1964, p. 16) expresses this relationship aptly and wryly in depicting bodily contact as the infant's earliest mode of communication with others. His entire body is stimulated when he is fed—his skin through touch and warmth; the prioceptors in mouth, tongue, and throat by the sucking movements; his nose by the smell of his mother's milk and his palate by the taste; his ears by her crooning; and his labyrinths by the motions of rocking and burping. He *needs* a nap after his bombardment to his central nervous system. The apron strings are, indeed, more difficult to sever than the umbilical cord, he says.

While this confusion of stimuli coming in from the outside might appear to be frightening to the infant, most writers agree that these bodily sensations, accompanied by what Van Riper has called a "bath of love," are of extreme importance to the continuing emotional development of the child.

Michell (1964, p. 43) in writing about the infant and his family stresses the importance of having available more scientific data concerning the infant vis-a-vis his family, particularly during the first year of life. In this regard he comments with satisfaction that more of these infant studies are now being conducted within the home setting rather than in the sterile strangeness of a laboratory where unnatural behavior is apt to be elicited.

There are indications that the infant can set up close and sensitive feeling patterns toward the parent. According to Michell (spast 45), infants seem to have an innate capacity for forming special ties with one person, with the corresponding emotional feelings of love, anger, and sadness. Continuous exposure to one person seems to elicit this response.

Many authors have commented on the fact that early language efforts are strongly based in emotion. Gordon (1962, p. 75) is of the opinion that the climate of feeling is perhaps the most important single variable in language development. If an infant is subjected to indifference, neglect, or emotional stress there may develop a related inhibition of language development. There are some indications that an infant is able to sense when a parent is caught up in ambivalent feelings toward him.

Van Riper (1963, p. 77) has frequently pointed out the crucial role the mother plays in the early parent-child relationship. Of necessity, the parents are the first teachers of language to the child and in Van Riper's opinion, are most often very poor teachers. Fortunately, there are other factors of even greater importance between parents and child.

Van Riper (1963, p. 77) noted that the comfort sounds are the ancestors of real speech, and that most parents seem to know this. The mother surrounds the child with the sounds of love, and the phenomenon of imprinting comes into play. According to scientists' findings, Van Riper reports, an animal's response to certain sounds is apparently imprinted soon after birth. He notes that babies whose parents take good care of them begin to talk sooner than orphanage babies and have fewer speech defects. It is necessary for a baby to hear a mother's voice if it is to be able to talk, and the mother's voice should have love in it.

From the foregoing discussion it would seem to be a straightforward conclusion that everyone interested in infants and children, and their speech development, should militate unceasingly for parent-child relationships where only love abounds. In practicality, this seems not to be possible, and one is grateful that most children can accommodate within reason to fluctuations in the physical and emotional environment around them. However, there do seem to be individual limits beyond which a child cannot cope successfully with a particularly threatening environment.

At one time we met a little three-year-old girl in a pediatric hospital where we were doing consultant work. This youngster had been born with a spinal defect—a spine bifida—where several vertebrae had not formed properly and allowed a bulging out of the spinal canal contents. This little patient had spent most of her life in the hospital, during which time several surgical procedures were carried out to correct the vertebral defect. During this entire time the child had shown very few of the signs of dynamic speech development—she was silent most of the time, although there appeared to be no damage to the speech and hearing structures.

It was of great interest to note that at age three, when surgery was complete and she was soon to be released from the hospital, this little girl began to produce babbling sounds for the first time. While we did not study this case in depth, it was our strong hunch that two events probably led to the slowness of speech to develop. The first was her long-term institutionalization which made it impossible to set up usual parent-child relationships. The other factor appeared to be linked with the organic defect itself. Although impossible to document, we felt that until recently this three-year-old had been fairly fully occupied in maintaining her own life forces. With surgery complete and recovery well advanced she seemed able to afford the relative luxury of babbling.

Developmental Stages of Language Learning

We have often had the occasion to set up systems of organization which relate to the human body and its functions. Likewise, we have frequently encountered an endless number of charts, diagrams, systemic postulates, and lists of anatomical parts—all designed to make the complexities of the body more understandable. As we begin a discussion of some of the developmental factors related to speech, we should like to stress that, while organizational charts make for easier understanding, we should never forget that none of the diagrams or charts are entirely correct, and that the body and its functions are likely much more variable and complicated than is indicated.

Before exploring some of the more detailed aspects of the speech developmental pattern, there are a number of general principles which deserve attention. Gordon (1962, p. 73, 78) has pointed out that before attention can be given to speech development itself, we need to ask ourselves what purpose it serves, what functions does speech serve for the child. In answering his own question he stipulates two major functions of language, that of clarifying meanings, and that of expanding relationships between people. In Gordon's opinion these functions are perpetuated from infancy throughout life.

McCarthy (1966, p. 503) in reviewing the findings of eight major studies in infant development, was impressed with the striking degree of uniformity which is noticeable for the age at which similar items are reported where more than one author has observed the same or similar behavior with the same or almost the same criteria. Such observations would be consistent with physiological timetable so apparent in other manifestations of pre- or post-natal life.

In briefly pursuing general motivational factors related to language development the comments of Carhart et al (1969, p. 2) are of particular interest:

> All normal persons, and most who are not normal, learn those portions of the language (or languages) of their culture that are essential to everyday exchange of ideas. Each then employs these skills as his major means of social adjustment. He thus functions amid the complex of social institutions that surround him, conforming to the mores of his culture and reaching such achievements as becoming gainfully employed. It is through the language he has learned that mass communications media can thus affect him. But probably most importantly, each individual uses the language he has acquired to carry on his daily private and his personal interactions with those few other individuals who are his intimates.

As we approach a discussion of the various stages of speech development we are immediately met with a variety of organization patterns which, while they generally show an underlying similarity, frequently use a varied nomenclature. For purposes of consistency, we shall arbitrarily use the Van Riper (1963, p. 79) version. It is widely used and is uncomplicated in its segmentation. A diagram of the Van Riper classification is included for reference purposes.

Period of Reflex Sounds. There is some disagreement among experts as to the importance of the speech role played by the infant cry and early reflex sounds. Speech sounds for infants are likely to be simply neutral stimuli with no reinforcing properties. Yet parents often speak in the presence of the infant many times while caring for the child. The act of caring for the baby involves removing negative reinforcers (wet diapers, other painful, uncomfortable stimuli, etc.) and providing positive reinforcers (food, warmth, tactual stimulation, etc.) This consequently causes speech sounds of the parent, along with other stimulus aspects of the parent, to become positive learned (conditioned) reinforcers.

Arnold (1965, p. 346) links the reflexive voice patterns with some of the motor reflex patterns. The continuing drive toward phonic expression is closely tied to the reflexive patterns of sucking, swallowing, and breathing. Implicit in this reasoning is the postulate that the infant's first vocal utterances are purely of a reflexive nature. On the other hand, Shohara (1935) feels that even at an early stage the reflexive pathways are influenced by generically preformed cerebral centers. At this stage,

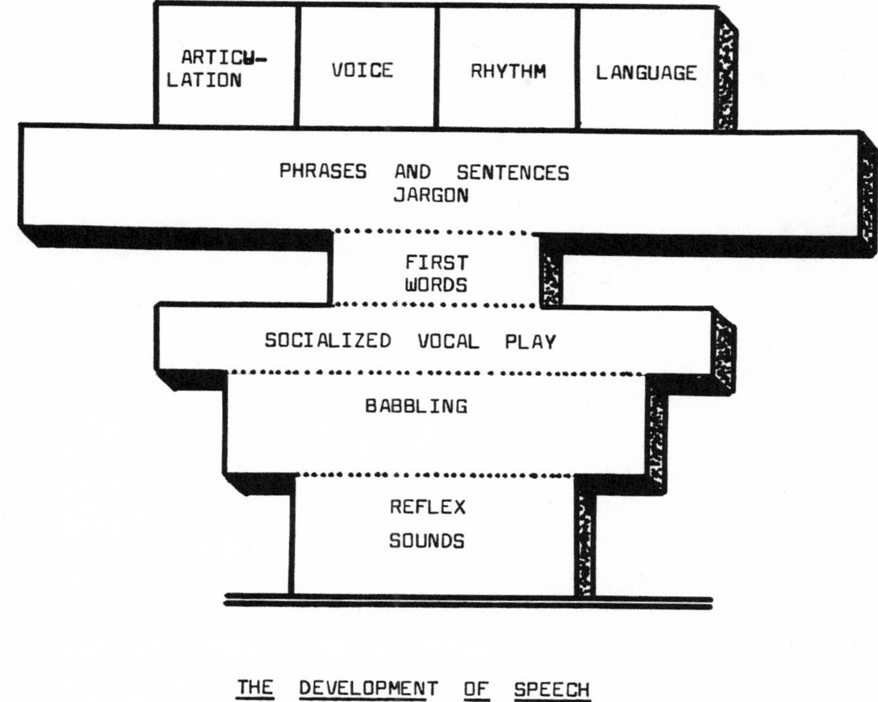

Figure 1

the infant cry is similar to an animal sound, representing an instinctive, inherited means of expression of cold, hunger, discomfort, and other physical sensations through an innate audiovocal mechanism.

We note above that Arnold postulated a physiological linkage between early vocalization and suckle, swallow, and breathing reflex patterns. One might point out that whether or not these sounds are emotionally or socially meaningful to the infant, the beginnings of basic neuro-motor coordinations are being made. McCarthy (1966, p. 505), for instance, points out that the reflexive cry marks the first use of the delicate respiratory mechanisms which will later provide an air source for the evocation of speech. Likewise, the early crying allows the infant to hear his own voice which marks the beginning of a monitoring circuit.

Concerning the sound patterns involved in the vocalizations of the infant in the reflexive period, many writers have indicated that there is a great variety of sounds, many of which do not appear in the child's environmental language. Van Riper (1963, p. 75) describes the first reflexive sounds of the baby as being "shrill nasal wails." These tend to persist during the first month of life. As the baby becomes slightly older he is likely to make comfort noises, such as cooing or laughing. Even at this early stage numbers of studies indicate that there are more vowels and consonants used in noncrying vocalizations than in whimpering or crying.

Truby and Lind (1965, p. 45) have studied the infant cry very extensively and in discussing the cry sounds of the newborn infant report that the sound is uniquely individual. While the cryprints, which are the visual-acoustic aspects of the crying, of a given baby may seem to be identifiable as his particular cry, each cry sound is actually physically different from any other due to the natural assymmetries of a human-produced sound which prevent iteration of that sound.

In another study of infant cry Bosma, Truby, and Lind (1965, p. 89–90) report the relationship between the act of crying and movements in the pharyngeal-laryngeal areas. They have found that the anticipatory anatomical posturing of the infant for the crying act is carried over to positions assumed for speech articulation, except that the feedback implications are different. They further note that while the paroxysmal anatomical patterns are commonly found only in infants, changes in frequency and volume of voice are found through maturation.

These authors stress their findings that the infant cry is physiologically a forerunner of other speech developmental patterns which will follow. The coordination of the larynx which occurs in the baby's crying is a mature coordination which is capable of producing a stable vocalization characterized at beginning and at termination by well-organized harmonic patterns.

Babbling. It must be stressed that the different stages of speech development do not represent abrupt changes in vocal behavior in the child, but an overlapping merging pattern which is modified slightly on a day-to-day basis. Inspection of the diagram by Van Riper showing the building blocks of speech and language development will indicate stippled lines drawn between the blocks. This line could more properly be fuzzy to denote the gradual and unequal flow of maturation from the simple toward the more complex neuro-motor patterns.

While there is naturally a great deal of difference in the chronology of child development, babbling will generally begin around the eighth week of life. McCarthy (1966, p. 507) notes that once the child has begun to make sounds there is a rather rapid increase in the variety of sounds, until by the third month babbling makes its appearance.

In discussing articulatory acquisition Winitz (1969, p. 20) cites an hypothesis put forth by Lenneberg and his associates. While acknowledging that the babbling activity of an infant is affected by reinforcement processes from the outside, these workers still feel that babbling is a genetic trait in man, the onset of which is not related to environmental or social forces.

To test their hypothesis Lenneberg et al (1965) compared vocalizations of infants of hearing and deaf parents, from about two weeks to three months of age. They found the frequency of vocalizations to be similar for the infants of both groups. Winitz (1969) noted that, unfortunately, there were contaminating elements in the research procedures which had some unknown effect upon the findings.

In Winitz' opinion there is no doubt that babbling is tied to maturational prerequisites, but much more carefully designed research needs to be done.

Arnold (1965, p. 347) refers to the babbling act as "instinctive." The urge to babble originates from the primary, inborn motor patterns of food intake, such as the reflexes of spitting, sucking, chewing, swallowing, etc. At about 2 months of age, the infant shows an innate drive to produce playful sounds with his speech organs, or to use the upper foodways for secondary, expressive purposes rather than the primary purpose of food intake. This drive toward playful babbling resembles the urge to move the arms and legs, promoting complete motor development of the body. Despite the possible existence of handicaps which can retard further language development, Arnold continues, the babbling stage is nevertheless present in all babies, although it may not develop beyond an incipient stage and may disappear before leading on to spontaneous speech.

Much work in the area of infant vocal behavior patterns has been done over a long period of years by Irwin and his associates. In summarizing a long series of Irwin's studies—all having to do with infant vocalization—McCarthy (1965, p. 509) notes significant points from Irwin's work which relate to the babbling period. It was found, for instance, that the frequency of vowel sounds is greater than that of consonant sounds in the first 30 months of life. There is a steady increase in the frequency of vowel sounds until two years of age. In early infancy there are about five times as many vowel sounds as consonants. Consonant frequency does not equal vowel frequency until about 2-1/2 years of age.

Murphy (1964, p. 12), a British writer, does not describe babbling as a separate entity but includes it as his Stage II of speech development which he calls "early articulation." He describes random tonal sound-making that usually occurs with the mouth wide open, and then combines "lalling and babbling effects" produced by articulation of the mid-mouth structures, or in the case of babbling, by the more anterior interruption of the air column by lips, tongue, tip, and alveolar ridges.

In terms of motivational factors involved in babbling Van Riper (1963, p. 78) stresses the pleasure principle which the infant is experiencing as he produces the vowel sounds of *ee, ih, uh* and other front vowels, and the *m, b and g* consonants, as well as the grunts, squeals, sighs, and gurgles that make up his own special language.

Socialized Vocal Play. The category of vocal play tends not to be included in most developmental models, but is rather merged with paralleling vocal behaviors. However, Van Riper (1963, p. 80) sees this as a new type of babbling which appears about the fifth or sixth month of life. Perhaps the most significant aspect of this development is the fact that the child is now responsive to sounds made in his presence. This is quite a step forward from the largely internalized earlier periods of sound-making.

The child begins to use his vocalization for getting attention and expressing demands and protests. According to Van Riper, he uses his developing speech to express himself and to influence the behavior of those around him.

When the infant reaches his eighth month, one is able to note elements of *inflected* vocal play. He has used pitch shifts earlier, but inflectional patterns become prominent and fairly stable during this period.

Changes are also discernible which allow one to see clearly the vocal foundations upon which true speech will emerge shortly. Van Riper (1963, p. 81) notes that during the period of from eight months to one year of age, the variety of sounds produced in babbling and vocal play increases. Back vowels and front consonants increase, and crying time becomes shorter.

It is during the general babbling period—as has already been noted—that one sees marked differences in the vocal behavior of babies who are deaf or severely hard of hearing. In part, the regression of babbling seems to be affected by a lack of the strong pleasure principle which Van Riper and others link with vocalization. The effects of deafness will be more extensively discussed at a later point. However, it seems appropriate to call attention to it while we are discussing babbling.

Among many other authors Van Riper (1963, p. 79) reports that even though deaf infants start babbling at a normal age, they don't hear the sounds they are making and probably engage in less real vocal play than hearing babies simply because they lose interest. Babbling in deaf babies has been increased, according to Van Riper, by suspending mirrors above their cribs to enable visual self-stimulation.

Echolalia. The phenomenon of echolalia, as an aspect of the speech developmental process, is frequently mentioned by writers in this field. It appears somewhat difficult to fit this pattern neatly into the developmental chart, and yet it is seen fairly consistently in children as they proceed along the pathway of speech and language development. Echolalia is often seen in a protracted and exaggerated form in children with severe mental retardation and those who present aphasoid symptoms.

Eisenson (1938) feels that echolalia becomes apparent after the child has learned to imitate many sound combinations of its own accidental making. Echolalia, then, is the imitation by the child of sounds it hears others make. The important feature in this situation is that the child does not yet *understand* the speech patterns it is repeating. This stage of development comes at about the ninth or tenth month. During this period more of the foundations are laid down upon which speech per se will develop.

According to Brain (1968), echolalia is very complex. We think of the child as imitating sounds others make and thereby producing the same sound himself. But this "same sound," although it may be the same phoneme, might be different in pitch or in another characteristic, and it may therefore sound quite different to the child. Thus, continues Brain, if the child is able to imitate the sound, he is learning to identify and reproduce the phoneme, for the phoneme is the pattern that is common to the sounds made by his parents and by himself, even though these sounds are different in other respects.

Brain's view of the child's echolalia embodying something more than a mere mimicry of sound patterns he hears, keys in with the postulates of a genetically determined language center which will be considered later.

The First Words. With the establishment of the first word, the child formally enters the world of speech-evoking creatures. It is a point of great interest to the professional investigator; it is a landmark of great personal satisfaction to the parent. Yet, as McCarthy (1966, p. 523) points out, the determination of the exact point in time when speech begins is not always easily achieved. There are a number of difficulties encountered largely because of the fact that the emergence of definite first words must be determined in terms of the child's internal linguistic processes which we can only view from the outside. The first word is usually linked with the first use of sound *with meaning* on the part of the child. Lewis (1951) recommends that we take special note of the function of a particular sound-group before and after a child seems to connect it with a particular object. We can learn how the meaning develops by noting the place of the word in the child's activities.

The literature reflects a wide range of difference as to when the first word is used, and perhaps this is partly a result of the difficulty in determining the precise onset of speech per se. However, most investigators place the age level at which first words are used at circa one year. McNeill (1968, p. 21) states that a normal child will begin to say words at about one. Van Riper (1963, p. 83) places the critical time between the tenth and eighteenth month.

Concerning the entry of words into the child's communication pattern, Lenneberg (1968, p. 32) reports that the onset of speech is an extremely regular phenomenon, which appears at a particular time in the child's physical development and follows a fixed sequence of events, as though all children progress according to the same general "strategy" from the time they begin to speak until they have mastered the art of speaking. In Lenneberg's opinion the first speech forms used are principles, not items—principles of categorization and pattern perception. Thus, the first words refer more to classes of things than they do unique objects or events. This line of thought would lead logically to a consideration of language in its broadest sense and the role which the first words play in the larger pattern.

Brain (1968, p. 317) has pointed out that when a child begins using first words—and for a long period thereafter—he often attaches strong emotional coloring to the words, probably related to the experience for which the word stands. Thus, there may be a significant difference between the basic character of the word spoken and the child's use of it. Brain notes that an adult's object reference of a word often differs from that of a child, and that a word used to name an object is many times incorrectly extended from one subject to another which is really not the same thing. We are therefore met with yet another dimension of the first words which does not make our efforts to comprehend the child's first true speech attempts any easier.

Once the child has acquired his first words the speech developmental process moves ahead. Winitz (1969, p. 46) reports that several word approximations will have been identified by parents by the end of the first year. The parent will predictably reinforce these utterances and in response, the child will gradually refine his word approximations until they eventually match the adult form. It is not necessarily true, according to Skinner (Winitz, 1969) that all the complicated forms of adult speech are present in the child's unconditioned vocal repertoire. At first the requirements for reinforcement of a response are very relaxed. The parents reinforce any response which vaguely resembles the standard. When such responses begin to appear more often, a closer resemblance is demanded—and the process continues in this way making possible the production of very complex verbal forms.

It is of great incidental interest to note that parents who know very little about teaching speech to their children, much less about learning theory, seem to give critical support and encouragement as their youngsters come to grips with the rigors of language learning.

Mention is frequently made of the fact that words stand for things—they are symbolic representations of the finite object. For a young infant to develop this kind of insight is certainly indicative of his having taken a giant step forward linguistically. However, Cherry (1961, p. 10), the British linguist, notes that "the suggestion that words are symbols for things, actions, qualities, relationships, et cetera, is naive, a gross simplification. Words are slippery customers. The full meaning of a word does not appear until it is placed in its context, and the context may serve an extremely subtle function—as with puns, or double entendre. And even then the 'meaning' will depend upon the listener, upon the speaker, upon their entire experience of the language, upon their knowlege of one another, and upon the whole situation. Words do not 'mean things' in one-to-one relation like a code." It is through this complicated and often bewildering mosaic that the young child must make his way.

Relative to the first words there is wide agreement among writers that a child must first comprehend spoken language before he can develop it himself. Sheridan (1964, p. 6.) agrees in principle with this concept and yet points out that performance comes after perception, so it is perhaps more correct to say that the child's spoken language echoes what he experienced through his hearing some months earlier. He states that handicaps such as a hearing impairment, mental retardation, rejection, or separation, which prevent the child from receiving the intensive individual coaching in his own language that he needs in order to learn and remember it (particularly in the critical period of the first two to four years) will seriously increase the child's difficulty in acquiring spoken language.

As we conclude the section of the first words, it is noteworthy that Van Riper (1963, p. 92) appears not to have the great confidence in the parent as an intuitional teacher of speech as others do. He states that the parents' teaching is usually poor, due to inadequate knowledge in the area of speech development and language teaching. The result is that many children do not learn to imitate sounds, do not practice their speech sounds in vocal play, do not learn that they can use sounds as useful, meaningful tools, do not make use of their jargon, and develop gestures and other substitute behavior patterns instead of gaining an increased vocabulary. This is the foundation for defective speech.

One is inclined to wonder if perhaps the parents are not being indicted somewhat unfairly in the light of the many and diverse dimensions of verbal language. Generations of individuals have lived and died as products of a universal exposure to poor, disorganized parental speech-teaching tactics. Undoubtedly, some learned to speak with great verve and effectiveness; others may have developed only the meagerest facility with language. The point in this situation appears to be that while, undoubtedly, the parental role is an important one, there are many other factors to speech development which also have their ultimate impact upon the quality of speech.

The Factor of Imitation in Speech Development. Implicit in much of our discussion thus far has been the role which imitation plays in the development of speech. The fact that a hearing child develops speech while a deaf child does not, easily leads to the notion of a one-to-one relationship existing between imitation and language acquisition. Certainly there is a relationship between the two and yet it appears not to be as simple and uncluttered as one might suppose.

For instance, Roger Brown (1964) has called attention to a common phenomenon in what he calls parent-child dialogues. This involves the parents' imitation of the child's speech, and, through this, their expansion of his utterances into complete, well-formed English sentences. To a child's statement, "Kitty cry," the parent can respond, "Yes, the kitty is crying," using the auxiliary verb and the progressive inflection *ing*. Both of these are examples of English transformations, and are being used in the context of the child's own speech. Brown has called this process "expansion," and finds that parents expand circa 30 percent of what two-year-old children say. Obviously, Brown sees this element of imitation as being a bi-directional, rather than a uni-directional process.

Somewhat in conflict with the statements made in the previous section by Van Riper, Lenneberg (1968, p. 33) adds further complications to the simple imitate-speak basis for speech acquisition. As we shall discuss in greater detail later, Lenneberg believes that the child inherits an aptitude for language and that this potential is very early operative in the life of the child. He grants that the language center must be sparked from the outside, but points out that man's ability to acquire language is so deeply rooted that, even in the face of serious handicaps, children can learn language. Children learn it even in the face of dramatic handicaps. He believes that the sounds of language and the configurations of words are quickly perceived by the young child and reproduced under universal linguistic principles.

Somewhat in the same general area of thought are Fraser, Bellugi, and Brown (1964) who have placed the factor of imitation in a chain of linguistic events made up of *imitation, comprehension,* and *production.* In commenting upon these three tasks, the authors state that imitation might work through the meaning system, rather than being strictly a perceptual motor task. They cite Decroy's argument (circa 1934) that a child can recognize only those words to which he attaches a meaning. He therefore cannot imitate a word he doesn't understand, since perceptual differentiation is essential for imitation.

Brain (1968, p. 315–316) has also described the factor of imitation as being more complex than many might think. He points out the fact that normal infants hear speech and respond to it, as basic aspects of the total developmental process. In contrast, he points to the deaf baby who begins to babble but soon gives it up. He cites Bühler, who has pointed out the psychological importance of the strong associations which are formed between the auditory impression and the movements which produce it. In Bühler's opinion this relationship is the essential basis of the later imitation of the sounds the child hears, in which it has to translate what it has heard into vocal movements of its own.

McCarthy (1966, p. 517) brings us back to the point that a child learns the language of his environment and this is evidence of the importance of imitation. She notes that children imitate all aspects of the behavior of others, especially in the verbal and motor areas. This imitative behavior most often is reported after the ninth month, and is especially noticeable at the beginning of the second year, the stage when language proper is just emerging. The importance of imitation is brought out, McCarthy feels, by the fact the congenitally deaf children do not learn to speak because they are deprived of the opportunity to imitate others.

As other writers have also done, McCarthy (1966, p. 517) points out that imitation does not imply a simple repetition of what the child is hearing. New sounds seem not to be learned by a simple imitation process but rather, they emerge from the child's vocal play as a factor in maturation. The child appears to imitate only those sounds which have appeared in his vocal play. Likewise, he is apt to imitate only those speech sounds he hears others make as they call attention to combinations of sounds he has already used.

Inner Language. Hopefully, it will be manifestly evident at this point that we are not able to view speech development as an entity unto itself. In our opinion, one could theoretically attempt to set up speech as an independent entity, a product of a basically independent speech mechanism. However, it would probably prove to be a remarkably abortive and unsatisfying experience. At the very least, it is in direct contradiction to all established concepts of the basic unity of the body and all of its processes.

In our discussion thus far, we have frequently made casual reference to "language centers" which appear to have a potent impact upon speech development from its earliest initiation. We have also cited other authors who have seen speech as having some type of inner organization. We have no interest in disregarding the peripheral speech mechanisms as we go along, any more than we would wish to undermine the influence, the impact, of the external environment on speech development. At the same time, it would seem naive to disregard the important work which has recently been done in the area of the central language centers.

The concept of inner language is certainly not a new one and yet it figures in the much larger picture of the brain as the chief implementer of speech and language.

Inner language is of particular interest to anyone working with deaf children since, despite the auditory defect, the youngsters will still develop inner language if there are no central complications. Sheridan (1964) defines inner language as an individual's personal store of concepts in a symbolic or code form. Just as a common set of symbols (expressed in speech, gesture, or writing and drawing) is necessary for inter-personal communication, symbols are also necessary for forming, codifying, and storing ideas in the memory. This is the inner language. It has both emotional and intellectual aspects, different for each person. Therefore, the process of encoding an outgoing communication or of decoding an incoming communication is a very personal one and is also a shared process. Sheridan continues to explain that the possession of inner language is dependent upon the child's ability to organize the impressions he derives through his senses into meaningful concepts. These then must be compressed and stored in his memory in some kind of code or shorthand. Thus, to achieve linguistic communication, it is necessary to possess and to be able to manipulate a code of symbols which is meaningful within the individual's social environment.

Sheridan (1964, p. 7) underlines the comment made earlier concerning inner language and the deaf child. She notes that barring other handicaps, the totally deaf child has the potential of understanding the world about him and of building an efficient inner language which can serve him in pantomime or drawing long before he has mastered the peripheral forms of language.

The Language of Gestures. One of the most fascinating areas of language, and perhaps the most prolific language form, is gesturing as a communication medium. It is evident in rather random forms in the neonate, and even in the most phlegmatic individual it is manifest in some fashion throughout life. The old elocutionary stances were based upon the premise that bodily postures communicate ideas. Psychologists have pointed out that gesture patterns need not be extravagant or obtrusive to carry impact. Reik has written about the clinical act of "listening with the third ear," to denote a therapist's sensitivity to the many subtle somatic clues we communicate. Bryngelson describes the "interpretive symbol" with much the same clinical thought in mind.

As far as the infant is concerned, McCarthy (1966, p. 452) points out that the child understands gestures before he understands words. He also employs gestures in his own responses before he uses language proper. McCarthy refers to Latif's statement (1934) that the general movements and postures of an infant gradually become symbolic gestures through the intervention of the child's elders. The hungry child seeking his bottle is seen as manifesting the language of the whole body because the activity and attitude of the entire body convey meaning to an observer.

There is evidence that the child's understanding of the people around him does not develop as an adjunct to speech understanding, but rather, the child picks up gestural cues from its elders and begins to understand. As Latif points out (1934), the gesture language begins to diminish when vocal language (verbal and tonal) develops; however, the gestures never completely disappear, even when vocal communication has reached its highest level.

Abercrombie (1964, p. 17) feels that although verbal communication becomes relatively more and more important as the child grows and matures, he is never totally emancipated from the nonverbal modes of communication, including gestures. Gestures, when used in a supplemental fashion to verbal communication, can be very significant in signalling fine nuances of meaning. On the other hand, when used in a solitary fashion, they can be very decisive, e.g., pointing a threatening finger, shaking the head vigorously.

Feldman (1959, p. 3), in his book on mannerisms and gestures, emphasizes that gestures and speech play an indispensable role in interpersonal communications. From the beginning of life, they are the most profound communications between individuals. As soon as a baby is born, the mother "talks" to it, and the infant responds to this, first by smiles, later by mimicry and gestures, and then by words.

Spitz (1964, p. 86) amplifies the early impact of gestures in the mother-child relationship. Spitz reports that in the second month the baby begins to become preoccupied with the visual patterns that he seems to be seeking from his mother's face. He gives it close and extended attention, possibly because of its physical closeness. Under conditions where the baby would receive pleasurable responses from this scrutiny he learns in the third month to reward the adult face with a smile. Spitz notes that this smile is the first active, intentional, directed manifestation of behavior on the infant's part.

The study of gestures as a communication medium is worthy of extensive attention, particularly when one is dealing professionally with children who are deaf or severely hard of hearing. In addition to the gesture patterns which our body postures continuously, reflecting many of our attitudes and inner feelings, one could devote profitable time to gesture language per se. Over and beyond the various visual communication systems used by the deaf, one is forcibly reminded that in our world of excessive noise, it is often necessary to devise systems of gesture communication. For instance, aboard aircraft carriers plane handlers have developed fairly extensive and quite explicit gesture signals. For many years the armed forces have used a gesture language in the battle areas.

In making a final comment on gestures and the total notion of communication by body postures, it would seem appropriate to note that teachers and clinicians often forget momentarily that they, too, are prey to the dangers of communicating messages we would just as soon keep under cover. The facial muscles are extremely sensitive mirrors of our feeling patterns, and they often betray us without our being aware of it. It is almost impossible for us to appear before one child or a group of children and impress them with our professional zeal if we are in truth bored or unwell. Our small muscle tensions will betray us. It recalls to mind the comments of Dr. Lilly in discussing the qualifications of those who would presume to serve as mentors to dolphins.

The Period of Speech Acceleration. One of the astounding aspects of speech development is the rapid development which takes place beyond the first year. According to McNeill (1968, p. 21), it takes only a little more than two years for children to acquire complete knowledge of the grammatical system of their native language. This is accomplished essentially through a process of invention.

After the appearance of the first words at circa one year of age it appears that he blossoms in all parameters of speech and language—vocabulary, sentences, grammatical function, language comprehension, speech formulation, articulation of speech sounds, command of inflectional patterns, and many more. The paradoxical aspect of this amazing feat is that the entire process develops so smoothly and painlessly that one is led to believe that language learning is easy. Only as one deals with the speech handicapped or attempts to cope with the rigors of Latin grammar in high school does the realization dawn that language development is probably the most complex thing which ever happens to man.

Many writers are convinced that children do not learn language by a simple imitative process. They point to the fact that earlier attempts to teach speech to subhuman forms using a variety of motivational stimuli have all failed. They indicate that when the broad spectrum of language is contemplated, it is unrealistic to suppose that such an unbelievably complex neuro-motor phenomenon could be achieved by the child within the span of a few years. There is general agreement that crucial and unique developments within man's brain have laid down a genetic language center which becomes activated early in the life of the child.

McNeill (1968, p. 21) has written extensively in the area of language development. He notes that a normal child, who suffers no hearing loss or speech impediment, will begin to say words at approximately one year of age and begins to form simple sentences of two or three words at one-and-a-half or two years of age. He has almost completely mastered the complicated structure of the English language by the time he is four.

McNeill states that language is created anew by each generation. An understanding of the creation of language can only be acquired by understanding what is being created. He suggests that language should be portrayed as a linguistic description, not an elementary school "grammar."

McNeill explains his concept of language learning in terms of linguistic frames of reference which are beyond our range of interest. However, it is appropriate to discuss the "black box" of the mind which is of considerable interest, if only to demonstrate again the limited knowledge available concerning the central language centers.

In discussing the "black box" McNeill (1968, p. 23) calls attention to a term borrowed from engineering and space science fields. The black box is frequently seen in sophisticated computers, modern aircraft, and space vehicles. It is typified by a plain black box into which numbers of wires lead, and out of which other wires emerge. It is known to perform almost unbelievable acts of technology when input leads and output wires are properly connected and activated. But no one knows what is in the black box, nor what transpires therein.

Using the black box as an analogy, McNeill discusses the central speech and language processor. He postulates that a young child has overheard a certain segment of speech, which he calls the "corpus of speech." By definition the corpus is a set of utterances, some grammatical, some not. This corpus is not particularly large—about the number of utterances one would expect to have been heard by the young child. The pattern which will be followed is illustrated below.

CORPUS OF SPEECH → [LAD] → GRAMMATICAL SYSTEM

The central language processor is called the Language Acquisition Device which McNeill calls LAD for short. The LAD receives the corpus of speech made up of a series of speech utterances. Upon receipt of this corpus the LAD—which is the equivalent of the black box of engineering—in some inexplicable fashion creates a grammatical system. Thus, language patterns can be received and appropriately manipulated.

While the total nature of LAD is not known, McNeill sets up several hypotheses: (1) As with any theory, LAD's grammatical system will allow predictions of future observations, predictions of which utterances will be grammatical sentences; (2) LAD creates a grammar by passing the evidence contained in the corpus through some kind of internal structure; (3) one hint about LAD's internal structure arises from the fact that it must be able to acquire any natural language; (4) whatever is contained in LAD must be universally applicable, so the theory of LAD will be, in part, a theory of universal linguistics; and (5) the problem of understanding LAD is exactly like the problem of understanding real children.

McNeill stresses the grammatical aspect of language learning inasmuch as he feels that grammatical relations must appear early because a capacity for language *is* the reason that children acquire language quickly.

The acquisition of grammar has also been considered by Menyuk (1967, p. 101) who notes that children proceed from physiological utterance, to babbling, to formation of words and sentences in a surprisingly short time. At the same time they acquire comparable grammars enabling them to communicate with their peers, family, and adults, and they do this after being provided with only a limited sampling of their language. In addition to being rapid, the processes of language development are also resistant to distortion, although a severely mentally retarded, physiologically impaired, or environmentally deprived child may suffer some language disorder when these processes are disturbed.

Ajuriaguerra (1966, p. 24) is of the opinion that the language centers in the child are fundamentally different from that in the adult. He has questions concerning preformed language centers in the brain. In children there are basic structures which are probably crucial, but they are less fixed and less well organized than in the adult. Basically, he feels that there are three underlying principles involved: (1) In the child, any interference with sensory motor processes may result in language disorganization; (2) there are no preformed centers of language in the young organism but these centers spring into life easily in the very process of organization itself; (3) hemispheric dominance is much more labile in the child than in the adult.

The author feels that for every function there are organizations laid down in the central nervous system, but they will not be functional without the process itself, which works back on these structures. This statement would seem to be pertinent in terms of basic speech development. Central language centers exist which can respond quickly to the speech experiences of the young child; however, they would lie essentially dormant in its auditory parameters in the case of a deaf child.

Lenneberg (1966, p. 37–38) calls our attention not only to the rapid development of speech during early years, but also to a sharp decline in speech acquisition facility at about the age of puberty.

This author cites studies done in Austria and in Great Britain on the onset of speech. The combined results indicated that by nine months of age only 20 percent of the children under study had acquired at least one word. However, by the time the children had reached 12 months, 75 percent of them had acquired at least one word. By the time the children reached age three years the acquisition curve had flattened out considerably.

Phrase and sentence development followed the same pattern with the point of onset at circa 18 months. The acquisition curve was very steep through about 30 months, when it tended to flatten out.

Lenneberg (1966, p. 48) notes the most rapid rate of language growth occurs during the first two years of life, and during this same period the brain more than triples its weight.

We have indicated that in the first three years of his life the young child makes a great amount of progress in his speech development—in many aspects, phenomenal. As if this were not enough, Van Riper (1963, p. 92) reminds us that the youngster is doing many more things than learning to speak. He has to learn to become a social being, whether he chooses to or not. He is exposed to prohibitions, which can cause him to become negative. He expresses his emotions through words, and words thus become very important to him. He can, through speech, manipulate those around him and satisfy his needs, so there is a necessity for precision and fluency in his vocal expressions.

Vocabulary Growth. Just as it is difficult to determine decisively when a child utters its first true word, there are problems involved in establishing the size of vocabulary at any given point. In this regard McCarthy (1966, p. 528) cites Vigotsky's (1939) comments to the effect that when a word is deprived of the meaning it has for the user it becomes not a word but an empty sound. In a child, or an adult, word meanings are not a static property of words, but they change and develop as the individual develops.

Despite the problems associated with vocabulary estimation, McCarthy (1966, p. 526) notes that a rapid increase in vocabulary takes place after the first few words have appeared. The child is acquiring the "raw material" of language, which he can later use in many different combinations to express various degrees and shades of meanings. One might note parenthetically that the rapid increase in vocabulary to which McCarthy refers might easily be linked with the subject matter of the previous section. McCarthy generally reinforces Lenneberg's findings when she writes of the rapid increase in vocabulary throughout the preschool period, followed by a slower rate until mental maturity is reached.

The first serious, organized effort to develop a vocabulary test to be used with young children was made by M. E. Smith in 1926. As cited in McCarthy's work (1966, p. 532), Smith built a test comprising 203 words selected by a systematic sampling method from the Thorndike 10,000 word list. The scoring of the test was based upon a composite of items, including allowing credit for recalling and speaking the word in the test situation, or giving indirect evidence of understanding the word.

Based upon Smith's findings with a total of 278 children representing an age range from eight months through six years, the accompanying table of vocabulary increase in children was devised. McCarthy gives considerable attention to these data and one also finds them reported in other professional writings. These data agree closely with estimates of vocabulary in children which are being cited in current literature.

It is interesting to note in this table that between the first and second years of life the child acquires 272 words, while between the second and

Increase in Size of Vocabulary in Relation to Age
(M. E. Smith, 1926)

Age					
Years	Months	N	Average IQ	Number of Words	Gain
	8	13		0	
	10	17		1	1
1	0	52		3	2
1	3	19		19	16
1	6	14		22	3
1	9	14		118	96
2	0	25		272	154
2	6	14		446	174
3	0	20	109	896	450
3	6	26	106	1222	326
4	0	26	109	1540	318
4	6	32	109	1870	330
5	0	20	108	2072	202
5	6	27	110	2289	217
6	0	9	108	2562	273

(from McCarthy, *Language Development in Children,* p 523)

third years, he acquires an additional 624 words. The never-ending character of vocabulary growth is more fully appreciated when one notes in McCarthy (1966, p. 529) that college undergraduates have a total vocabulary estimated at 155,736 words, with a range of from 112,110 to 192,575.

Development of Phrases and Sentences. In this discussion on speech development it is inevitable that we would not be able to conform to a neat organizational pattern. As we have already indicated, the very complexity of language and the many factors—simultaneously operative—which are important in building up language skills, make it difficult to categorize cleanly. In this regard we have referred to sentence development several times thus far, although we are just now bringing it into sharper focus.

It has already been mentioned that at the age of circa two years the child begins to use simple sentences. This is an achievement of considerable note, since it is outward evidence of the youngster's awareness that words can be linked together to expand communication. Yet, as with all other developmental stages we have looked at, there is much more to the sentence than meets the casual eye. In this regard, McNeill (1968, p. 21) helps to put the sentence into perspective by contrasting the surface structure of the sentence with the "deep" or "underlying" structure—that aspect of the arrangement of words which enables us to extract meaning from the sentence.

Brain (1961, p. 16) feels that the relationship between the words of a sentence and the order in which they are used is a very complex one, yet something of the rules involved must come to the child's early awareness as he proceeds to coin his version of sentences. The order appears to be determined by the meaning of the words, and yet in some cases the meaning of a word is determined by its position in the sentence.

As one charts the chronology of speech development, and particularly the many confusing elements of linguistic function in sentences, he can only conclude that the youngster must have available the LAD device—or some equivalent—as described by McNeill.

Following some of Lashley's ideas, Brain points out that when one is faced with the expressions of one thought, there are a variety of ways in which it can be expressed—the analog being the situation where numbers of geographic routes may be taken to arrive at a single destination. Persons who have toiled with the complications of a foreign language will recall the ingenuity they developed in expressing themselves with limited vocabulary and a limited grammar.

Following this line of thought Brain writes:

> . . . In translating into speech, the idea to be expressed must be represented physiologically by a diffuse simultaneous excitation of widespread cortical and subcortical areas; that is, it is spatially extended and for practical purposes simultaneous. An idea is not structureless, but possesses its own structure, which may be partly logical and partly emotional. Speech involves the conversion of the structure of the idea as a system of simultaneous relationships into the syntactical structure of words in a sentence succeeding one another in time. Like the walker, the talker has alternative routes to his objective, that is, alternative ways of constructing his sentence, and a sentence, like a route, is a whole which determines the relationship of the different parts to each other in such a way that the choice of the later parts is influenced by the choice of the earlier one.

Van Riper (1963, p. 92) has described the language status of children two years of age when they have begun to come to grips with sentence structure. Speech has now become a very useful tool for the child as well as a safety valve to dissipate emotions. He tends to use many two-word sentences at this point although more complex ones are occasionally heard. His articulation is still error-ridden and it will be some time before all sounds are accurately produced. Speech rhythms are not smooth. But the highly significant thing is that he is now speaking—he has learned to talk.

The Speech Chain. Thus far we have restricted our presentation largely to the evocation aspects of language, except for occasional references to the impact of deafness upon the early stages of speech development. However, we feel that the entire "speech chain" must be looked at briefly if the speech process is to be appreciated in its true perspective. For this purpose, we are including a diagram which appears in *The Speech Chain*, written by Denes and Pinson (1963).

In looking at the simplified circuitry of the speech chain we are reminded again of Fry (1957) who described spoken language as implying communication between two minds. This concept further implied a three-part system: *Reception,* which begins in a sensory stimulus; *Interpretation* which is an intellectual process; and *Expression* which terminates in motor activity.

When we think of the dynamics of the speech chain we operate on the premise that the entire circuitry is functioning reasonably well, thus allowing the process of communication to proceed. For those who have responsibilities for handicapped children it is important to reaffirm the fact that a break can occur at any point in the chain—or multiple breaks may occur. It is also possible for the chain to become weakened at one or more points. In these cases the communication chain can be impeded in performing its functions in a variety of ways, depending upon the locus of the disruption.

A. The Auditory Link. Arnold (1965, p. 346) has noted that the newborn infant hears and responds to sound through inborn hearing reflexes. At birth the central hearing pathways are functioning at the level of the primary hearing center in the inferior colliculi of the midbrain.

Some writers are confident that the ears become functional as soon as the amniotic fluid has drained out of the middle ear cavity. At any rate, it is generally agreed that the hearing mechanism is operational early in neonatal life.

Jean-Claude Lafon (1968, p. 76) in discussing the auditory basis of phonetics points out that one should not think of the ear alone when audition is described. One should also consider the reception of the acoustic message by the ear, the transformation of the message into a nervous message which is received and integrated by the neurological circuits, the identification of the message, and finally, the recognition that it is a structural element which belongs to a language system familiar to the subject. The latter two elements cited by Lafon in his pathways would impinge upon central processing areas of the brain, which points again to the limitations of categorization.

Kevin Murphy (1964, p. 12), the British writer whom we have cited earlier, points to an interesting study which involved the listening patterns of a very young child:

> The function of hearing in relation to the production of . . . sounds is interesting. We recently made serial tape recordings of an infant and observed the child's reactions to various stimuli. At six weeks old the infant could be stimulated into vocalizations by voice when he saw the face of the vocaliser. By 12 weeks he could be stimulated into babble by voice alone and this was particularly interesting when one played back his own tape recording. When a happy, playful sound was heard he would respond with happy noises similar to, though not identical with, the stimuli. When cries were played back quietly they were listened to, i.e., there was stilling, eye widening, and cessation of noises. When the volume was turned up to reproduce the originally recorded intensities, he would begin to show signs of distress.

B. The Central Processor of Language. Earlier we considered the Language Acquisition Device (LAD) which was proposed by McNeill. Various writers have given a variety of names to this central processor

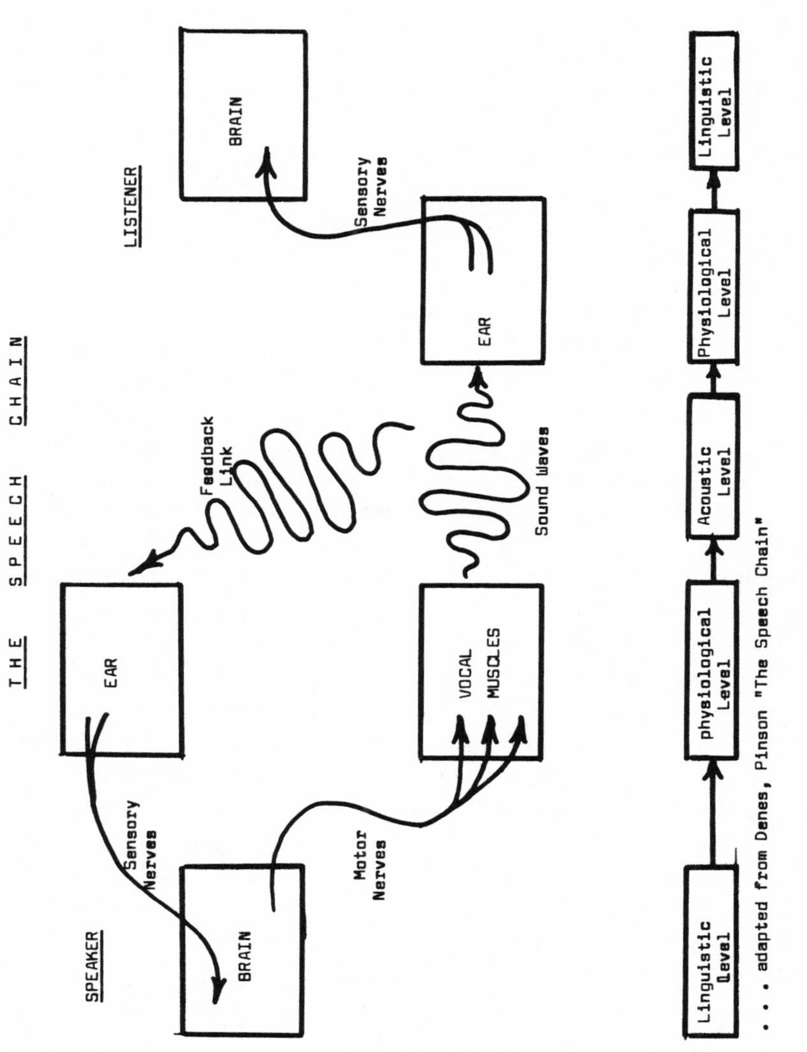
THE SPEECH CHAIN
SPEAKER
LISTENER
BRAIN
EAR
Sensory Nerves
Motor Nerves
VOCAL MUSCLES
Feedback Link
Sound Waves
EAR
Sensory Nerves
BRAIN
Linguistic Level
physiological Level
Acoustic Level
Physiological Level
Linguistic Level
. . . adapted from Denes, Pinson "The Speech Chain"

Figure 2.

which is unique to man. Several have postulated the anatomical whereabouts of the language center; however, at the moment any speculations are guarded. Many are just as content to think about it in "black box" terms for the time being.

As was indicated by Lafon, auditory messages reaching the brain are received in the language center, they are decoded, they are analyzed for meaning and then passed on for any action which may be indicated. Carhart (1969, p. 4) and his associates recently discussed the functions of central language in a document which was prepared for the Institute on Neurological Diseases and Stroke:

> Each sensory complex encodes incoming stimulation into patterns of neural impulses which, after recoding and processing enroute, reach the appropriate primary sensory area of the cerebral hemispheres. The end result is the delivery of patterned neural impulses which are transformed into a symbolic and linguistic stream within the central processor. This central processor is shown in the diagram very simply because its complexity defies any reasonable schematic representation on a single sheet of paper. Moreover, we still know practically nothing about what events occur here or how they proceed. However, we can say that in consequence of these events each incoming neural message is structured into a symbolic and linguistic entity. It acquires meaning and becomes the focus of consciousness. We can also say that these events often trigger reactions which culminate in a reply.

The diagram to which Carhart refers above is being presented here. In a sense it is an expansion of the "speech chain" diagram, except that it is limited to one-half of the speech chain circuit. While the Carhart diagram appears fairly complex it can be very helpful to the reader in understanding some of the language processes which take place within the central processor. Incidentally, we have some question as to whether the "receptor segment," the "central processor," and the "effector segment" are properly indicated in terms of physiological function. At the same time, if other than broad concepts were portrayed, the purposes of the diagram would be defeated.

C. The Speech Function of Language. In the Speech Chain motor nerves lead from the brain to the speech mechanism where speech is actually effected. While we do not propose to go into a detailed description of psycho-neuro-motor processes, it seems inappropriate to contemplate speech from a simplistic point of view.

As Carhart et al have observed, the speech act is made possible by the amazing capabilities of the central language processor. The speech mechanism has often been looked upon as a kind of anatomical orphan child—having borrowed one anatomical part here, and another there, until in some sort of higgledy-piggledy fashion a functioning mechanism was achieved. While it is true that there is literally no speech mechanism per se, and that it is composed of bits and pieces, the crucial feature in this portrayal—and a rather marvelous thing to contemplate—is that the "speech mechanism" functions as excellently as it does because of the unbelievably intricate integrating forces residing within the language formulation area of the brain.

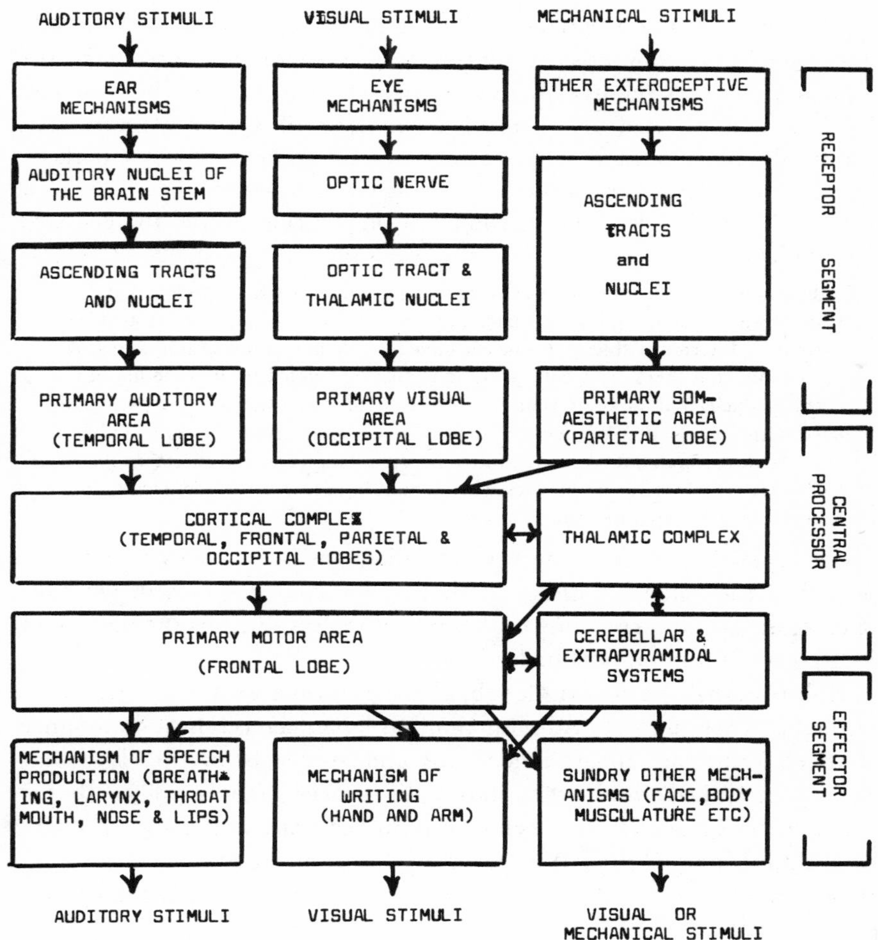

Schematic Diagram of Neural Mechanisms for Human Communication . . . from Carhart et al, "Human Communication and Its Disorders"

Figure 3

As Van Riper has observed, a child *does* learn to speak. He does learn to marshal the encoding process of language; he does achieve the exquisite coordinations among tongue, lips, pharynx, larynx, thorax, and numerous other facilitating body parts so that meaningful speech is formed and communication is established.

D. Feedback Links in Speech. One of the important circuits portrayed in the Speech Chain is the feedback link which allows the speaker to monitor his speech constantly. As with so many other facets of the speech process these feedback pathways are seldom thought of or fully understood. Yet they are constantly at work sending reports in to the central processor relative to the quality of articulation, the loudness level of speech, and the proper sequencing of speech sounds. We ordinarily make minute adjustments in our speech patterns without being consciously aware of the monitoring circuits.

Carhart et al (1969, p. 83) comment on the role played by feedback mechanisms:

> It is now apparent that every sensory system in the body has a feedback mechanism through which input is regulated at various levels. The auditory system is no exception. Efferent pathways to the ear have been demonstrated and it is reasonably certain that there are feedback stations directly related to the function of the cochlear nuclei and the brain stem. It is quite possible that they play a role in children with delayed development of language, and some aspects of adult aphasia. . . . Again, although it is easier to study hearing, language, and speech as though each were a kind of entity, the fact remains that in both normal and deviant function none can be separated from the others.

An inspection of the Speech Chain diagram as it moves over to the person of the listener will reveal that as the circuit is closed, we have once again begun a recycling of the entire process. Such is the pattern of interpersonal communication.

Relationship between Cerebral Dominance and Speech. One of the manifestations of brain function has long been cerebral dominance as it relates to body function generally and to speech specifically. It has long been linked—and not without differences of opinion—with the problem of aphasia. It has been closely linked with stuttering, although to a diminishing degree. We have long been intrigued with the notion that lack of cerebral dominance may be related to delayed language development.

Mountcastle (1962) and other authors have given basic consideration to the phenomenon of cerebral dominance. In this publication Teuber (1962, p. 131) discusses hemispheric brain lesions and also the physiology of cerebral activity:

> As a paired organ, the vertebrate forebrain with its conspicuous cerebral hemispheres poses questions of origin and present function. The evolution of this twin structure is undoubtedly related to the bilateral symmetry of the body itself; the widespread decussation of neural pathways, connecting one halfbrain with the opposite half of the body, reflects the need for contraversive movements in any bilaterally symmetrical organism as it strives to maintain its course and posture in water, air, or on the ground.
>
> Given this quality of cerebral hemispheres we have the question of how these paired structures normally interact.

In this same publication Neff (1962, p. 196) concludes that man demonstrates measurable differences in the functioning of the two cerebral hemispheres. He states further that the differences are not confined to behavior which involves language. Critchley (1962, p. 210) discusses the phenomenon of speech and of man's handedness preferences, and feels that there are more dimensions to cerebral dominance than these two features.

Brain (1961, p. 24–28) has written about the relationship between speech and cerebral dominance at some length. However, as is true with most writers, there appears to be greater interest in which hemisphere is playing the dominant role and the speech and language sequelae of hemispheric lesions.

In terms of basic speech development we are rather more interested in the phenomenon of cerebral dominance and its possible relationship to delayed speech. We have seen many children with marked speech and language retardation who at the same time have no appreciable laterality preferences, as far as we are able to determine. We know that one can portray laterality along a single continuum in which case the plotting of a reasonably large population would yield a bimodal curve. The question then arises as to what happens when a child has no laterality preference. We feel that more research could profitably be done in this area.

In conjunction with his work with Penfield, Roberts (1966, p. 18) has studied the dynamics of cerebral dominance in considerable depth. He expresses the general opinion of contemporary writers in the field when he states that regardless of handedness, the left cerebral hemisphere is usually dominant for speech, except in individuals who have incurred left cerebral damage early in life. Roberts also makes the impressive statement that the left cerebral hemisphere dominant for speech is the most important thing that man inherits.

The Speech Environment. It takes little thought to establish the importance of environmental factors in the life of an infant learning how to speak. We have already noted that certain environmental stimuli will facilitate the sound-making pattern, while others will cause the baby to fall silent.

Since the element of practice of speech sounds is very important to continuing development we should examine those factors in the environment which can be most productively used. Spitz (1963, p. 180) calls attention to the sudden shift in attitude which takes place within the baby when he begins to locomote on his own. Automatically the child's operational horizons are tremendously extended and his earlier dependency upon his mother is now markedly changed. The parent-child communication patterns likewise undergo a change. In contrast to the period when the infant was relatively passive and maternal behavior consisted of endearment and supportive action, the exchanges between mother and child now include commands and prohibitions of the mother and bursts of infantile activity in the child.

Some authorities comment on the manner in which speech can be used to influence one's own behavior as well as the behavior of those about him. In their opinion we often control another's behavior by what we get them to say.

Such a line of thought leads toward the philosophical purposes served by speech, and the point at which they influence the child's life. McCarthy (1966, p. 562) is interested to learn of factors which initially induce speech attempts in the child, what specific situations are apt to motivate him to speak, what satisfactions he derives from his environment when he attempts speech, and what internal needs are satisfied by speech.

Many writers feel that the impact of institutionalization is of great moment in the speech developmental life of a child. McCarthy (1966, p. 584) states that recent studies of the effects of environmental deprivation in hospital, orphanage, or institutional environments have shown challenging results. He notes that it is surprising how early the effects are manifested and how lasting these effects are.

McCarthy cites Gatewood and Weiss (1930) who reported that in situations where newborn infants were allowed to lie naturally without any external stimulation there were fewer vocalizations than usual. They feel that apparently the sheer monotony and the impersonal character of the institutional life environment provide little motivation for vocalization.

Other environmental elements contribute to emotional climates in which the infant engages in the speech-learning process. Arnold (1964, p. 349) tends to summarize them when he points to the linkage between built-in language potentials and the triggering mechanism of a stimulating environment. Without a speech environment, speech development will suffer. Arnold feels that if inheritance can be looked upon as the potential for the development of functions and structures, then maturation would be the development of the functions and structures under the conditions of the environment.

The Reticulo-Limbic Complex. Passing mention must be made to a function of the brain which appears to be of great importance in the conscious aspects of audition and also in the emotional displays which frequently become a part of our speech patterns. This complex function has been variously called the "reticular core," the "reticular activating system" or a combined "reticular-limbic complex."

Berry (1969, p. 71) notes:

> Because relatively recent research has brought the reticular system out of limbo, and put it in an orbit of great importance, it demands a consideration that long established systems do not require. Moruzzi and Magoun describe the system as a "cephalically directed brain-stem system, apparently consisting of reticular relays ascending to the basal diencephalon and further to the cortex where it was found to desynchronize the high-voltage slow wave and create a pattern of low voltage, high frequency activity the so-called arousal reaction."

The key word in the reticular system seems to be arousal, although other functions are now being ascribed to it. It might be thought of as an energizing or organizing system. It seems to act both as an augmentor and inhibitor of impulses coursing along conventional nerve pathways through the nervous system.

While arousal mechanisms can act in conjunction with most of the sense modalities, it would be of greatest interest for us to consider the reticular core vis-a-vis the auditory function. In the first place, it is important to point out that we are always hearing—there is no analog to the eyelid to shut off the flow of sound patterns along auditory pathways. Thus, unless there were some inhibitory mechanism built into the auditory circuitry, we would live in a bedlam of uncontrolled sound bombardment. However, thanks to this suppressor mechanism we are able to listen selectively.

On the other hand, with the suppressor mechanism obtaining, there needs to be a counter-acting arousal mechanism to alert the brain to sounds which have some sort of significance. It is thought that the reticular core plays an active role both in the inhibitory function as well as in arousal. A recent Pfizer publication on the *Functioning Brain of Man* describes elements of reticular activity (1966, p. 11). It states that the reticular core has a dual function: it activates the neocortex and other portions of the brain enabling them to respond in a meaningful way to incoming coded signals; and it serves to selectively prevent most potential stimuli from affecting us, so that we can concentrate on the stimuli that are momentarily significant.

The limbic system, thought to involve the hypothalamus of the brain and other structures surrounding the thalami, figures prominently in our emotional life. We have already noted that the early content of a child's speech is largely emotional in character. Additionally, speech continues to serve throughout our lives in close conjunction to our emotional patterns. Often it serves an important role in the ventilating of emotional tensions. The exact anatomical limits of the limbic system are not known at present, nor the precise manner in which our emotions are keyed into our language processing units. We can only postulate that the relationship must be a close one.

Speech Development of the Deaf Child. As our discussion of speech development has progressed we have often mentioned the impact of deafness upon all facets of emergent sound and word patterns. Different writers have pointed to the deaf child as firsthand evidence of the need for an encouraging speech environment.

The general rule expressed by most writers in the field is that a deaf baby will engage in self-reflexive sounds during the early months of life, but because of the sound vacuum will regress and gradually become essentially silent, whereas the normal infant will move forward to the babbling stage. In this regard Roberts (1966, p. 19) states that auditory, kinesthetic, and visual systems need to be intact if the child is going to speak normally. If one sense modality is defective, speech can be learned, although with difficulty.

Lenneberg (1968, p. 33) points out that it is difficult to suppress language development in children. He states that even congenitally deaf children who may be unable to acquire vocal speech can learn language with little difficulty through a graphic medium when written materials are presented to them. According to research now in progress, reports Lenneberg, children who suffer severe parental neglect, or whose parents speak no language at all, may nevertheless acquire speech with a minimal delay.

The psychological impact of deafness upon the speechless child is stressed by McCarthy (1966, p. 493). She feels that one should never lose sight of the relationship between language and the psychological development of the child. She points out the difference between the "mental vacuum" in which the young deaf-mute lives before he is exposed to any means of communication and the mental state of the normal child, who is able to gain a great deal of information not only through his understanding of the speech of others, but also through his ability to express his own ideas, wants, and needs through language, and to therefore affect the behavior of others.

Lewis (1963, p. 75–76) also emphasizes the other-than-speech deprivations which the deaf child is likely to encounter. In addition to speech and language problems, he points to the effects of deafness upon the social, emotional, and intellectual lives of these children. He observes that, although deaf children are no less able than normal children to deal with concrete situations which immediately face them, their cognitive retardation becomes more evident when there is need for generalization and abstraction.

It is interesting to note that in almost every aspect of habilitation, as practiced today, great emphasis is placed upon reaching the handicapped child at the earliest possible age. The same holds true for the deaf child and one sees many moves in this direction in a variety of facilities. Murphy (1964, p. 12) stresses the time factor in commenting on speech and language problems of the deaf child: "It is important to remember that unless he is either very profoundly deaf or his deafness is of central origin, even the deaf infant makes sounds and it is, of course, essential that these vocalizations should be maintained. The reasons for this are twofold: (a) because maintained vocalization implies maintained interest in and therefore preparedness to continue in vocalization; (b) if vocalization is not maintained and muteness supervenes, the consequent delay in therapy relates not only to the redevelopment of interest in voice and skill in its use, but also to overcoming the developing skill in gestural communication which may have reached the stage of becoming his 'mother tongue.' In all stages of handicap, skills which are learned with difficulty have a very distorted status value for their learner and are therefore less readily or easily unlearned."

Other Parameters of Speech Development. There remain numbers of other basic and important parameters of the speech developmental process, some of them at least as important as those which we have discussed. Much more could be said about the external environment in which the infant finds himself; we have scarcely mentioned the critical area of emotional well-being and the psychological features of speech development; we have said little about individual differences as they affect language learning; we have only vaguely pointed to the anatomical end organs which actually produce speech.

In short, we have reaffirmed the innate complexity of speech development and the frustrations attached to presenting an abbreviated version of it. Fortunately, there are excellent supplemental readings from which an interested person could glean the missing elements

TRENDS IN THE AREA OF SPEECH AND LANGUAGE DEVELOPMENT

Early Therapy

In recent years there has been a mass of evidence accumulated, all pointing to the importance of the earliest possible introduction of habilitative procedures into the lives of children presenting handicaps such as congenital deafness. We believe this policy has very important implications for handicaps which call for long-range therapy. In the past we have too often been lulled into the false notion that we have an endless period of time available in which to achieve maximum habilitation.

Investigating the Black Box of the Mind

There is a strong and welcome trend in speech pathology-audiology, teachers of the deaf, teachers and clinicians working with brain-damaged children, and others, to look beyond the obvious peripheral symptom patterns and begin probing into some of the central functions of speech and language. This move challenges the professional person to extend his vistas of knowledge into linguistics, psycholinguistics, anatomy and physiology, and child psychology. We see it as a tremendously important trend, worthy of anyone working with the language handicapped.

Taking the Child out of the Laboratory

For many years the convenience of the professional worker has been served by conducting research in the laboratory or in the classroom. Unquestionably, important work has been accomplished, but for certain types of child studies, stress is being placed upon studying the child within his own home environment. Child researchers are coming to the awareness that an uncontrolled variable is being introduced into any study where one assumes that the child's behavior in the "test tube" is identical with his behavior at home.

Issues in the Area of Speech-Language Development

It has been remarkable and depressing to be forced to an important awareness during the course of the voluminous reading we have done in the area of general linguistics and in language development in recent months. We have been depressed to acknowledge that professionals skilled in speech and hearing handicaps are notably absent on the roster of persons actively studying the central language processes. There is great activity among the linguists, psycholinguists, psychologists, neurologists, neuro-physiologists, and even psychiatrists. However, with the exception of Wepman and Roberts, representatives of the speech-hearing professions are generally absent.

It is heartening, however, to recognize that colleagues with vision have recognized the direction in which the profession must move and important steps are in process to assure greater representation in the future when central language functions are discussed.

Prospective Research Areas

Without going into specifics at this point, we might note that broad areas of prospective research have been included in the discussion of speech development. Much of the oft-quoted research is still meaningful; however, with the relatively sophisticated instrumentation now available to the investigator, many areas of speech development could be probed which were not possible even a few years ago. Certainly the unanswered questions surrounding normal speech and language development are legion.

Perhaps some of our lack of finite knowledge has been encapsulated by Cherry (1961, p. 12):

> It is remarkable that human communication works at all, for so much seems to be against it; yet it does. The fact that it does depends principally upon the vast store of habits which we each one of us possess, the imprints of all our past experiences. With this, we can hear snatches of speech, see vague gestures and grimaces, and from such thin shreds of evidence we are able to make a continual series of inductive guesses, with extraordinary effectiveness.

BIBLIOGRAPHY

Abercrombie, M. L. J. Non-verbal communication. In C. Renfrew and K. Murphy (Eds.), *The child who does not talk.* London: William Heinemann Medical Books, Ltd., 1964.

Ajuriaguerra, J. de. Brain mechanisms in speech. In E. C. Carterette (Ed.), *Brain function.* Vol. 3. *Speech, language and communication.* Berkeley: University of California Press, 1966.

Berry, M. F. *Language disorders of children.* New York: Appleton-Century-Crofts, 1969.

Bosma, J. F., Truby, H. M., and Lind, J. Distortions of upper respiratory and swallow motions in infants. In J. Lind (Ed.), *Newborn Infant Cry.* Uppsala, Sweden: Almquist and Wiksells Boktryckeri, Ab., 1965.

Brain, Sir R. *Speech disorders: Aphasia, apraxia and agnosia.* Washington, D.C.: Butterworth, Inc., 1961.

Brain, Sir R. The neurology of language. In R. C. Oldfield and J. C. Marshall (Eds.), *Language: selected readings.* Baltimore, Md.: Penguin Books, 1968.

Brown, R., and Bellugi, U. Three processes in the child's acquisition of syntax. In E. H. Lenneberg (Ed.), *New directions in the study of language.* Cambridge, Mass.: M.I.T. Press, 1964.

Carhart, R. (chairman). *Human communication and its disorders.* NINDS Report, NIH, Public Health Service, Bethesda, Md., 1969.

Cherry, C. *On human communication.* New York: Science Editions, Inc., 1961.

Critchley, M. Speech and speech loss in relation to the duality of the brain. In V. B. Mountcastle (Ed.), *Interhemispheric relations and cerebral dominance.* Baltimore, Md.: Johns Hopkins Press, 1962.

Denes, P. B., and Pinson, E. N. *The speech chain.* New York: Bell Telephone Laboratories, 1963.

Eisenson, J. *The psychology of speech.* London: F. S. Crofts, 1938.

Feldman, S. S. *Mannerisms of speech and gestures in everyday life.* New York: International Universities Press, 1959.

Fraser, C., Bellugi, U., and Brown, R. Control of grammar in imitation, comprehension and production. In R. C. Oldfield and J. C. Marshall (Eds.), *Language: selected readings.* Baltimore, Md.: Penguin Books, 1968.

Fry, D. B. Speech and language. *Journal of Laryngology and Otology,* 1957, **71,** 434.

Goldstein, K. *Language and language disturbances.* New York: Grune and Stratton, 1948.

Gordon, I. J. *Human development.* New York: Harper and Row, 1962.

Lafon, J.-C. Auditory basis of phonetics. In B. Malmberg (Ed.), *Manual of phonetics.* Amsterdam: North Holland Publishing Co., 1968.

Latif, I. The physiological basis of linguistic development and of the ontogeny of meaning. *Psychological review,* 1934, **41,** 55–85, 153–176.

Lenneberg, E. H. A biological perspective of language. In R. C. Oldfield and J. C. Marshall (Eds.), *Language: selected readings.* Baltimore, Md.: Penguin Books, 1968.

Lenneberg, E. H. Speech development: Its anatomical and physiological concomitants. In E. C. Carterette (Ed.), *Brain function.* Vol. III. *Speech, language and communication.* Berkeley: University of California Press, 1966.

Lewis, M. M. *Language, thought and personality in infancy and childhood.* New York: Basic Books, 1963.

Lilly, J. C. *Man and dolphin.* New York: Pyramid Books, 1961.

Lilly, J. C. *The mind of the dolphin.* New York: Doubleday, 1967.

Lilly, J. C. Dolphin's vocal mimicry as a unique ability. In K. and S. Salzinger (Eds.), *Research in verbal behavior and some neurophysiological implications.* New York: Academic Press, 1967.

Lind, J. (Ed.) *New born infant cry.* Uppsala, Sweden: Almquist and Wiksells Boktryckeri, Ab., 1965.

Luchsinger, R., and Arnold, G. E. *Voice, speech and language: Clinical communicology, its physiology and pathology.* Belmont, Calif.: Wadsworth Publishing Co., 1965.

McCarthy, D. Language development in children. In P. H. Mussen (Ed.), Carmichael's *Manual of child psychology.* 3rd ed. New York: John Wiley and Sons, 1970. (Cited as 1966).

McNeill, D. The creation of language. In R. C. Oldfield and J. C. Marshall (Eds.), *Language: selected readings.* Baltimore, Md.: Penguin Books, 1968.

Menyuk, P. Acquisition of grammar by children. In K. and S. Salzinger (Eds.), *Research in verbal behavior and some neurophysiological implications.* New York: Academic Press, 1967.

Michell, G. The infant in his family. In C. Renfrew and K. Murphy (Eds.), *The child who does not talk.* London: William Heinemann Medical Books, Ltd., 1964.

Mountcastle, V. B. (Ed.) *Interhemispheric relations and cerebral dominance.* Baltimore, Md.: Johns Hopkins Press, 1962.

Murphy, K. Development of normal vocalization and speech. In C. Renfrew and K. Murphy (Eds.), *The child who does not talk.* London: William Heinemann Medical Books, Ltd., 1964.

Neff, W. D. Difference in the functions of the two cerebral hemispheres. In V. Mountcastle (Ed.), *Interhemispheric relations and cerebral dominance.* Baltimore, Md.: Johns Hopkins Press, 1962.

Oldfield, R. C. and Marshall, J. C. (Eds.) *Language: selected readings.* Baltimore, Md.: Penguin Books, 1968.

Pfizer Laboratories. *The functioning brain of man.* New York: Charles Pfizer, Inc., 1966.

Roberts, L. Central brain mechanisms in speech. In E. C. Carterette (Ed.), *Brain function.* Vol. 3. *Speech, language and communication.* Berkeley: University of California Press, 1966.

Sheridan, M. D. Development of auditory attention and language symbols in young children. In C. Renfrew and K. Murphy (Eds.), *The child who does not talk.* London: William Heinemann Medical Books, Ltd., 1964.

Shohara, H. H. The genesis of the articulatory movements of speech. *Quarterly journal of speech,* 1935, **21,** 343.

Spitz, R. A. and Cobliner, W. *The first year of life.* New York: International Universities Press, 1965.

Teuber, H.-L. Effects of brain wounds implicating right or left hemispheres in man. In V. Mountcastle (Ed.), *Interhemispheric relations and cerebral dominance.* Baltimore, Md.: Johns Hopkins Press, 1962.

Truby, H. M. and Lind, J. Cry sounds of the newborn infant. In J. Lind (Ed.), *Newborn infant cry.* Uppsala, Sweden: Almquist and Wiksells Boktryskeri, Ab., 1965.

Van Riper, C. *Speech correction: Principles and methods.* (4th ed.) Englewood Cliffs, N.J.: Prentice-Hall, 1963.

Warfel, H. R. *Language: A science of human behavior.* Cleveland: Allen Publishers, 1962.

Wepman, J. and Jones, L. V. Studies in aphasia: A psycholinguistic method and case study. In E. C. Carterette (Ed.), *Brain function.* Vol. 3. *Speech, language and communication.* Berkeley: University of California Press, 1966.

Winitz, H. *Articulatory acquisition and behavior.* New York: Appleton-Century-Crofts, 1969.

CHAPTER VI

Speech Pathology for the Deaf

JOHN W. BLACK, PH.D.

This chapter summarizes the disorders of speech that are singular to the deaf, particularly deaf children. These disorders arise from an incomplete feedback loop and the resulting inability of a person to follow his own speech aurally. The significance of the ability and inability to hear one's own voice is dramatically and positively illustrated with these disorders of speech. The self-monitoring system is known to affect loudness of vocal output and is sometimes hypothesized to be related to stuttering. This same causal chain in the instance of the deaf is both dramatically present and is beyond conjecture. Without hearing, one does not learn to speak normally. The experience of hearing oneself talk is a link in the cybernetic loop that fashions an individual's speech and makes it conform to the mode of society. This average behavior is learned not only by the youthful talker, but by his peers as well and has been learned earlier by his parents and teachers. It is called *normal speech* and becomes a target behavior for a person, his family, and his community. In normal development and in day-to-day behavior, the principal channel for matching one's speech production with what is expected—with what is "right"—is through the auditory feedback loop.*

The different feedback loops as diagrammed by Fairbanks are shown in the top portion of Figure 1, that is, Figure 1A (Fairbanks, 1954). This model assumes that a body of experience has accumulated in "storage."

*Vegely has shown that deaf individuals learn through experience the words and sounds that they make unintelligibly. This is a long-term feedback loop that permits deaf adults to predict with some success their speech that will be understood (Vegely, 1964).

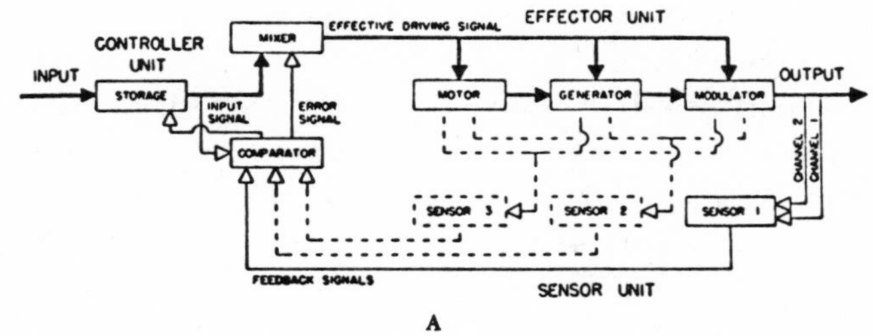

A

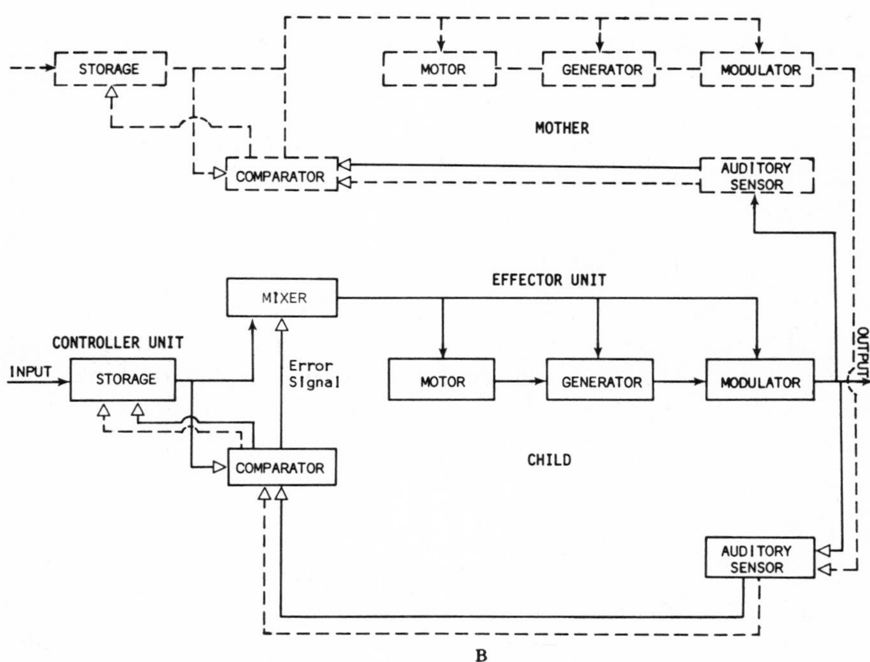

B

Figure 1. Model of a Closed Cycle Control System (top, A, after Fairbanks); and of a modification to accommodate the sensory deficit of a deaf child (bottom, B). The experience (storage) and evaluations (comparator) of an outside person, a mother or teacher, substitute for those of a normal child (Black, 1969; Fairbanks).

The normal talker draws upon a learned vocabulary, practiced linguistic principles, familiar facts, and habitual manners of exposition in order to frame his utterance. The deaf child, however, draws largely on a vacuum in these regards, for he has no accumulated experience in successful oral communication. The model becomes active as it is "primed" by an outside or a substitute "storage."

The lower portion of the same figure largely repeats Figure 1A; however, the writer has suggested in another context the addition of the upper portion of Figure 1B to the Fairbanks diagram (Calvert, 1964). The suggestion was made in connection with an explanation of one's acquiring a pronunciation dialect. The principle, however, holds equally well here. The exterior "storage" may be provided by the parent or a teacher. It is the sum of his experiences with normal speech and serves as a substitute source for the content and form of oral expression of the deaf child. In like manner an exterior "comparator" of the parent or teacher provides the judgments of "suitable - unsuitable," "expected - unexpected," "meaningful - unmeaningful" with each oral production by the child. The target is normal speech. This is beyond reasonable expectation; hence intelligible approximations to normal are acceptable.

The speech of deaf children differs from normal speech in all regards. Possibly these dimensions are encompassed by three headings, (a) articulatory characteristics, (b) aspects of voice, and (c) matters of language. The present chapter includes limited discussions of only the first two of these. The former will be alluded to as understandability and the latter as uniqueness. One writer concludes that the speech of the deaf imposes a hearing loss of the discrimination type on the listener (Thomas, 1964).

Both voice and articulation are represented visually by spectrograms, although no portrayal of the acoustic event is complete. Figures 2–6 show spectrograms of the pronunciations of five words by each of three deaf children, ages 5 and 8, and two normally hearing children of the same ages. The children were known to be cooperative; otherwise the recordings were unselected. One teacher elicited the pronunciations from the children in the manner of repetitive exercises. Recordings were made on magnetic tape and copied on the spectrograph.

A spectrogram shows four physical dimensions of speech. (1) The horizontal length of the picture represents the total duration of the segment of speech. This is limited to 2.4 sec.; however, a single syllable is typically about 1/5 sec. (2) The frequencies (Hz or cps) at which energy occurs typically fall in clearly defined bands and appear as dark horizontal markings at different locations on the vertical dimension of the spectrogram. Those that are present simultaneously are directly above and below each other. (3) The relative intensities of these bands of frequencies are shown by the degree of blackness of the markings. (4) The vibrations of the vocal folds, termed the *fundamental frequency* and causally

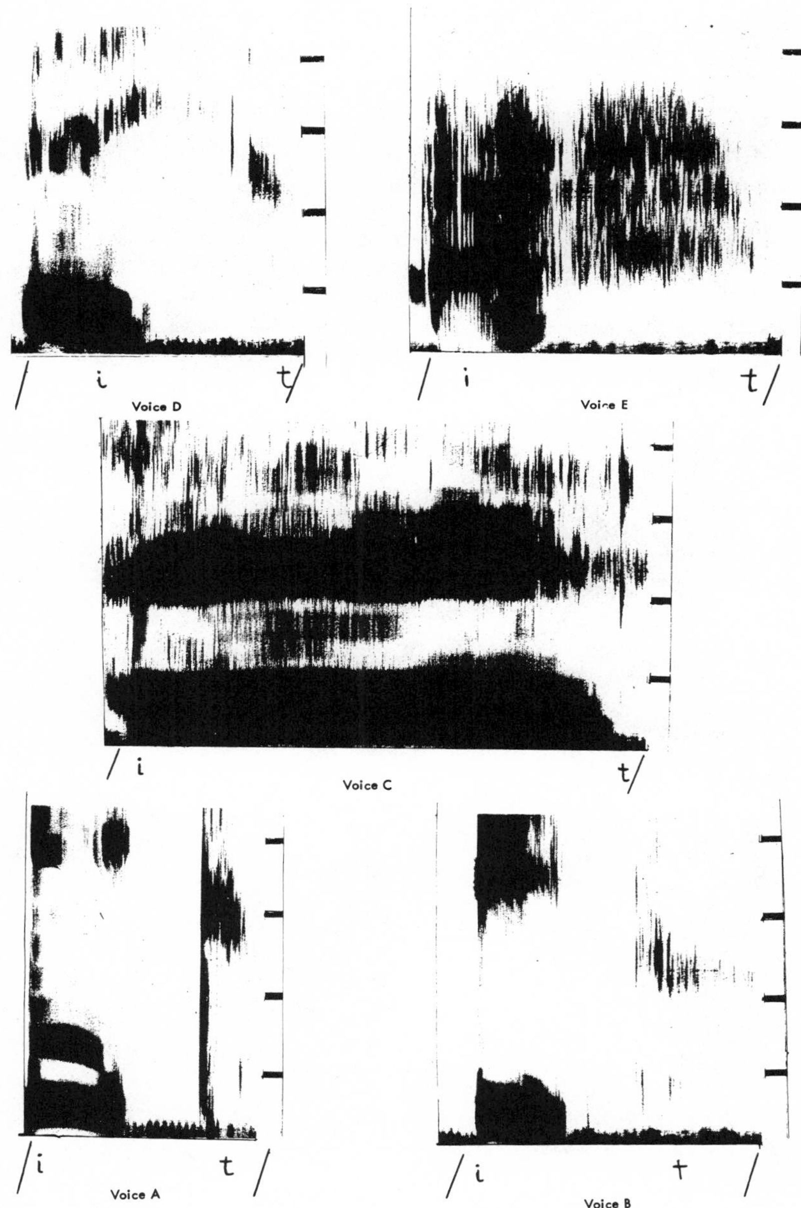

Figure 2. Spectrograms of five pronunciations of eat *as spoken by five children. Voice A, normal hearing girl of 5 years; Voice B, normal hearing girl of 8 years; Voice C, deaf boy of 8 years; Voice D, deaf girl of 8 years; and Voice E, deaf girl of 5 years.*

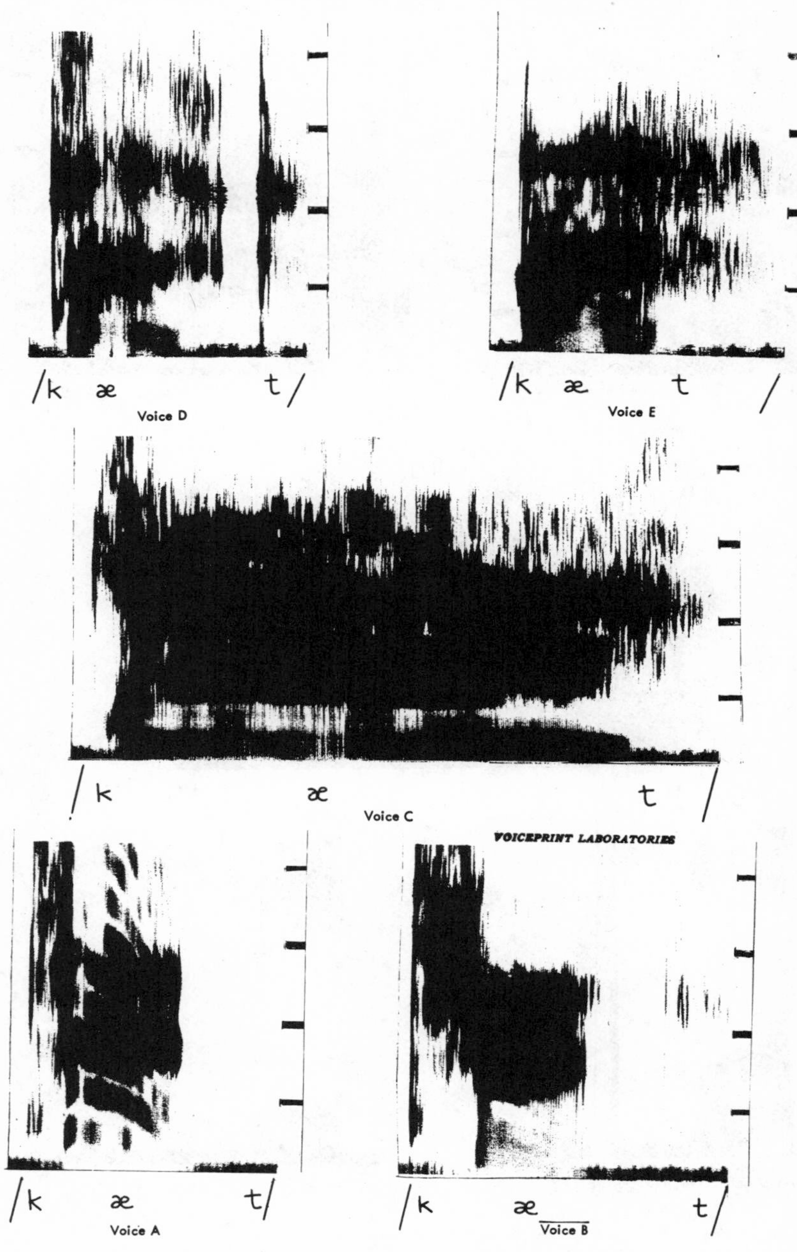

Figure 3. Spectrograms of five pronunciations of cat *as spoken by five children. Voice A, normal hearing girl of 5 years; Voice B, normal hearing girl of 8 years; Voice C, deaf boy of 8 years, Voice D, deaf girl of 8 years; and Voice E, deaf girl of 5 years.*

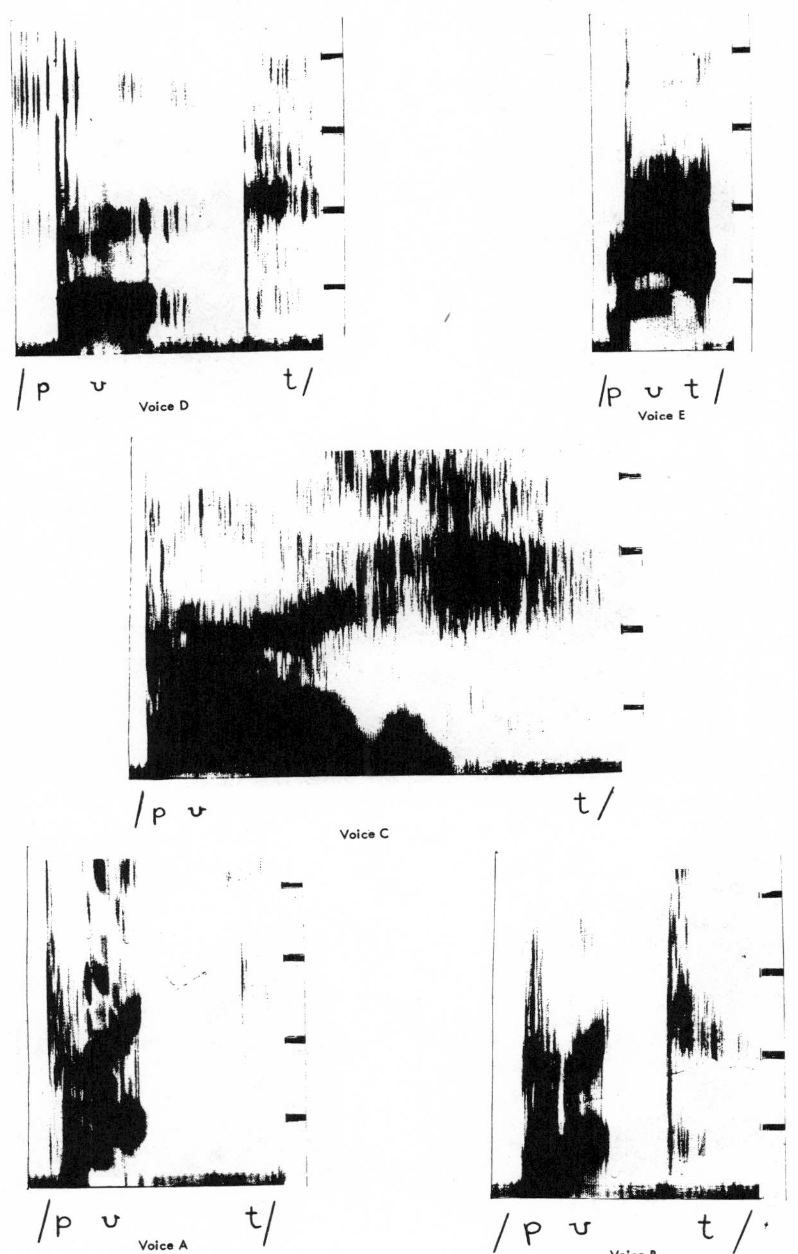

Figure 4. Spectrograms of five pronunciations of put *as spoken by five children. Voice A, normal hearing girl of 5 years; Voice B, normal hearing girl of 8 years; Voice C, deaf boy of 8 years; Voice D, deaf girl of 8 years; and Voice E, deaf girl of 5 years.*

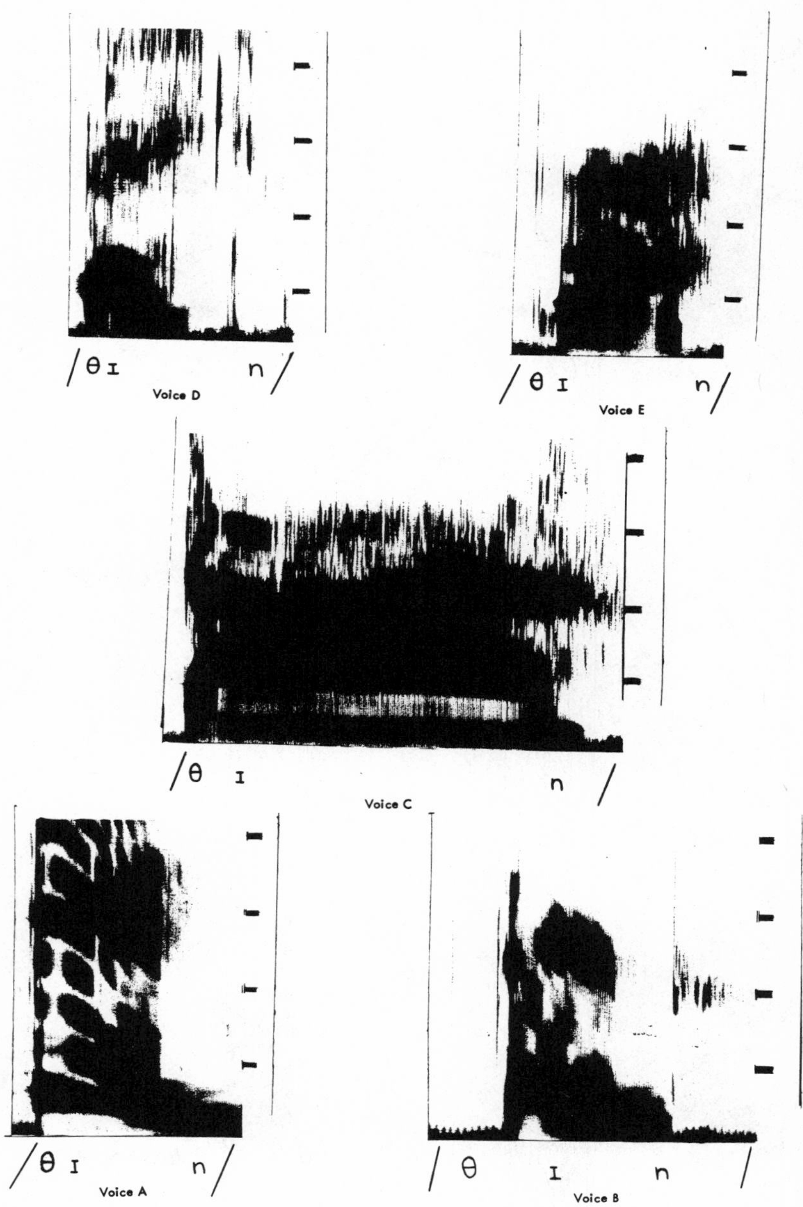

Figure 5. Spectrograms of five pronunciations of thin *as spoken by five children. Voice A, normal hearing girl of 5 years; Voice B, normal hearing girl of 8 years; Voice C, deaf boy of 8 years; Voice D, deaf girl of 8 years; and Voice E, deaf girl of 5 years.*

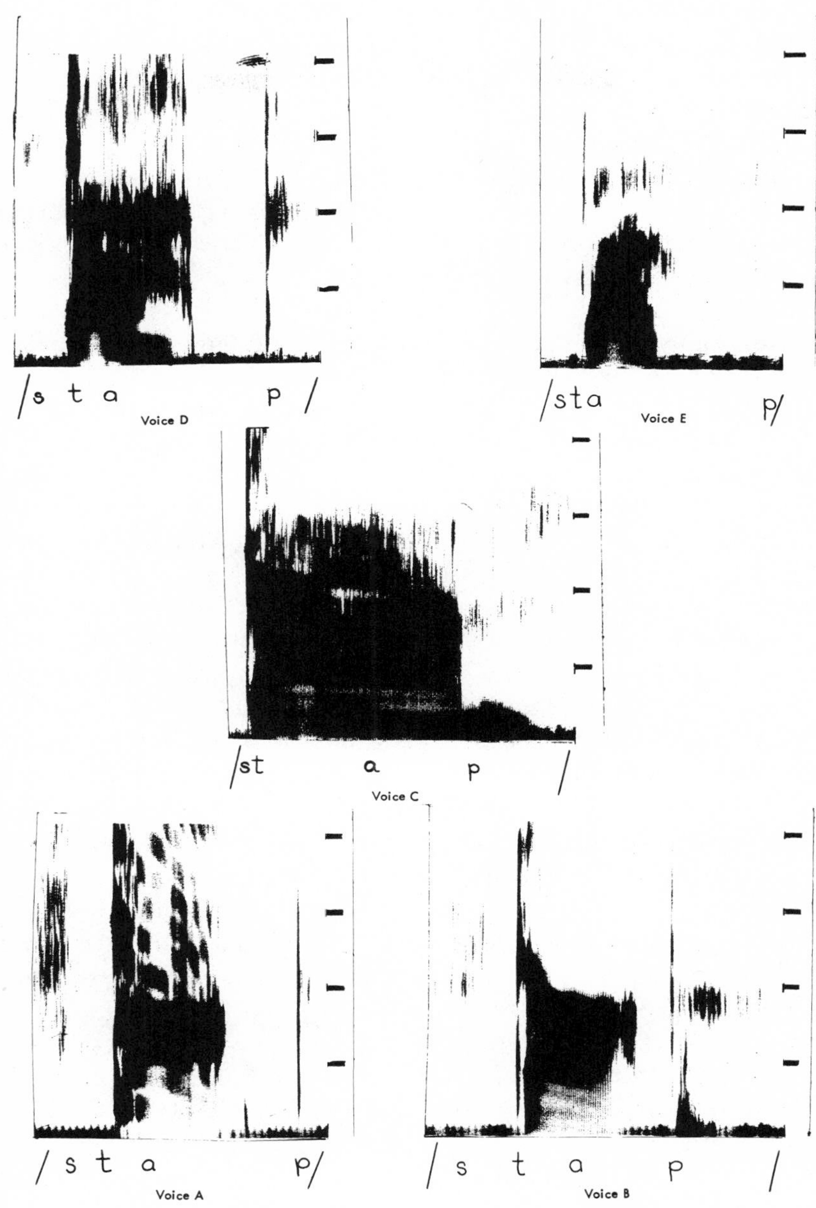

Figure 6. Spectrograms of five pronunciations of stop *as spoken by five children. Voice A, normal hearing girl of 5 years; Voice B, normal hearing girl of 8 years; Voice C, deaf boy of 8 years; Voice D, deaf girl of 8 years; and Voice E, deaf girl of 5 years.*

related to the pitch of the voice, appear as the number of vertical striations per unit of time. Thus, those that accompany a high-pitched voice are close together; a low-pitched voice, more distant. These four physical dimensions of an utterance convey both the voice and articulation of the speaker as he produced the utterance.

Figures 2–6 are not offered as data from which generalizations are to be drawn, but only illustrations of spectrograms of children's speech. They conform to some generalizations that are made about the speech of deaf and hearing children and not to others. The five words represented are eat /it/, cat /kæt/, put /pʊt/, thin /θɪn/, and stop /stap/. Child A was a girl of 5 years with normal hearing; Child B, girl, 8 years, normal hearing; Child C, boy, 8 years, deaf; Child D, girl, 8 years, deaf; and Child E, girl, 5 years, deaf. Sets of similarities that might be expected include those among the representations of the same word and those that reflect the traits of a particular voice.

Attention is invited to representations of /it/ spoken by the two normal hearing children, Voices A and B. The vertical dimension of Figure 2 represents linearly a band of 4000 Hz. From accumulated data about phonetics the expected characteristics of the vowel /i/ include concentrations of energy in bands of frequencies of 250–400 Hz and 2000–3200 Hz. These are the first and second formants of the vowel, and their pressure and prominence relate closely to the intelligibility of the sound. Other prominent frequencies, if present, are singular to particular voices. These bands contribute especially to the recognizable voice quality of the speaker. These additional and desirable concentrations of acoustic energy, of course, must not override or mask the characteristic formants of the vowel. The displays of both Voices A and B show formants at the expected frequencies. In addition, Voice A has prominent individual formants at 800–1000 Hz. The durations of the two vowels are similar, about 1/12 sec. A period of "silence" of about the same duration ensues. This corresponds to the time the tongue blocked the outgoing air stream. The release of the pent-up air caused an explosion that registered energy throughout the 4000-Hz band and trailed into scattered frequencies. In Voice B these were near 2000 Hz; in Voice A, slightly higher.

The fact that the dark representations of the formants of /i/ in Figure 2 seem to be solid bars results from the time scale of the spectrogram. A more careful examination of the /i/ of Voice B shows that the solid bar is a number of discrete vertical lines, each of which represents one sound wave or one vibration of the vocal cords. Those of Voice A are closer together than those of Voice B. To the listener, the pitch of Voice A would be higher than that of Voice B.

The foregoing description of the spectrograms of *eat* in the two normal pronunciations should enable one to make comparable observations of the normal pronunciations of *cat, put, thin,* and *stop* in Figures 3–6. An additional factor that appears clearly in some of these is the marked changes in the frequencies of the formants with the temporal progress of the vowel. These changes occur with opening and closing the jaw and shifts in the position of the tongue as the word progresses from one phoneme to another. However, the formants are within the tolerance limits of the target vowel for sufficient time to convey the intended sound to a listener. The expected frequencies of the two principal formants of the vowels of Figures 3–6 are: / æ /, 600–900 and 1600–2200 Hz; / ᴜ /, 400–500 and 900–1300 Hz; /ɪ/, 300–500 and 1900–2700 Hz; and / ɑ /, 700–900 and 1000–1300 Hz.

Note may also be made that some of the words were spoken with a changing pitch, particularly a downward inflection. This appears in the figures as a decreasing number of vertical striations (vocal cord vibrations) per unit time with the temporal course of the vowel. Thus, if there were 25 striations in the first one-half of the vowel /i/ and only 16 in the latter half, the vowel would be heard as a downward inflection.

All the pronunciations of the normally speaking children were highly intelligible.

The spectrograms of Voice C reflect many typical abnormalities of deaf speakers. First, the vowels are strikingly prolonged (Calvert, 1964), Four of the five were sustained for almost one second. This corresponds to the average duration of five or six normally spoken syllables. Second, the vowels are distorted as is shown by formants of the improper frequencies. In this regard only /æ/ resembles the target vowel. In turn, listeners uniformly reported it as satisfactory. The /i/ of *eat* was recognizable if a listener knew what to expect; and the / ɑ / of *stop* bore some likeness to the intended vowel. Third, the formants were broad, not concentrated bands of energy, and considerable energy was spread throughout the full band width of the spectrogram as is the case with many noises. This scattering of acoustic energy is often even more markedly present in analyses of the speech of the deaf than appears in these samples. Fourth, the analyses reflect speech that does not change in fundamental frequency except in the instance of *put;* nor do the formants change in frequency with ongoing time. These imply a monotonous experience for a listener in terms of pitch. In keeping with this, the relative darkness of the picture is essentially the same from moment to moment, indicative of monotony in loudness as well. Fifth, a few errors of articulation, clearly present to the auditor, are shown in the figures: (a) a whispered vowel begins *eat;* (b) the final sound of *cat* is a continuous post-vocalic noise with no explosion; (c) evidently the same foregoing fricative that is in *cat* serves also as a substitute for /t/ to terminate *put;* (d) the initial sound of *thin* is voiced and unusually brief; (e) the final /n/ of *thin* turns into a voiceless sound; (f) the /s/ is omitted from *stop;* and (g) the /p/ of *stop* is a voiced fricative for at least one-half of its duration.

In contrast to the typical speech of deaf children, the pronunciations of Voice D were unusually intelligible. The principal difference between this speaker and a normal one was the practice of saying each word a second time in the responses. This type of repetition occurs more frequently in the speech of deaf school children than with normal hearing children.

Voice E produced only one vowel that was recognizable as the target sound, the / æ / of *cat.* The others were neither intelligible nor differentiated from one another.

The few deviations in speech discussed above are typical but not exhaustive of disorders of speech that can be traced causally to deafness. Dr. C. Holm, who has worked in depth with deaf children in Freiburg, West Germany, generalizes one of these discrepancies in Figure 7(b). Four vowels are represented as having formants that are as well separated as the coordinates of the figure. The deaf speaker, however, fails to maintain their clear discreteness. Instead, he tends to lower the higher formant and raise the lower one. This results in a more neutral vowel sound than would accompany the well-made, differentiated, and concentrated formants. Thus the diagram shows that the formants of four vowels—and these are approximately the cardinal vowels—tend to be made as neutral instead of well differentiated as they are pronounced by deaf children. By way of explaining "neutral," the distinction among / ə /, / ɜ /, and / ʌ / is conveniently labelled a difference in amounts of stressing in forms of a "neutral" vowel.

The abnormalities in the speech of deaf children, whether reflected in spectrograms or generalized in the manner of Figure 7, affect both the timbre or quality of the voice and the intelligibility of the utterance. Hudgins and Numbers referred to both in a descriptive reference to the uniqueness of deaf voices (Hudgins and Numbers, 1942). They pointed out that persons who are totally unfamiliar with the speech of deaf pupils

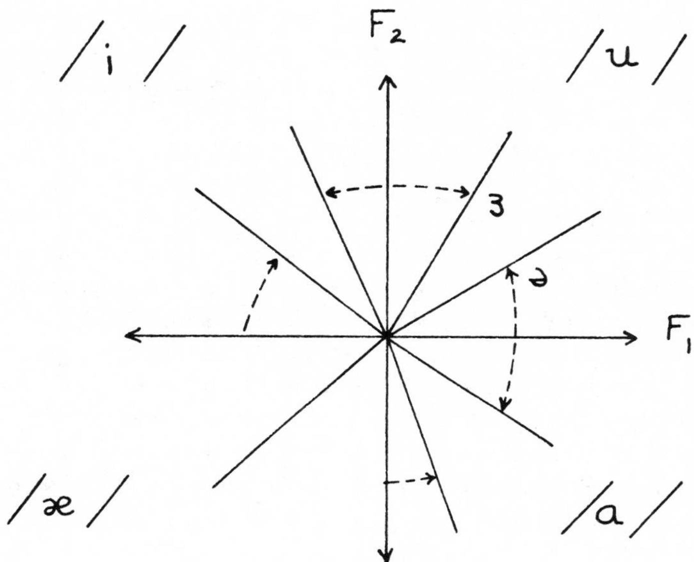

Figure 7. A schematic representation of the distinctly discrete formants of four normal vowels, and of the displacing of these formants by deaf speakers through collapsing them (after Holm).

would not have much value as auditors since they are often distracted by *the voice qualities peculiar to deaf pupils* and because of this, lose much of the content.

An earlier observation, as well as being a segment of the foregoing one, is echoed in a report by Calvert (1964).

> In analyzing the results of the present study, it was shown that deaf speakers typically distorted the duration of most phonemes by extending their average duration three or four times that of hearing speakers. There was also distortion in that the systematic variation of relative duration of a phoneme as a result of the effects of adjoining phonemes was not present for deaf speakers. This durational distortion by deaf speakers was not phonemic for vowels but may be an acoustic characteristic which is a factor in *the unique sound of deaf speech* [italics mine].

The same author also catalogued the many words that are used to describe the deaf voice. Fifty-two were suggested, of which 33 were identified with voice quality (Calvert, 1962).

The flow of air through the trachea and larynx of the deaf child is poorly coordinated with voice production. This relates to rhythm; the temporal sequencing of sounds, words, and phrases; and the evenness of the stream of speech. Although some deaf children experience a somewhat normal period of babbling, the experience does not lead to a habitual integrating of air flow and sound production, with an awareness and appreciation of syllabic-like bursts and of appropriate variations in loudness and pitch. The valving action of the larynx during speech is not developed. Dr. Holm cites the mean airflow of deaf children while speaking as being three times the similar flow of normal children (Holm, 1970). With a medical orientation, he refers to the structures of the larynx that are usually prominent in speaking as resembling partially atrophied ones. He estimates the laryngeal development at the level of the vowel folds of a deaf child of 2.5 years to be equivalent to that of a normal child of 6 months, and that of a deaf child of 6 years as resembling a normal child of 2 or 2.5 years. Importantly, the deaf child has difficulty approximating his vocal folds and maintaining tension in them. This affects his efficiency in converting the breath flow to acoustic energy and results in an overlay of whispered noise along with voiced sounds. The wastage of air impairs the talker's ability to continue a vocalization without interruption.

Hudgins was an especially capable experimentalist in regard to speech and respiration. He had studied this under Professor R. H. Stetson and had learned it in a context of rhythm and speech. His five types of anomalous exhalations for speech relate closely to poor rhythm as well as to other properties of the speech of deaf talkers (Hudgins, 1946).

(1) Short irregular breath groups often only one or two words in length with breath pauses interrupting the speech flow at improper points;
(2) Excessive expenditure of breath on single syllables resulting in breathy speech;
(3) False grouping of syllables resulting in the breaking up of natural groups and the misplacement of accents;
(4) A slow methodical utterance resulting in a complete lack of grouping; and
(5) A lack of proper coordination between breathing muscles and articulatory organs.

The peculiarities of spectrum and timing of the voices of deaf children are sufficiently unusual that the utterances frequently are not readily identified with speech. The descriptive word *snort* is often used and is apt. A similar quality—although more rhythmical than a deaf child's speech—can be simulated through generating short bursts of saw-tooth sound waves electronically. The snort is excessively nasal and often does not have a speech-like rhythm.

Hudgins and Numbers (1942) classified the rhythms of 192 deaf children as normal (approximately 45 percent), abnormal (approximately 35 percent), and non-rhythmical (approximately 20 percent). The abnormal instances were unusual groupings of words and syllables with stress in atypical places and degrees—again, resembling snorts. The non-rhythmical speakers, in contrast to the abnormal ones, seemed to stress equally all of the vowel-like sounds of an utterance. If reproduced as backward-played speech, this non-rhythmical speech would be heard as having minimal variety in stress while the abnormal and normal speech would sound much alike. Of course, as forward-played speech, intended to be comprehended, the abnormal speech would have stress, but unusual stress. The speech with normal rhythm accounted for 75 percent of the intelligible sentences (N = 1900 sentences); (these were 1900 different sentences, not repetitions of a few sentences).

The preceding sentence and the bibliographic reference lead the discussion easily to speech articulation instead of voice. Hudgins and Numbers also devised and used a system for classifying the errors of articulation of the recordings of the 1900 sentences. Each of the pair of collaborators said aloud what he heard from the recording and his partner transcribed the rendition phonetically. The two transcriptions were subsequently compared and discrepancies were reconciled through repeated listening, saying aloud, and transcribing. The final transcription was compared with the target sounds, that is the ones that would have been spoken in a good rendition of the sentence.

Seven categories of errors in the articulation of consonants were sufficient to describe all incorrect sounds:

(1) Voiceless-voiced confusions,
(2) Substitution of one consonant for another,
(3) Nasality (failure of the speaker to close the nasal pharynx),
(4) Mishandling of consonantal clusters,
(5) Mishandling of abutting consonants in different syllables,
(6) Omission of terminal consonant, and
(7) Distortion or failure in releasing pent-up air pressure.

The comparable classification for vowels included only five categories:

(1) Substitution of one vowel for another,
(2) Improper sequencing within a diphthong, for example (a) making two syllables out of a diphthong or (b) omitting one element of the diphthong,
(3) Diphthongizing a vowel,
(4) Nasalizing a vowel, and

(5) Neutralizing a vowel.

Panels of listeners, experienced with deaf speech, also heard the recordings and wrote the sentences in the manner of dictation exercises. Consonants that appeared to be associated with articulatory errors on the basis of the responses of the panels of listeners were /dʒ, d, h, b, g, ʃ, l, r, tʃ, j, s, z/; the least troublesome ones were /v, ŋ, m, n, p/.*

Importantly here, teachers' reports of the sounds that are judged most difficult for their students to master do not include /b, d, g/. This inconsistency suggests the superiority of the responses of listening panels that follow a rigorous procedure over the subjective impressions of professional workers.

This chapter has been limited in subject matter to the speech pathologies that are directly related to deafness. These are ones of voice and articulation. The more severe the hearing loss and the sooner in a person's life the onset occurs, the more devastating are the effects. Deafness may not be the sole cause of the subnormal speech of an individual. He may have almost any of the pathologies of hearing persons brought about by brain damage, a cleft palate, mental retardation, and the like. There are interesting discussions about whether a deaf person may also stutter. These are inconclusive. The documented instances usually or always relate to persons who have stuttered as hearing persons and who later lost their hearing and continued to stutter. In any event, a discussion of the wide scope of these pathologies is beyond the treatment of the present summary and is available in many standard references. They, in turn, include scant treatments of the speech behavior of deaf children, emphasizing educational procedures (Silverman, 1957).

BIBLIOGRAPHY

Black, J. W. Communication behaviors: Acquisition and effects. In R. J. Kibler and L. L. Barker (Eds.), *Conceptual frontiers in speech communication.* New York: Speech Association of America, 1969.

Calvert, D. R. An approach to the study of deaf speech. *Report of the Proceedings of the International Congress on Education of the Deaf.* Washington, D.C.: U.S. Government Printing Office, 1964, 242–245.

Calvert, D. R. Deaf voice quality: A preliminary investigation. *Volta review,* 1962, **64,** 402–403.

Carr, J. Early speech development of deaf children. *Report of the Proceedings of the International Congress on Education of the Deaf.* Washington, D.C.: U. S. Government Printing Office, 1964, 261–267.

*Carr in a study of the development of speech sounds in deaf children included m, n, p among the earliest sounds mastered by deaf children (Carr, 1964).

Fairbanks, G. Systematic research in experimental phonetics: A theory of the speech mechanism as a servosystem. *Journal of speech and hearing disorders,* 1954, **19,** 133–139.

Holm, C. (Freiburg, W. Germany), Oral Presentation at the First International Colloquium on the Verbotonal System. Primosten (Yugoslavia), January 29–31, 1970.

Hudgins, C. V. Speech breathing and speech intelligibility. *Volta review,* 1946, **48,** 642–644.

Hudgins, C. V., and Numbers, F. C. An investigation of the intelligibility of the speech of the deaf. *Genetic psychology monographs,* 1942, **25,** 289–392.

Peterson, G. E., and Barney, H. L. Control methods used in a study of vowels. *Journal of the Acoustical Society of America,* 1952, **24,** 175–184.

Silverman, S. Clinical and educational procedures for the deaf. In L. Travis (Ed.), *Handbook of speech pathology.* New York: Appleton-Century-Crofts, 1957.

Thomas, W. G. Intelligibility of the speech of deaf children. *Report of the Proceedings of the International Congress on Education of the Deaf.* Washington, D.C.: U.S. Government Printing Office, 1964, 245–261.

Vegely, C. Monitoring of monosyllabic words by deaf children. *Report of the Proceedings of the International Congress on Education of the Deaf.* Washington, D.C.: U.S. Government Printing Office, 1964, 735–744.

CHAPTER VII

The Psychology of Communication

FREEMAN McCONNELL, PH.D.

To consider the psychology of communication first requires defining communication as conceived by a particular speaker or writer. Perhaps the most common connotation brought to mind for most individuals is that communication implies some form of *verbal interaction between two or more persons.* Discussing the psychology of communication in such terms as it relates to the deaf child, however, is to impose an unduly narrow construct on the subject, since for him meaningful interaction with his environment must maximize all incoming sensations and perceptions of events and objects around him, as well as his relations with other individuals. It is therefore important at the outset of this discussion to adopt a frame of reference which provides a broad view of communication.

COMMUNICATION, LANGUAGE, AND SPEECH

Moores (1969, p. 4) has stated that communication broadly defined involves any interaction between living organisms, and it can be observed up and down the entire genetic scale from the amoeba to the most complex form of primate life. Not only do the same species communicate with each other, but there is also interspecies communication, which is evidenced among various forms of animal life in their mating, fighting, and specialized signaling systems, and which may even occur between plant and animal forms of life. Thus it becomes apparent that communication in this more total sense is universal among the various forms of life that inhabit the earth.

With this broadly based frame of reference, it is of interest to consider the deaf child's plight in relating to his environment as he develops. If he is otherwise unimpaired and is an average child in an average family, it will be seen that he does automatically acquire various modes of communication which enable him to adapt to his silent world despite the great void created by not hearing, and he does indeed progress in a reasonably normal manner in the various spheres of development other than language, particularly in the prelingual years. For example, the deaf child at one year of age can hardly be distinguished from a hearing child by many observers, and indeed his deficit often goes completely unnoticed even by his parents and by the physician who follows his physical development. The two-year-old deaf child deviates more, but still is not unlike a hearing child of the same age to many casual observers. By the third year of life, however, during which the onset of connected speech normally occurs, the differences which mark him as a deaf child seem to progress in almost "snowball" fashion.

This rapidly increasing manifestation of the effects of the hearing impairment is integrally related to the development of that aspect of communication which involves verbal interaction with other humans. It is thus that anyone who is familiar with the deaf can attest to the extremely crucial role which language plays in man's growth and development. It is by far the most important subcategory in communication, notwithstanding the many other types of communication, including those which are nonverbal.

Language as a uniquely human phenomenon transcends the animal limitation to the here and now. It is dependent upon learning, and it is modified by experience. Sapir (Eisenson *et al.*, 1963, p. 4) states that language is "a purely human and non-instinctive method of communicating ideas, emotions and desires by means of a system of voluntarily produced symbols." Hill (Eisenson *et al.*, 1963, p. 4) describes language as "the primary and most highly elaborated form of *human symbolic* activity." These symbols of language are comprised of sounds produced by the vocal apparatus and arranged in classes and patterns which make up a complex and symmetrical structure. This structure of language provides an individual the possibility of making a linguistic response to any experience. Hill obviously refers only to oral-aural components of language, but the point is made that the term language of necessity involves symbolization, and this is true whether heard, spoken, read, written or manually transmitted by signing or fingerspelling.

It would undoubtedly follow that if language is the most important subcategory of communication for humans, the most important subcategory of language, in turn, is speech. Thus, one must also distinguish between speech and language. Lenneberg (1970, p. 68) refers to speech as "the skills of making special noises, namely of shaping the muscles in and around the mouth and in the voice box in such a way as to produce speech sounds," while language is "the capacity to understand what is being said and the capacity to construct sentences." Black and Moore (1955, p. 2)* describe speech as "a form of human behavior in which words may serve both as substitute stimuli to evoke responses in others and as substitute responses." Speech then may serve as both a stimulus to behavior and a behavioral response to a stimulus. An infant first responds to speech in a signal manner; that is to say, the word "mama" or "milk" simply implies for him a given auditory clue associated with a given experience in a particular setting. After becoming conditioned to the signals, repeated experience reinforces and familiarizes the meaning of the signal so that response to the same words in a symbol rather than signal manner becomes habituated.

Because speech is the most common means of communication between humans, and because it appears to have some innateness in man, many have equated speech and language. Without question, the ability to express one's self in spoken language is highly desirable in our society, but the fact that language and speech cannot be equated is strikingly evidenced by the deaf, many of whom may communicate through language which is read, written, or manual, without having any capacity for heard or spoken language. Such individuals are indeed greatly restricted both in the number of humans with whom they can communicate, and in the relative effectiveness of the communication process, for spoken language orally transmitted and aurally received is indeed a highly efficient means of communication between persons.

Innateness of Language for the Deaf Child

In the area of child language acquisition, a widely held view today is that language is characterized by an innateness which is universal in human development (Lenneberg, 1967). This view would hold that language is inherent in the child's maturation, and appropriate environ-

*From *Speech: Code, Meaning and Communication* by John W. Black and Wilbur E. Moore. New York: McGraw Hill, 1955. Used with permission of McGraw Hill Book Company.

ment is the factor which merely triggers a process that has been anticipated by millions of years of evolutionary development. Admittedly, this view holds small comfort for the parents of a young deaf child, since his physical impairment alters his environment so drastically that it becomes incapable of triggering this development, regardless of its universal nature. Thus, for the deaf child, language is not learned in this automatic manner, but must be taught. Normal language competence is achieved, if at all, only painstakingly over a period of many years. This is not to say, however, that teachers of the deaf are not aided in this struggle by the natural language capacity which is part of the human potential in all children. It may indeed alter the approach to language teaching in search for methods which more effectively take advantage of built-in phenomena.

Lenneberg (1970, pp. 61–71) has pointed out that man's capacity for verbal communication is primarily dependent upon the operation of his brain. Thus, he believes the various stages of language onset and acquisition are regulated by the sequence of maturational states in the brain. Between the ages of two and ten the brain is in an optimal condition for acquiring language. This facility afterward declines, however, so that by the late teens it is virtually impossible to acquire language if one has not yet learned to speak it. He postulates that the brain function is best suited to learning language in the early period of life, and that indeed the brain itself is not quite mature as long as language is learned with ease. Once it has matured, functions are locked into position, so to speak, and readjustment does not take place after destruction.

The association between language acquisition and man's natural history of maturation also suggests that the capacity for language is indirectly connected to the action of genes (Lenneberg, 1970). This is so because all maturational phenomenon are under the control of genetic factors, and this control accounts for the fact that normal children all over the world will go through the same sequence of developmental stages as they learn to talk. Such a premise does not deny that environmental influences are unimportant, but simply confirms the interaction between environmental and biological factors.

Perhaps the most cogent principle which has emanated in recent years from the research, practice, and theory characterizing communication and the deaf child, is the importance of the first years of life. Whetnall and Fry (1964) contend that because the infant or young child at the proper age is able to make certain sound discriminations that will later be impossible, the deaf child should have from the first year of life the opportunity to have his poor hearing boosted by use of a suitable hearing aid. It is the hearing aid which for him brings the auditory feedback loop into play. Thus, establishment of this auditory feedback loop, even though not as perfectly as in the normally hearing child, does provide the environmental manipulation most likely to overcome the sensory barrier which prevents the child's utilization of his inherent capacity to learn to talk. These authors believe that much of the severe handicap of deafness could be eliminated insofar as speech and language are concerned, if all deaf children could be exposed to special help through boosting hearing in the first 18 months, which is the period when the hearing child is storing auditory experiences preparatory to learning spoken language.

CURRENT APPROACHES TO COMMUNICATION DEVELOPMENT FOR THE DEAF CHILD

Auditory versus Visual Input Systems

There are today two major trends in the teaching of speech to deaf children. Although both are similar in that they encourage the importance of early intervention, they differ in the method by which this process should occur, one espousing the introduction of fingerspelling and the other emphasizing parent instruction and acoustic input. About a decade ago Morkovin (1960) reported that the neo-oral approach developed in the Soviet Union, and involving the simultaneous use of fingerspelling and speech with young children, was yielding better results than the so-called oral method in the United States. He reported that through the use of fingerspelling from the age of two, deaf children in Russia were able to develop vocabularies of several thousand words by the age of six.

Moores (1970, p. 46), too, advocates the use of signs and fingerspelling in the early period of life with deaf children. He argues that fingerspelling affords the child better linguistic models in that the entire grammatical structure is presented to the child. He indicates that the oral-aural method, which relies upon visual and auditory reception, cannot as adequately present this better structured material to the child.

Quigley (1969) showed that the use of fingerspelling in a controlled experiment affected neither the speech nor speech reading ability of children in schools for the deaf. The subjects, however, were not exposed to fingerspelling until they reached school age, and thus had already exceeded the age at which the critical period of language learning normally occurs. Furthermore, as DiCarlo (1969, p. 10) has pointed out, none of the subjects came from programs exemplary of oralism. Thus, one can agree with Moores (1970, p. 47), who concludes that the effectiveness of such an approach for very young deaf children remains a matter of conjecture, since in this country it has never been tested on a systematic basis. It is his opinion, however, that it is sound both practically and theoretically.

It may be noted that the same situation exists for a number of other approaches. In view of the pliable status of the infant, it might well be conjectured that any language acquisition method used would incur much greater success if initiated in the first years of life (0 to 3 years). As a matter of fact, detailed investigation of practices used by those purporting to apply the oral-aural method in this country might well find that most teachers place far greater emphasis on visual reception than on aural as the primary input modality. Indeed, such investigations might show the widely embraced multi-sensory approach as practised by many teachers of the deaf is essentially visual, not acoustic. Evidence of this situation is demonstrated in the assumption, and in fact the dictum, so frequently heard in repeated counsel reminding parents that no communication with their child can occur unless the child is watching the speaker. This implied denial of auditory potential thus introduces a psychological barrier which will be manifested from the beginning in communicative relations of the child with his family. That is to say, the child may be expected to assume the characteristics which are projected on him by others. If he is treated as not-hearing, he will indeed not hear. The infant years are crucial ones in the establishment of attitudes of parents toward their deaf child, whom they must learn to view positively with respect to his capacity to hear if he is to be maximally successful in his experience with the oral-aural approach.

Emphasis on Parent Involvement

Regardless of the method, early intervention is widely being recognized to be the key for optimal programs designed to develop communication in deaf children. Such an approach of necessity stresses parent involvement and a wholly new frame of reference for teachers of the deaf and audiologists, who have primarily been experienced in and trained in those methods which are child-, not parent-, oriented. Parent teaching models which have been established fall primarily into three categories:

the home visitation type program, in which the professional person visits the homes of deaf children to work with the parents in their own individual setting; second, the clinic visit type, in which the parent instruction is provided individually or in groups in the clinic setting; and third, the home demonstration program, in which the parents bring their child to a setting, usually near or adjacent to a clinic, furnished as an ordinary home, where the teacher applies to her teaching those principles of child development relating to parents' management of the child.

Among the first exponents of this latter model in the early 60's were the John Tracy Clinic in Los Angeles and Central Institute for the Deaf, in St. Louis. Developed a few years later were similar programs at the Bill Wilkerson Hearing and Speech Center, Nashville, Tennessee, and the University of Kansas Medical Center, in Kansas City.

While the rationale and philosophy of these four programs have a high degree of commonalty, there are of course certain differences among them. The present discussion will reflect primarily the writer's experience in the Nashville program, where the parent teaching is largely focused on the mother's role in stimulating the child's awareness of and interest in his sound environment, the foundation for auditory communication. To accomplish these goals, the teacher does what the mother of any young child does—she prepares snacks or meals in the kitchen, she washes dishes, and she feeds the child (Knox and McConnell, p. 184). She also performs other household chores, such as sweeping, dusting, folding clothes, and bathing and dressing the child, but *as* she carries out all these tasks, she demonstrates that every activity provides a means of communication with the child and an opportunity to call attention to the many environmental sounds, as well as speech, that the child must learn to recognize.

While visual stimulation is not excluded, the teacher's major effort is to show that most deaf children have sufficient residual hearing when wearing hearing aids to respond to and recognize the majority of sounds in their environment. For the parents, emphasis is placed on the fact that the deaf child needs to undergo the same kinds of experiences as does any other child his age; the difference is that the parents must assist him in deriving meaning from these experiences which his sensory deprivation has prevented. He needs to be given words for all that he sees and does in relation to his environment. This emphasis is on communicating about those things that relate to the immediate present and on developing the capacity to recognize first daily environmental sounds and what they mean.

With the hearing child each sound is automatically related to its source, for the first months of life have laid a foundation of sound perception upon which later finer discriminations can be developed. Todd and Palmer (1968, p. 595), reporting results of a study on the relation of human presence to conditioning of infant vocalizations, conclude that only through hearing voices of others does the infant's babbling get reinforced. It is not surprising that the effects of not hearing in the early infancy period will already have been felt by the deaf child by one year of age. The diminution of babbling rather than increased use of vocalization is the result, and even at this early stage of life, development of the auditory function has suffered a serious setback. Normally hearing individuals, on the other hand, from birth have automatically developed such an efficient auditory monitoring of their environment they are able to scan it at an unconscious level, bringing to the conscious level only those sounds which signify an event to which they should respond. Surprisingly enough, few parents have considered how they actually function themselves in their own sound environment. Thus, they must first learn to analyze their own auditory behavior as it relates to the many sounds constantly occurring and to which they react at an automatic level. At first it will be necessary for them to exaggerate their reflexive responses to sounds that occur in the home, such as the dropping of the cookie tin off the table so the child can clearly learn the meaning. Only after the child has learned to accord this meaning and to differentiate between environmental sounds, can we expect him to differentiate between sounds which make up speech. Thus, while he is learning these everyday life sounds, the teacher demonstrates how parents can reinforce communication by giving names to the sounds or to the events, objects or persons signified by them.

Once the child has begun to respond differentially and meaningfully to nonverbal sounds, he can begin to learn language from his family. To maximize these opportunities, both the parents and the child must be in harmony with one another and the goals. Information from professionals must be given out a little at a time in order for parents to absorb it. Frequent sessions are therefore important. The parent who is fearful and anxious needs to be encouraged to use more verbal interaction with the child. The natural tendency is for parents to cease talking when they have learned their child is deaf, or talk *only* when the child is looking at them, neither of which strategies is designed to help auditory communication. In the end, the success of the parent teaching program is dependent upon the kind of communicative relation which the parents are able to establish and maintain with their deaf child. If they can succeed in this effort, the child is truly given a headstart on his road to learning through language.

The Years under Three

Recent trends in the management of the deaf child's communication problem have been generally consistent with respect to the importance of early intervention, even though methodologies espoused are quite different among educators of the deaf and audiologists. Unfortunately, facilities for treating the deaf infant and the very young deaf child are still sparse, and furthermore, those trained in education and habilitation of the hearing impaired child have had relatively little experience with children under three, either in their training institutions or in their experience settings.

A "psychology of communication" for the deaf child must of necessity involve the type of rapport developed by the parents with their child in these early critical years of language acquisition. Moores (1970, p. 43) postulates that the specific ability to develop language appears to peak around ages three to four and declines steadily thereafter. Thus, he affirms that any language program for the deaf child initiated after the age of five, regardless of method, is doomed to failure. The key to successful acquisition of language, therefore, becomes dependent upon the kind of input to the child in these first years. Because the child's natural milieu in this period of life is not the school, but the home, whatever communication he develops must be that which originates within the confines of his home. Granted, then, that professionals must place emphasis on the home and on parent teaching procedures, several working principles are of great significance in establishing a communicative base between the child and his parents.

Parents must be helped to recognize that language is best learned, and most readily, when it grows out of direct experience. Therefore, language instruction must derive naturally from the child's own daily activities and experiences which have maximum meaning to him. It is also vital that the parents themselves view language as the manipulator of the environment, for learning to talk occurs most readily when it is seen to be a mediator of environment change—that is to say, when language is used, it causes something to happen. When the child learns that he can control his own environment through his use of words, the most important motivation principle is established. Obviously for the deaf child, this use of language as a tool for manipulation of environmental changes is not learned automatically, and he must perforce adopt other modes of environmental manipulation if he is not early introduced to methods of enhancing verbal communication. For the normal child, language input occurs in great quantity and variety before any language output is expected. In the early life of the deaf child, therefore, parents must maximize both quantity and quality of auditory verbal input through the help of wearable hearing aids.

When counseling parents regarding the most effective manner of talking with their hearing impaired child, they can be shown several quite basic guidelines to follow. First, it is important for them to make *consistent and appropriate use of short, simple sentences and phrases appropriate to the child's level of understanding*. Second, early language input *should stress the concrete but not to the exclusion of the functor words.* That is to say, a speaking vocabulary of 50 single words in isolation is a sterile kind of goal, compared to words used appropriately in syntax with intonation and applicable to more than one setting. Conceptual language making use of prepositions, conjunctions, and adverbs can indeed be part of the young child's language input, if they are presented in relation to an idea that is current and meaningful. Talking about the here and now is indeed important for the young deaf child, because only as he learns to relate his rudimentary speech to the present will he be able to use it to project into the past and future. Third, the use of *meaningful and somewhat exaggerated patterns of inflection* should be employed.

It is indeed the intonation patterns in our speaking which give so much of the variety of meaning to what we say. For the deaf child who learns language only through a visual medium, the prosody of our language is lacking. Not hearing or understanding the importance of pitch and duration changes, his own speech output is characterized by monotone and unnaturalness of quality, hence carries less meaning. Greater emphasis on this aspect of language through early auditory stimulation aided by wearable amplification greatly enhances his communication effectiveness. Indeed, it is only through auditory reception that this component of language can be acquired successfully, for unfortunately, it is not available to those totally deaf children who must rely upon the visual modality exclusively through means of speechreading, sign language, or fingerspelling.

Communication development in deaf infants requires also that parents capitalize on all talking times throughout the day and that they make every effort to create opportunities for such talking times about everyday activities that are related either to the child's own physical comfort or his natural tendency to explore. Expansion of the child's speech utterances through consistent feedback is necessary to stimulate syntactic and morphological growth. In other words, when the child says "dada go" to indicate his father is leaving to go to work, he should receive the complete reinforcement pattern from his mother—"Yes, Daddy is leaving; Daddy is going to work; see, Daddy is getting in his car to go to work." These attempts at communication will be more effective if the parent remembers to direct verbal output at the eye and ear level of the child, where more direct contact is available.

Finally, the significance of wearable hearing aid use for every deaf child as soon as possible to bring into play the function of audition cannot be underestimated (McConnell, 1970, p. 361). Even when such children show little or no response to sound, hearing aids on a trial basis should be fitted to observe if any early auditory reinforcement from babbling and vocal play might occur, and thus stimulate fragmentary hearing not previously detected. The more severe the hearing loss, the more important is early amplification if hearing is to become in any way functional.

Directions for Educational Management and Research

There is an abundance of past experience with deaf children which demonstrates what the end-product is when no acoustic stimulation is provided until the child reaches school age of six years. What is needed are far more data on what can happen if *all* deaf youngsters receive intensive acoustic stimulation from infancy throughout the preschool period.

Audiologists themselves need to become more attuned to the special needs of the very young deaf child. Clinical experience with the very young has shown there is indeed some danger in labeling the infant with negative connotations regarding his ultimate hearing potential. To establish true threshold at these early age levels is a difficult audiologic task. Comparison of test results obtained on the same children later suggests that all hearing impaired infants are likely to show greater severity of impairment than later measurements bear out. In other words, the first evaluation is useful only if it is followed by frequent periodic tests, the results of which must be viewed as an aggregate. It has, in fact, been shown in one program that the amount of language gain achieved was not significantly correlated with initial hearing test results (McConnell and Horton, 1970, p. 48). This finding implies that regardless of the level of hearing obtained with an infant, he should have the benefit of wearable amplification on a trial basis. If he, in fact, has better hearing potential than the first test suggested, he will make much more rapid advancement in his ability to use the residual hearing. On the other hand, should he prove to be a profoundly deaf child, early hearing aid use may enable him to take better advantage of the feedback principle in monitoring his own vocalizations, even though intelligibility for speech is not possible. In consequence, his attention for sound is established and may result in a surprising degree of aural language development.

As public school systems enter the field of deaf infant education, there will be a need to employ audiologists on the educational team. A completely new kind of orientation to her role will be needed by the teacher, who must be able to work effectively in a "non-teacher" kind of counselor approach. She must teach the parents, not the child, since their involvement is crucial to the success of any program with a child too young to enter into a formal education experience. Further, the public schools must be willing to remain flexible in their programming for such children, since working with parents in the home requires a non-school, non-clinic type of atmosphere. Educational concepts applicable to deaf children of school age cannot be applied as a simple downward extension to include the infant and nursery age child.

In essence, the auditory modality should become the lead sense if at all possible through use of wearable amplification and parent instruction. The use of the visual channel can then develop naturally and as needed. Conversely, if the visual channel is established first as the main input source of the child's perceptions and information, the use of hearing does not come naturally, but only laboriously and slowly, and with much intensive training, if at all. This position does not ignore the fact that some severely impaired children will be unable to use hearing as their primary receptor sense, but a far larger number will be able to do so if the acoustic channel is made available to them very early through the wearable hearing aid, parent guidance, and skilled audiologic management.

In conclusion, a psychology of communication for the deaf child in the '70's should be one which reflects the advancements that have been made in acoustics, engineering, early childhood education, and linguistics. The principles of child development dictate that a deaf infant must be given the opportunity to use audition in as nearly as possible the same manner as the normally hearing child if he is to benefit maximally from whatever residuum of hearing he possesses. Since it is hard to determine this level, all deaf infants should be given the opportunity to hear through use of wearable hearing aids to make possible consistent and continuing acoustic input from the beginning. While the degree of benefit will remain in part a function of the degree of impairment, it will also be dependent upon parent participation and involvement. Such intervention applied even to the profoundly deaf child will result in his learning to attend, thereby early developing a communicative attitude which enhances either visual or auditory learning for the future.

BIBLIOGRAPHY

Black, J. W., and Moore, W. E. *Speech—code, meaning, and communication.* New York: McGraw-Hill, 1955.

DiCarlo, L. M. Old oil in a different lamp. *Bulletin, Education of the Hearing Impaired.* Washington, D.C.: American Organization for the Education of the Hearing Impaired, Winter 1969, 9–14.

Eisenson, J., Auer, J. J., and Irwin, J. V. *The psychology of communication.* New York: Appleton-Century-Crofts, 1963.

Knox, L., and McConnell, F. Helping parents to help deaf infants. *Children,* 1968, **15,** 183–187.

Lenneberg, E. H. *Biological foundations of language.* New York: John Wiley and Sons, 1967.

Lenneberg, E. H. What is meant by a biological approach to language? *American annals of the deaf,* 1970, **115,** 67–72.

McConnell, F. A new approach to the management of childhood deafness. In D. Karzon (Ed.), *Pediatric clinics of North America,* 1970, **17,** 347–362.

McConnell, F., and Horton, K. B. *A home teaching program for parents of very young deaf children.* Final Report, Office of Education, Bureau of Research, Project No. 6-1187, Grant No. OEG 32-52-0450-6007. Nashville, Tenn.: Vanderbilt University, 1970.

Moores, D. F. Communication, linguistics, and deafness. *Proceedings of the Teacher Institute,* October 17, 1969. Frederick, Md.: Maryland School for the Deaf, 1969.

Moores, D. F. Psycholinguistics and deafness. *American annals of the deaf,* 1970, **115,** 37–48.

Morkovin, B. Experiment in teaching deaf preschool children in the Soviet Union. *Volta review,* 1960, **62,** 260–268.

Quigley, S. P. *The influence of fingerspelling on the development of language, communication, and educational achievement in deaf children.* Institute for Research on Exceptional Children. Urbana: University of Illinois, 1969.

Todd, G. A., and Palmer, B. Social reinforcement of infant babbling. *Child development,* 1968, **39,** 591–596.

Whetnall, E., and Fry, D. B. *The deaf child.* Springfield, Ill.: Charles C Thomas, 1964.

CHAPTER VIII

Social Aspects of Speech

D. M. C. DALE, PH.D.

It is not uncommon for sociologists, psychologists, and linguists to suggest that "the time spent out of school can be more important to a child's linguistic development than the time spent in school." Bernstein, for example, in much of his work (Bernstein, 1960, 1961a, 1961b), has shown that wide differences in the amount and type of language used exist between children from middle class and lower class homes. Such differences appear most marked when children enter the high school stage and are called on to undertake what Piaget has classified as "formal operations." The lower class child is more likely to be restricted to concrete operations. Sociologist Strodtbeck refers to "the hidden curriculum of the middle class home." Philip Vernon, in his latest book (Vernon, 1969), describes the influence of environmental factors and shows clearly the effect of culture and type of upbringing on the development of abilities.

In *Special Education in Denmark* (Jorgensen, 1970) the officer responsible for special education lists "the standard of the home" as first of the three priorities which determine whether a child with a hearing handicap can be educated outside a school for deaf children.

The important role which parents and house parents of residential schools can play in assisting deaf children to acquire language and speech is appreciated by many, but by no means all, of their teachers.

To obtain statistical evidence of the value of parental participation, a research project was conducted in 1970 with 60 deaf children and their parents. The hypothesis tested was that educational attainments and social adjustment of children from families which appeared to be working hard with them would be superior to those of children whose parents were not.

Head teachers of five day schools for deaf children and two regular schools which contained special units were asked to suggest names of severely deaf children who might be suitable for this study. On receipt of these, the writer visited each school and administered three tests to each child: Owrid's Oral Language Vocabulary Test (Owrid, 1960); Schonell's Reading Vocabulary Test (Schonell, 1960); and Dale's Speech Production Test (Dale, 1968). Better ear thresholds for pure tones over the speech frequencies 500, 1000 and 2000 Hz, date of birth, and teachers' ratings of IQ on an A-E scale were obtained. The head teachers then sent a letter to the parents, and two graduate research workers visited the homes to interview the parents. A structured interview technique was used (Appendix A). When all parents had been interviewed, a final questionnaire was sent to the parents to obtain further information on the nature of the guidance offered by teachers of the deaf during the pre-school years. It was decided to investigate further the nature of the guidance received from teachers of the deaf at the pre-school level. Questionnaires were sent to the parents of 49 children who had indicated that they had had at least some assistance from a teacher at this time. Replies were received from 31 of these homes.

Eighteen mothers had had 21 or more guidance sessions and 10 of the remainder had had more than 11 sessions. In 16 cases, visits were made each week and in nine they were made every two weeks.

During the sessions, the visiting teacher usually talked about "deafness and its problems" and often showed the parents how to work with the child. It was not so common, however, for the teacher to ask the parents to work with the child and then to discuss the methods used by them (in only eight cases had this happened often). On the other hand, Professor Ian Taylor at the University of Manchester (Taylor, 1964) and others have found this an invaluable technique in parent guidance.

In only half the replies received had the teacher regularly checked the performance of the hearing aid. Recent statistics for school-age children show how essential regular checking of hearing aids is and careful checking at the clinic or on each home visit gives parents encouragement to do this regularly at home. No less than 50 percent of the individual hearing aids tested in schools and units in the London area were found not to be performing at maximum on the day of testing (Martin and Lodge, 1969).

All 60 children in the current project were day students and their ages ranged from 4.8 to 15.9 years (Mean 9 yrs., 4 months with an S.D. of 2 yrs. 3 months). The mean hearing loss for pure tones in the better ear was 93.72 dB and the standard deviation 15.34 dB. The majority of this group were deaf from birth (42 children) and all were deaf before the age of 3 years. Teachers' ratings of the children's intelligence on a 5-point scale, indicated that 30 were of average intelligence (IQ:90–110), 15 were above average (111–125), 10 were below average, two were very bright and two very dull. In Schonell's Reading Vocabulary test, Mean Reading ages were 6.02 years with S.D. 1.13. This result is not dissimilar from that obtained in the United States Survey of attainments of children in schools for the deaf.

On Owrid's Vocabulary Tests the Mean score was 16.93 and the S.D. 7.20. This test, although designed for deaf children, is equated for assessing vocabulary in normally hearing children up to an age of only 5 years. Although it proved too easy for some children in this research, it is noteworthy that so many of those aged 10, 12, and even 14 years, failed to complete this test up to the 5-year level. Total scores on Dale's Speech Production Test (Dale, 1968, pp. 218–220) gave a Mean of 16.67 and an S.D. of 9.25. This test consists of 20 words containing 23 different consonants and 17 vowels and diphthongs. The overall scores in many cases were far too low to obtain intelligible speech and these results present further evidence that the teaching of the articulation of sounds needs to be increased as well as concentration on rhythmical functional speech.

Interviews were held with 34 mothers, three fathers, and in 23 cases with both parents. Ten of the 120 parents did not speak fluent English—four of these were deaf themselves and the six others were immigrants from other countries. Two other parents were deaf but spoke fluently.

To obtain adjusted scores for language, reading, and speech, each of these variables were separately included in a regression as the dependent variable with age in months, hearing loss, and IQ grade included as the independent variables. The residuals from the regression were used as adjusted scores which were given a grade so that frequency could be produced.

Two-thirds of the mothers had received at least 21 guidance sessions either at home or at a clinic when their child was of preschool age. There was no evidence statistically that children whose parents had had most such meetings made most progress either educationally or socially (X^2 = 2.90, 0.11, 0.02 and 0.11).

Hearing Aids

Fifteen of the 60 children were attending units in regular schools and the remaining 45 were in schools for deaf children. Table I illustrates a very significant difference between the two groups in the use of hearing aids out of school time.

Table I. Use of hearing aids at home by children from deaf schools and units in regular schools.

Hearing aid worn	Schools for deaf children (Mean hearing loss 97.7)	Units in ordinary schools (Mean hearing loss 90.0)
All the time	12	14
Often	7	1
Sometimes	9	
Rarely	8	
Never	9	
Totals:	45	15

It was first thought that this might be due to the fact that the children in the schools for the deaf were overall, some 8 dB more deaf than those in the units. No relationship was found, however, between use of hearing aid and extent of hearing loss (X^2=0.11). This bears out Justman and Moskowitz' findings of 1956 and numerous others, that children attending regular units become more interested in wearing hearing aids than do those in segregated schools for the deaf. Evidence was presented of a relationship between use of hearing aid and the frequency with which it was checked by the parents (X^2 = 6.04). No less than one parent in three said that they did not ever check the performance of the hearing aids. There are implications in this, of course, for visiting teachers of deaf children as well as class teachers—specific guidance and regular encouragement is needed by parents especially in the early years of the child's life.

Language

One hundred and eight of the 119 parents stated that they taught their children new words and phrases quite regularly each week. In view of the relatively low scores on Owrid's vocabulary test, however, these responses should be treated with caution.

Only six of the homes kept a grammar dictionary, (i.e., lists of common phrases written as occasions arose and classified under headings such as "meal times," "at the shops," "going to bed," "when people are sick," etc.) One-third of the group had never taught their children nursery rhymes. Only 10 of the homes had a street map of their local district, 15 had a map of Great Britain, and 17 a map of the world or a globe.

Pictures, maps, and photographs are felt by the majority of teachers to be a very necessary aid to developing and recapitulating language forms. The interviewers asked to see what samples of these had been collected. Fifteen of the 60 homes had no pictures at all and 11 said they never used photographs. More positively, 35 homes had collected more than 50 pictures and 34 used photographs either "a great deal" or "often." No parents kept their pictures alphabetically or with a library type catalogue, although one family had 1000 pictures and nine had between 250–500.

Television sets were possessed by all but one of the families and 51 out of 60 of the children were reported to like to watch it. One child did not like television at all and eight were said to be indifferent to it. Half the group watched for between one and one-half and two hours each night during the week; ten watched for one-half an hour or less daily; ten others watched for one hour, eight watched two and one-half to three hours, and one 15-year-old boy watched for six hours each night. On weekends, half of the group watched television for a total of between three and six hours, and a quarter for a total of between seven and ten hours. The 15-year-old boy watched for 12 hours, and a 7-year-old boy in the Midlands viewed for no less than 14 hours each weekend. Twenty-eight of the 60 homes said that they explained things on the television programs "all the time." This, however, was felt by the interviewers to be a not too highly objective rating.

There was evidence to show that children with low language scores found signs and gestures more useful than those who had high language scores ($X^2 = 4.09$).

Evidence was produced when a correlation matrix was completed which showed that the children of those parents who had worked hardest on language, had in fact achieved higher scores on the adjusted language test ($r = .316$—significant at the 5 percent level of confidence).

Reading

Thirty-three of the 60 homes said that they were devoting 5–15 minutes each day to helping the deaf children with reading. Only 16 of the 119 parents said they devoted no time at all to helping with reading.

In the writer's experience, perhaps the most useful aid to reading is a family diary (Dale, pp. 62–63, 1968). Only three of the 60 homes were keeping these. A child's dictionary was possessed by 30 of the homes and 33 of the children used a children's library with any degree of regularity. Notebooks or something similar were kept in various rooms of those homes by 38 of the children's parents to help them explain things to their deaf child. It appeared that in most cases, parents were using these pads more as an aid to communicating some difficult point, than as a useful educational tool. Simple words and sketches were obviously better than nothing, but phrases and sentences which occurred during the day and could sometimes be used again in the evening for reading, auditory training, and language development should be recorded. No significant relationship was found between the parents who seemed to be working hardest on reading and those who were doing least ($X^2 = 2.673$).

Speech

The subject which causes parents most anxiety (Dale, 1971) and teachers to feel most inadequate (Her Majesty's Stationary Office, London 1964) appears to be speech, i.e., obtaining intelligible utterance from the children.

Teachers of deaf children frequently have recommended that parents should not try to teach speech to the children. This is primarily due to the fact that some parents, in their enthusiasm and due to their apprehension, have attempted to manipulate the children's tongues and lips and in other ways have created a sense of failure and frustration in the children which does more harm than good to the speech and often to the relationship between child and parent. There are, however, a number of things which parents can do which are felt to encourage the child to speak more clearly and at the same time, let the children know that the parents appreciate clear speech. In such speech activities (as in most of the work which parents do at home with the children) the feeling that it is a "game" should prevail—"Try this for fun and see how you get on." Parents were asked about such activities.

Just over half of the parents said they listened regularly to their deaf children as they said various words and phrases and tried to understand which one the child said. Over a third of the group, however, never did this. In 18 of the homes, the parents said that they regularly tapped out the syllables of new and unfamiliar words when they were said; again, just half of the group of parents said they never did this.

It is interesting that 40 of the 60 pairs of parents said that they let their children know "every time" that they pronounced a word well. Twelve other homes said they "usually" did. The remaining eight pairs of parents said they "never" did this. Less credible was the finding that no less than 34 of the pairs of parents said that they told their children "every time" that a word was mispronounced. In one of these cases, the child was only able to articulate correctly three of the 40 phonemes tested; in two others five and in seven others, less than 11 phonemes were accurately produced. If it were true that these 68 parents were correcting these particular 11 children "every time" they said a word incorrectly, it would seem to be a quite undesirable policy, since the children possessed few if any intelligible words.

Parents in 26 of the homes said they used the telephones once or twice each week to give practice to the child in speaking clearly. Parents in six others said they did this every day. Thirty-four of the 119 parents said they did not ever use a telephone for this purpose.

Thirty-seven of the 60 homes reported that they regularly asked their children to repeat words and phrases from reading material until they said them more clearly. Thirteen homes said they never did this.

The children whose parents paid most attention to the aspects of speech production listed above, were found to speak more intelligibly than those whose parents had not (r=.366, significant at the 1 percent level of confidence).

Social Adjustment

Parents and teachers completed Rutter's Social Adjustment Schedules (Rutter, Tizard, and Whitmore, 1970) for all 60 children. Twenty-one of the 60 children tested with the Rutter A Schedule (parents) and 21 of the 59 children assessed by teachers on the B Schedule, showed evidence of some maladjustment. Although the numbers in this study were relatively small, they do make an interesting comparison (Table 2) with those obtained in the large-scale study on the Isle of Wight reported by Rutter et al (Ibid. p. 104).

It will be seen that the overall scores for a group of deaf children and a

Table 2. Social Adjustment: Parental and Teachers' Questionnaire Scores

Questionnaire	Isle of Wight Control group (Normally Hearing Children)		Deaf group (all but 2 of whom were retarded in reading		Isle of Wight Children with reading retardation		Deaf children rated D & E on 5 point Intelligence Scale		Isle of Wight Children with IQ below 70	
	No. of children	%	No. of children	%	No. of children	%	No. of children	%	No. of children	%
Parental Questionnaire										
Score 13+	11	7.7	21	33	20	24.1	6	54.5	17	30.4
Neurotic	3	2.1	4	6.7	6	7.2	1	9.1	8	14.4
Antisocial	4	2.8	14	23.3	10	12.0	5	45.4	7	12.5
Undesignated	4		3		4	2	0		2	
Total numbers	143		60		83		11		56	
Teachers' Questionnaire										
Score 9+	14	9.5	21	35.6	32	37.2	6	54.5	23	41.8
Neurotic	7	4.8	10	17.0	11	12.8	3	27.5	10	18.2
Antisocial	7	4.8	8	13.6	20	23.8	2	19.0	11	20.0
Undesignated			3		1		1		2	
Total numbers	147		59		86		11		55	

group of normally hearing ones show a much greater degree of maladjustment in the former than the latter (Table 2). When considering, however, that virtually all the deaf groups were quite retarded in their reading skills, the results, although still disturbing, are much more understandable. The number of deaf children with low IQ in the research group was too small to draw any valid conclusions, but the indications are in line with Rutter's Isle of Wight findings (i.e., there is a great deal more social maladjustment among children of low IQ than among those of normal intelligence).

Relationships with School

Five-sixths of the parents said that their relationship with the school was either "close" or was "quite happy and useful." The remaining sixth said that the relationship was "not very close" or that there was "very little contact." This finding was felt to be a tribute to the friendliness of the teachers in both deaf schools and regular school units. Despite this, however, when one considers the number of points which so many of these parents were not taking up in the educational training of their children, one cannot but feel that the relationship must be much stronger on the professional side.

Parents regularly received suggestions of what they could do at home with their children and this was felt by 23 of the 31 parents to be the most valuable information received at the guidance session. Some consideration was given by teachers to showing the parents books and pamphlets, but in half the cases this was never done and is felt to have been another weakness.

The last question asked the parents was:—"On looking back at those early years, what do you think the teacher might have done to help you more?" Three parents wished that the visits could have been of one hour's duration rather than the half or even the quarter of an hour that they had received. One said they should be made once a day to begin with and then taper off to once every week. It used to be believed that once parents had attended some 20 weekly or fortnightly guidance sessions it was only necessary for them to be seen once a month or even two months. The rationale for this was that after 20 guidance sessions the parents were well informed. This view, however, overlooks the tremendous value to most mothers of regular discussions with a well-informed outsider who can sometimes guide, but often just confirm, the mother's thoughts about her child or the problems of deaf children and adults in general, and can always be sympathetically interested and encouraging.

Two parents mentioned a lack of help with emotional problems, and this is felt to be a case where assistance should be sought by the teacher of the deaf from the school medical officer and an educational psychologist and then to follow the suggestions of these professionals.

The mother of a very deaf and backward child felt that too much of the information and literature given her was concerned with children less handicapped than her own, and she found it rather depressing. The practice of demonstrating and writing about only the highly successful cases is not uncommon, and although valuable for raising the levels of aspiration of some parents, house parents, and teachers, it can, as in the above case, have a very negative effect on those who are dealing with less gifted children.

Sixteen of the 31 parents who returned the questionnaires felt that there was nothing more that could have been done. Of the remainder, the commonest suggestion for improving this service, was that help should have been given regarding the future, e.g. discussion of possible educational placement, visits to schools and units, information about helping the child when he was older. One parent said, "I was told to live one day at a time and not to think of the future. I disagree with that." Although caution must be shown in predicting educational attainments, one feels that parents can be told about possible educational placements after a teacher has worked for several months with a child and has received reports from medical workers and an educational psychologist. In addition, although class teachers in schools and units for deaf children are becoming more aware of the need for active collaboration between home and school, it is felt that the preschool teacher who is specializing in parent guidance can play a highly significant role in showing parents what they can do at home when the child is older; parents' replies in this study indicate they would appreciate such information very much.

One of the most disturbing findings resulting from this survey was the lack of participation of most of the parents in giving educational assistance to their deaf children. Usually this was not through lack of warmth or feeling for the children, but through ignorance, and this, after 39 of the 60 mothers had had at least 20 sessions with a teacher of the deaf when their child was at the preschool level. If preschool guidance workers are only going to concern themselves with the day-to-day problems of the children under 4 or 5 years of age, then the service will be much less effective than it can be and there is likely to be considerable frustration and disappointment experienced by parents.

The manner in which many of even the most able parents interviewed were missing opportunities to assist their children gave cause for very real concern. The advantage of speaking close to the microphone of a hearing aid has been common knowledge to audiologists (and hearing aid users) for the past 25 years (John and Thomas, 1957; Dale, 1967), yet parents in 33 of the 60 homes visited did not ever do this. Only eight said they did this daily and a further eight that they did so on some days. Daily checking of hearing aids has been shown to be essential for ensuring their satisfactory performance (John and Thomas, 1957; Dale, 1967). Yet 22 of the parents interviewed said that they did not ever check the child's hearing aid. Daily diaries kept by the parents concerning the family's activities have been found to be perhaps the biggest single contribution that they can make to helping their child to read. Again only eight of the 60 homes were keeping such diaries. It is often recommended that a child should have books by his bedside and available at other times. Parents are encouraged to tell stories from the excellent books now available. Nineteen of the 60 children did not belong to a children's library, although these were accessible to them all. This negative list could be needlessly extended, but suffice it to say that teachers do have a responsibility to see that parents are much better informed about the opportunities to assist their deaf children.

Residential Care of Deaf Children

Some of the problems of helping deaf children in their own homes have been discussed above. When children are removed from their homes and placed in groups of 10 or 20 or even more to be supervised by one houseparent it can be seen that their difficulties may be magnified considerably. Because the handicap of deafness is a relatively rare one, it is inevitable that a certain number of children will have to live away from home if they are to receive daily assistance from teachers of deaf children. Much care must be taken in planning such out-of-school facilities if the children are to be educated, as well as just cared for.

In my experience in the four schools for the deaf in which I have lived for a total of nine years, and in my visits to 115 deaf schools in 13 different countries during the past 15 years, I can say that out-of-school facilities for deaf children's educational development are in nearly all cases quite inadequate. Some of the worst treatment has been observed in the largest residential schools. The difficulties frequently arise from inadequately qualified (although often dedicated) staff, being asked to manage groups which are far too large. In one of the schools in which I lived for two years in England 14 years ago, one member of the staff was required to supervise the going-to-bed routine of 40 boys in one dormitory and 45 boys in another. On Sunday mornings, one teacher or housemaster supervised the play activities of no less than 90 boys. I recall the only play equipment provided for this group one morning was a length of heavy knotted rope. One of the children held an end of this and spun so that the rope moved in a merry-go-round style of action and the remainder of the children jumped it as it turned. When the rope struck any child he was "out" and left the game. Most of this type of Dickension treatment of children has changed today, but certainly not all. The case of four housemasters in one large residential school who regularly play cards together for an hour or so each evening before lights are turned out for the children is not an isolated one. This incident regularly occurs at the present time.

When I asked in a large residential school in the United States recently if I could observe the routine followed while the children ate their lunch I was informed, "Well yes, you could if you like, but it's rather like 'slopping the hogs.' " It was. It is sobering to compare the language and speech opportunities afforded to children in the following two situations: In dining room one, containing a total of 20 children, four children and a teacher or houseparent sit at one table with places carefully set. There are flowers on each table and a menu of today's and tomorrow's meal. The older children at each table are asked to help the little ones when they require it. In the second dining room, 280 children sit 20 at each table. No adults sit with the children and food is distributed rapidly by staff who have not time even to ask the children to say, "Thank you."

In two large schools in East Germany I was shown ten dormitories, immaculately cleaned and polished, but with not one picture on any of the walls nor a personal item visible which belonged to any child.

One very intelligent deaf boy who went to work on a farm after he left school wrote, "Please send me some pictures from calendars to put on the walls of my room. The walls are bare and at night before I go to sleep, I can't think of anything." By placing deaf children in virtually bare rooms, as is so frequently the case, we are really simulating one of

Hebb's boxes when it is remembered that they are receiving so little stimulation auditorily.

In discussing school entry with a group of 10 deaf boys and girls, aged 15 years, in New Zealand, I was astonished to learn that in every case, when they first came into residence at the age of 5 or 6, they believed that they would never return to their homes again. One Maori boy, who had helped his father round up sheep and put them on a train to be slaughtered, even believed that when he was placed on a train with a group of other children, he was going to be killed himself. He said that the sight of his mother on the platform and some of the children in the train crying, as well as his father looking very upset, convinced him that this must be so. It is some consolation that this boy and the nine other members of the group were, at 15 years, happy and very pleasant young people. With the development of visiting teacher services to the homes, there will doubtless be fewer instances of this type which have occurred in the past. It must be said, however, that some of the things that have gone on under the name of special educational treatment have been exceedingly unfortunate.

Those of us who have worked in the traditional large schools have all seen cases where a young child has entered full of confidence and initiative and after a few months has lost a great deal of this buoyancy, spontaneity, and speech. This has frequently occurred through having to fit into the routines which are necessary when a small staff cares for large groups of children. The individual approach which is so important in speech work and for psychological well-being is just not possible.

What can be done about the present large residential school problem? The physical magnitude of some of the largest schools which evoke delusions of grandeur in some superintendents and aspirants for their positions, is the same physical magnitude which can be quite overwhelming to a small deaf boy or girl. The huge assembly and dining halls and great corridors and stairways are often quite intimidating to them, and some children take several years to become accustomed to such facilities. Others, of course, never learn to accept them.

If deaf children are to be segregated in schools with enrollments of 200 and even up to 600 (which a growing number of workers and parents believe to be quite the wrong policy), then at least a great effort should be made to modify the internal structure of many of the existing schools. This would allow for much smaller grouping of children and more intimate, personal care of them in more home-like facilities. One school in

Canada has recently placed a large number of dividing walls throughout the huge dining hall so that alcoves have been created. This has helped a little acoustically and a great deal psychologically by making meal times more personal and homey.

The size of the groups for which a houseparent is asked to take responsibility is perhaps the most critical question. For supervision of getting up in the morning, going to bed, and for indoor activities such as hobbies, homework, and indoor games, groups should only consist of ten children or less, if an educational role is expected of the houseparent and personal attention is to be given to each child. Houseparents need to know details such as the birthdays of each child in the group, the names and ages of each child's brothers and sisters, what each home is like, what pets the child has, what games he plays and how he spends his time. Time should be taken to listen patiently to things the children are trying to communicate. The houseparent, often aided by the children, should make dormitory and playroom walls as attractive as possible with posters, pictures, photographs, displays of the children's work, notices of coming events, and other news items. For little children, especially, home/school notebooks should be conscientiously read and filled in by houseparents. A group diary should also be kept in the dormitory, the ideas for which have been suggested by the children and then written and illustrated by the houseparent.

Another aspect of the work which administrators can make easier for houseparents is in the provision of adequate play materials and hobby equipment for each group. Staff members, of course, need training in how to make the most of this, and courses in this field should be a regular part of their training. Eva Burmeister in "The Professional Houseparent," an excellent book for residential care workers, suggests a very useful list of equipment for a supervisor.

Recommendations such as reducing the size of supervision groups to ten children or less, may appear extravagant where present programs have 30 or 40 children in each group. It is difficult to justify removing children from their homes, however, unless something approaching life in a good home can be offered to them.

Far too little attention has been paid in the past to the use that can be made of out-of-school hours, both at home and in hostels.

APPENDIX A.
PARENT INTERVIEW

1. Name of Child ______________________________

2. Interview with—Mother ☐

   Father ☐

   Both ☐

3. Age of Onset of deafness ______________________________

   (a) Before your child went to school about how many times did you see a teacher of deaf children (either at a clinic or at home)? ______________________________

4. Nationality ______________________________

   (a) Nationality—Mother ______________________________

   Father ______________________________

   (b) Use of English—Mother ______________________________

   Father ______________________________

   Key: A—fluent English
   B—limited English
   C—very limited English
   D—no English

   (c) If parents are deaf please indicate with a cross ☐

5. The aid is worn (a) all the time
   (b) often
   (c) sometimes
   (d) rarely
   (e) never

6. How often do you check that the aid is running satisfactorily?

   (a) three times each day
   (b) twice each day
   (c) once a day
   (d) once or twice a week
   (e) never
   (f) no hearing aid

7. If (a)–(d), what is done? ______________________________

____

8. Do you make any special use of the hearing aid? Please specify:—

Open	Coded

(a) do you have a session when you speak close to the microphone of the hearing aid:
- (i) every day
- (ii) nearly every day
- (iii) some days
- (iv) very occasionally
- (v) never
- (vi) not applicable

(b) Do you "direct your child's listening," e.g. to tap running, music on radio:

Open	Coded

- (i) frequently each day
- (ii) several times each day
- (iii) once or twice each week
- (iv) very rarely
- (v) never

(c) Other

Language Development—(learning new words and sentences)

9. What ways have you yourself found that seem useful in helping your child learn new words and phrases? ________________________________

____

____

Open	Coded

(a) Do you teach your child new words?
- (i) every day
- (ii) once or twice each week
- (iii) once or twice each month
- (iv) never

(b) Do you teach him correct phrases? e.g. "Where's my coat?" instead of "Coat—where?" or "Coat—nothing?"
- (i) every day
- (ii) once or twice each week
- (iii) once or twice each month
- (iv) Never

(c) Do you keep a "grammar dictionary" of common phrases and sentences used at say meal times, when getting dressed, when washing, when being courteous, when questioning, etc?
- (i) Yes
- (ii) No
- (iii) Others, e.g. not now.

	Open	Coded

(d) Do you (or did you) teach your child nursery rhymes?
(i) often
(ii) sometimes
(iii) rarely
(iv) never

(e) Do you have maps of your town or district on a wall at home?
(i) Yes
(ii) No

(f) Do you have a map of Great Britain on a wall at home?
(i) Yes
(ii) No

(g) Do you have a map of the world on a wall at home?
(i) Yes
(ii) No

(h) Do you use photographs to help your child with language?
(i) a great deal
(ii) often
(iii) a little
(iv) not at all

(i) Approximately how many pictures have you collected to help your child with language?

(j) Other

10. Do you have a television set?
(i) Yes
(ii) No

11. Does your child like television?
(i) very much
(ii) quite a lot
(iii) not very much
(iv) dislikes it
(v) don't know

12. How long does he watch (average) week nights? (hours) ____________________

13. How long does he watch (average) at weekends? (hours) ____________________

14. Does someone explain things to him?
(i) all the time
(ii) often
(iii) sometimes
(iv) never

15. In understanding you, when you speak, do you think your child finds lipreading:
(i) a tremendous help
(ii) very helpful
(iii) quite helpful
(iv) very little help
(v) no help
(vi) a hindrance

16. In understanding you, when you speak, do you think your child finds his hearing aid:
    (i) a tremendous help
    (ii) very helpful
    (iii) quite helpful
    (iv) very little help
    (v) no help
    (vi) a hindrance

17. In understanding you, do you think your child finds signs and gestures from you:
    (i) a tremendous help
    (ii)
    (iii)
    (iv)
    (v)
    (vi) a hindrance

18. On average, about how many minutes would you spend talking (or signing, etc) with your child at:
    minutes
    (i) breakfast
    (ii) lunch
    (iii) tea

19. On average, during term time, about how many minutes would you spend talking with your child on a:
    minutes
    (i) Saturday
    (ii) Sunday
    (iii) Monday
    (iv) Tuesday
    (v) Wednesday
    (vi) Thursday
    (vii) Friday

(Interviewer and parent calculate together)

Reading

20. What have you yourself found helpful in the teaching of reading?

	Open	Coded
(a) How much time do you spend on helping him with his *reading*?		
(i) 1/4-hour per day		
(ii) 3/4-hour five times a week		
(iii) 1/2-hour two or three times a week		
(iv) 1/2-hour per week		
(v) a few minutes (5–6) each day		
(vi) a few minutes (5–6) each week		
(vii) very rarely help		
(viii) no time at all		
(ix) don't know		
(b) If (i)–(vii), state what you do (i) now		
______________________________		
______________________________		
and (ii) what you have done earlier		
______________________________		
______________________________		
(c) Do you keep a family diary?		
(i) Yes		
(ii) No		

(Coded)

(d) Do you use a children's library
(i) every week
(ii) once a fortnight
(iii) once a month
(iv) very rarely
(v) not at all
(vi) inaccessible

(e) Do you keep jotter pads in different rooms in the house for writing messages to your child?
(i) Yes
(ii) No

(f) Do you have a child's dictionary in your house?
c(i) Yes
(ii) No

(g) Other ______________________________

____

____

Speech

21. Have you found any ways for yourself that seem to help your child improve his speech?

Open | Coded

(a) When your child is at home, do you ask him to say words or phrases (e.g. from a list or from a book or from a group of objects on the table) while you, without looking guess what has been said?
(i) daily
(ii) once or twice each week
(iii) once or twice each month
(iv) never

(b) Do you tap out syllables of words said incorrectly and unfamiliar phrases and sentences?
(i) every time
(ii) usually
(iii) once or twice each week
(iv) once or twice each month
(v) never

(c) Do you tell your deaf child when he pronounces words wrongly?
(i) every time
(ii) usually
(iii) once or twice each week
(iv) once or twice each month
(v) never

(d) Do you tell your deaf child when he pronounces words well?
(i) every time
(ii) usually
(iii) once or twice each week
(iv) once or twice each month
(v) never

	Open	Coded

(e) Do you use the telephone (e.g. child "talking" to father or Grandma on the telephone) to encourage him to speak clearly?
(i) every time
(ii) usually
(iii) once or twice each week
(iv) once or twice each month
(v) never
(vi) no telephone

(f) When reading with your child, do you ever get him to repeat a word or phrase or sentence 4 or 5 times until he gets it clearer?
(i) every time
(ii) usually
(iii) once or twice each week
(iv) once or twice each month
(v) never

22. Has your relationship with the teachers at the school on school subjects generally been:
(i) close
(ii) quite happy and useful
(iii) not very close
(iv) very little contact
(v) other relationship

23. Have you other comments to make about helping your child educationally or socially?

____

____

____

(a) If you have other children living at home besides ______________, what are their ages?

(b) How much help do they give to ______________ educationally (i.e. help him/her to learn, say or read new words or phrases)?

(c) How much help do you think they give to ______________ socially, (i.e. help to make him/her a pleasant person who most people seem to like)?

Age in years	Educational	Social
Under 1 year		
Under 2 years		
Under 3 years		
Under 4 years		
Under 5 years		
Under 6 years		
Under 7 years		
Under 8 years		
Under 9 years		
Under 10 years		
Under 11 years		

Age in years	Educational	Social
Under 12 years		
Under 13 years		
Under 14 years		
Under 15 years		
Under 16 years		
Under 17 years		
Under 18 years		
Under 19 years		
Under 20 years		
Over 20 years		

Key: A—very helpful
B—helpful
C—a little help
D—of no help
E—other (specify)

Copy of booklet "Suggestions to Parents of Deaf Children" can be given to parents, if they have not already received one, after the interview.

BIBLIOGRAPHY

Bernstein, B. B. Language and social class. *British journal of sociology,* 1960, **11,** 271–276.

Bernstein, B. B. Aspects of language and learning in the genesis of the social process. *Journal of child psychology and psychiatry,* 1961, **1,** 313–324. (1961a)

Bernstein, B. B. Social class and linguistic development. In Halsey, A. H., Floud, J., and Anderson, C. A. (Eds.), *Education, economy, and society.* New York: Free Press of Glencoe, 1961. (1961b)

Dale, D. M. C. *Applied audiology for children.* Springfield, Ill.: Charles C Thomas, 1967.

Dale, D. M. C. *Deaf children at home and at school.* London: University of London Press, 1968.

Dale, D. M. C. *Language development in deaf and partially hearing children.* Washington, D.C.: Alexander Graham Bell Association for the Deaf, 1971 (in preparation).

Department of Education and Science. *The Health of the School Child, 1962 and 1963.* His Majesty's Stationary Office, London, 1964.

John, J. E. J., and Thomas, H. Design and construction of schools for the deaf. In A. W. G. Ewing (Ed.), *Educational guidance and the deaf child.* Manchester, England: Manchester University Press, 1957.

Jorgensen, I. S. *Special education in Denmark.* Det Danske Selskab, 1970.

Justman, J., and Moskowitz, S. *The integration of deaf children in a hearing class.* Pub. No. 36. New York: Board of Education of the City of New York, 1956.

Martin, M., and Lodge, J. J. A survey of hearing aids in schools for deaf and partially hearing units. *Sound,* 1969, **3,** 2–11.

Owrid, H. L. Measuring spoken language in young deaf children. *The teacher of the deaf.* 1960, **58,** Part 1: 24–34; Part 2: 124–128.

Rutter, M., Tizard, T., and Whitmore, K. *Education, health and behavior.* Longmans Appendices 5 and 6, 1970.

Schonell, F. J. and F. E. *Diagnostic and attainment testing.* Edinburgh, Scotland: Oliver and Boyd, 1960.

Taylor, I. G. *Neurological mechanisms of speech and hearing.* Manchester, England: Manchester University Press, 1964.

Vernon, P. E. *Intelligence and cultural environment.* London: Methuen, 1969.

Part III Speech Teaching

CHAPTER IX

The Acquisition of Speech

Sophie L. French, M.A.

Most speech skills are best learned through use of speech itself.

Mary C. New

The above words will have a familiar ring to all who studied under or worked with Mary C. New of Lexington School for the Deaf. She firmly believed that deaf children must be helped to pass through the normal developmental stages of speech acquisition and that they will best learn to talk through talking. Her philosophy stands the test of time well and is surprisingly compatible with new insights into the development of speech and language for both hearing and hearing impaired babies. Miss New's theme will be the theme of this chapter, restated and reinforced by the findings of modern research which increasingly emphasize the importance of utilizing the auditory and proprioceptive feedback systems at the appropriate developmental age. Such an approach requires early identification, parent counseling, home training, and special educational assistance if the child is to reach his maximum speech potential. The environment must be modified and the child's own sensorimotor perceptions stimulated to the fullest. The goal is to enable the child to acquire speech and language as normally as possible.

How are speech and language acquired by the normal child? This is the topic of previous chapters. Therefore, let us merely summarize some of the factors that must be present.

It is generally assumed that the time of speech emergence is during the first three years of an infant's life. This assumption presupposes a child who possesses a normal central nervous system, the musculature and physiology necessary for speech production, and a functioning hearing end organ. He lives in an environment that provides him both with the sensory stimuli that set his receptive-expressive system in operation and with positive responses to each step that he takes toward speech and language acquisition. The process begins with the production of vocal signals which all babies give, whether hearing or deaf. These vocalizations contain both changes in pitch and intensity. Very early in life the child uses intonation patterns first to indicate an afferent state, later to impart a message. As he begins to perceive the phonological components of speech, he imposes these on his intonational patterns in babblings, jargon, words, phrases, and finally in complete utterances having proper syntax. He masters during this process the melody of speech (pitch, intensity, duration, and quality). He learns to integrate his utterances into appropriate breath groups and develops the ability to handle all necessary articulation skills. Simultaneously, he begins to associate these activities with meaning. All of this has been possible because of the auditory and proprioceptive monitoring (feedback loop) systems. All abilities have emerged in an integrated cyclical pattern without conscious effort or imposed practice.

But what about the infant with a hearing impairment? He suffers limitations or deprivations in most of the areas vital to the development of speech. The sensorimotor input is limited to the extent that his hearing is non-functional. His environment is severely modified, not only by the fact that it is soundless, but also by the fact that the discovery of the hearing loss usually causes great strain and stress for the parents. Positive responses to the child's early efforts may be lacking. The child's early vocalizations may not be continued and a series of omissions occur in the feedback loop system. Because the child fails to hear himself and others, he ceases to babble and fails to enter the jargon stage. This cessation prevents his experiencing all the tactile-kinesthetic sensations that enable him to master the movement patterns of speech. This further increases the difficulty of perceiving the association between speech movement patterns and linguistic units. Speech and language do not develop in the normal fashion. Immediate special assistance is needed if the child is to develop speech. This assistance must come at the appropriate developmental age. It must focus on reducing the child's hearing impairment to the minimum through use of amplification and auditory training. It must focus on manipulating the environment through parent counseling to provide for both maximum stimulation and for maximum reinforcement of the child's earliest vocal attempts. Finally, it may have to focus on finding means for stimulating babbling and use of articulatory movements to provide maximum information to the proprioceptive system.

When, where, and how do we begin? Obviously as early as the hearing loss is detected, if possible during the first few months of life. The feasibility of this has been amply demonstrated (Downs, 1967; Pollack, 1967; Griffiths, 1967; Whetnall and Fry, 1964). Despite the observations of Lenneberg (1967, p. 140) that cooing and babbling may not necessarily be vital practice stages for future verbal behavior, it is clear that maximum input of auditory stimuli at the appropriate developmental period is an essential for learning. If we are to begin working with the child at this period it is apparent that most of the work must take place within the home, and parents must be very much involved. The first efforts will have to be devoted toward three areas: (1) increasing sensory input; (2) stimulating or maintaining vocal expression and (3) developing the essentials of speech. We shall deal with all of these areas separately, but it is of vital importance that they be seen as completely integrated. Parallel development must take place.

Sensory Perception

The young deaf infant in the home is, of course, receiving much sensory information through his visual and tactile senses and it is primarily the auditory input that is lacking. We will, therefore, focus our initial efforts in the area of auditory training. The first steps must be to condition the youngster to respond to sound, to realize that sound has significance, and to learn that listening is pleasurable. Even before hearing aid selection takes place, auditory stimulation can begin.

Parents take naturally to the practice of singing, humming, vocalizing close to their baby's ear. They see and feel his response and they continue this practice for the satisfaction it gives both parent and child. This type of auditory input should continue even after the acquisition of a hearing aid, for it provides the child with an opportunity to hear amplified but undistorted speech as well as continuing a very satisfying experience. Fathers, in particular, should participate in this activity for the lower-pitched male voice will reach the child better than that of the mother.

It is while the baby is still in arms, not yet totally immersed in the joys of running, climbing, and exploring that initial auditory stimulation should take place. If the child hears voice through the naked ear, he will vocalize. Parents must continuously talk to their child and draw his attention to vocalizations. They should, if possible, alert him by use of voice, not by touch or visible gesture. They must attempt to teach him to identify a speaker and locate his position. Finally, they should frequently imitate the child's own vocalizations, especially during the babbling stage, for in this way they can fulfill their appropriate role as providers of speech models as well as stimulators of auditory feedback (Wyatt-1969, p. 19).

There are, however, other aspects of auditory awareness with which parents should be concerned. They can note the sounds to which the child does pay attention (the doorbell, the telephone, father's voice, the plane overhead) and be sure the child understands the sound source. They can then go on to draw his attention to other sounds that hitherto have gone unnoticed (the vacuum cleaner, the timer, the radio, the television). Many of these sounds become meaningful once the child's attention has been drawn to them. We know of one child whose earliest vocalizations were stimulated by Lucille Ball. The child loved to watch Lucy as she sang on the *I Love Lucy* show. The very alive face, very close to the screen, highly attracted her. The mother perceived this, moved the child closer to the screen, turned the sound up a bit, and the little deaf girl responded.

It is of great importance that parents acquire a functional understanding of their child's hearing potential. Not, what is his loss, but what does he hear? What loudness level for voice is necessary? At what distance can he respond? Under what circumstances does he hear best? Most parents readily understand a simplified version of information theory which has much revelevance for developing speech in an acoustically handicapped child (French, 1967). They easily comprehend that varied pitch, a slightly higher than normal intensity, a slightly slower (but not distorted) rate helps the child understand. They can also learn that "too much noise on the channel" can interfere with messages sent and received, and they will provide for quiet, with minimal distractions, at certain periods of the day. They see that repetition (redundancy) can increase the input and facilitate recognition. Without these understandings, parents seldom provide the most beneficial environment for the child. Quite the opposite is apt to occur, for they will then perceive their child as not responding; they will fail to receive satisfactory responses themselves; and as a result they will talk less and less to the child. Thus, input is reduced, rather than increased and further deprivation is added to a child already deprived. The above statements do not imply that one should turn parents into teachers of the deaf. On the contrary, the attempt is to enable parents to fulfill their natural role as providers of input for their child's speech and language development.

In addition to an understanding of the child's hearing potential and becoming skillful at providing maximum sound input, the parent must also learn what a hearing aid can and cannot do for their particular child. The work of Guberina (1964) and Ling (1964) have made us cognizant of the fact that hearing that exists below the speech range is still extremely useful. Mildred Berry (1969) helps us to understand this phenomenon as she refers to neural plasticity (page 48), the ability of alternate neural pathways to take over the functions of a damaged route. "When certain neural highways are closed to the tactile, kinesthetic, and auditory signals of speech, for example, the possibility of alternate routes will be determined largely by neural plasticity." The child can learn what was formerly considered the impossible; that is, to decode and encode speech via the auditory channel despite the fact that he has little or no hearing in the speech range. It is imperative that parents have some understanding of these facts or they will fail to see how the hearing aid, which sounds so dreadful to them, will still be of great use to their child.

Despite the fact that we are emphasizing auditory input, we must not overlook two other areas of sensory perception: the visual and the tactile-kinesthetic. Visual perception is vital for oral learning whether specific lipreading is taught or not. "We know that the baby learning oral language depends heavily on *speech as he sees it*" (Berry, 1969, p. 286). The child gets much additional information from watching a speaker, and all babies do this. They become aware of facial expression, the visual movements of speech, the temporal aspects. Why else did the little baby referred to earlier become attracted to Lucy?

Little children love to imitate funny faces, learn finger-play songs and follow-the-leader games. Participating in these play activities serves many purposes. The child develops imitative skills, of course, but beyond this he is, by visually imitating others, experiencing many kinesthetic sensations that are vital for speech. He can experience changes in the rate of movement, size of movement, and the tension and relaxation of muscles. Parents and siblings can lead babies in games that involve gross body movements, fine finger movements, movements of the face, and movements of the articulators. We raise the arms up, then down, up then down, and the child follows. We open the hands wide apart, then only a tiny bit, wide apart, and a tiny bit. Clap hard, then softly, hard, then softly. All are visually imitated, all stimulate imitation and memory, but also all give the baby vital kinesthetic sensations.

At this stage of development, perception of movements is probably the most important and appropriate aspect of visual training. The more conventional concept of visual training, where the child learns to classify by color, shape, sequence, etc., belongs to a later developmental level and is related to other aspects of learning more than to speech development.

The development of tactile-kinesthetic perception should also emphasize the feedback that comes from perceiving rate, size of motion, and tension rather than the perception of likenesses and differences of shape, size, and texture of objects. Again, as the baby plays imitatively with his parents, shifting from imitations of gross motor activities to very fine ones leading up to imitation of speech productions, he begins to experience the kinesthetic sensations that cannot really be taught or overlaid. When being held closely, he can feel his parent shifting from loud to soft voice or high to low pitch. In time he will incorporate these variations into his own vocalizations. Only by the performance of motor activities himself can he experience and master the motor skills needed for speech.

At this point one should consider the apparent dichotomy between the unisensory and the multisensory approach. Are these necessarily opposed? We think not. It is rather a matter of the roles played by each and the appropriate use of each. The work of Gaeth (1967) makes it abundantly clear that it is impossible for children to learn from signals in two different modalities at the same time. Initial training must be unisensory and should be in the auditory area, both because this modality is most closely linked to speech development and because it is the weakest input system. However, unisensory training does not preclude the use of other modalities to set off a response once it has been learned. Both visual and kinesthetic perception are tied in with the proprioceptive loop system. There may be times when unisensory training is required in these areas, also. Eventually, all sensory perceptions will be integrated, mutually supporting each other in the establishment and recall of speech patterns (Berry, 1969, p. 124). Speech is a visuo-motor-kinetic activity. Perception and production of speech require the use of all modalities, each developed to the maximum level. We should plan for unisensory and multisensory training at appropriate times and places.

Essentials of Speech

What are the essentials of speech that must be acquired? These must be a combination of vocalization, intonation, and phonemic production.

We have already discussed the continuation of natural phonation emphasizing the auditory, but utilizing all sensory systems for stimulation. If there has been a lapse in vocalization, parents and therapists will have to work out together a conditioning situation for this activity. A reversal of the Ewings' classic "go"activity used primarily for testing can be useful here. The child learns to perform an activity in response to a spoken sound. As he performs this activity he usually begins to vocalize and wants to take over the situation so that he can play examiner and make his parent be the person examined. He has found a useful purpose for his voice. He can control others with it, at least in this particular situation. However it is achieved, the establishment of voice is the primary step.

Once the child vocalizes there must be concern for the quality of these vocalizations. Are they pleasant and comfortable or are they too loud, strident, and harsh? Are they monotonal or do they contain both pitch and intensity changes? Krijnen (1967) cautions us to be aware of these qualities, not only to prevent voice damage, but also to promote the use of the voice that appears to be most natural and easy for the child. The more residual hearing a baby has and the more efficiently he uses this hearing, the more natural will be his voice. But beyond that there are other factors involved. The relationship between parent and child and teacher and child is of vital importance. The relaxed infant will produce a relaxed and pleasant voice; a tense infant will not. Forced training, roughly imposed vocalizations, long prolongations of any one sound produces tensions and may result in a youngster damaging his voice. Furthermore, these activities may develop in the child the wrong kinesthetic sensations. Krijnen (1967) urges us to find the situations which bring out the most natural and relaxed voice from the child. Only after that can one begin to impose intonation changes.

Finally, through playful babblings, the development of consonants and syllables can take place. One should always move from the easily produced to the more difficult. If at any time the effort to produce the new, whether it be a pitch modulation or the imposition of a new phoneme, creates an undue strain on the voice, then one should go back to the simple vocalization and start anew.

As the baby listens, feels, and watches his parents producing slightly accentuated intonation patterns, he will learn to imitate and produce similar patterns. The parents should say, "oh, oh, oh," with rising and falling intonation curves. They should also vary the intensity patterns within such utterances. Auditory perception of such changes is possible even for the very deaf child; however, he can also feel and see tension in the facial and throat muscles. Changes in pitch can be felt in the throat and chest. Even the arch of the eyebrows can give him information. As he perceives, he will imitate and produce. The family's delighted responses will stimulate him to repeat and repeat.

It may be that a baby who has not spontaneously continued vocalizing from the infant stage will need assistance in learning how to blow, to give a prolonged breath or to give many shortened breaths. Parents enjoy teaching children these skills through games and other activities. These skills are fortunately easy to teach and are extremely valuable for speech acquisition. We suggest such activities as: blowing on feathers or bits of tissue; blowing ping-pong balls across a table; learning to prolong the breath as one blows out a paper party whistle and attempts either to hold the end uncurled for a longer and longer time or make many short little unfurlings.

Movements of the articulators are another area that may need specific attention. The early vocalizations are primarily vowels. Some children need help in such seemingly simple activities as closing and opening the lips. The use of the mirror for visual feedback and simple, gentle manipulation of the lips can take place. Such a simple skill as letting the tongue lie flat in the mouth may need practice. You can use the mirror or even place a flat bit of candy on the tongue to give the child the feel of this position. A child may have to learn to play with his tongue, extending it in and out of his mouth, curling it up and down, making it broad and thin or narrow and thick. A full-length mirror in which the child can see himself as well as his parents and siblings who are giving him these patterns to imitate can be much fun and permits view of the total person.

We wish to emphasize again that while these games are being played, important kinesthetic sensations are being experienced. Such games may begin without vocalization, but soon voice should be added, via the auditory channel if possible, via the tactile channel if necessary. But voice must be added at some point for proper proprioceptive feedback. Eventually such imitative games should evolve into lalling practice where the child imitates patterns presented and also imitates himself. Curling the tongue tip up and down evolves into *lu, lu, lu.* Protruding the tongue slightly and then withdrawing it becomes *thu, thu, thu.* All these activities may be more pleasurable and will continue longer if the parent at times imitates the child instead of trying to force the child to always follow the parent's pattern. Throughout this babbling and lalling the baby is developing tactile and kinesthetic sensations and adding them to his already developed phonation and intonation skills.

From the beginning a discrimination between voiceless, voiced, and nasal sounds is important. The earlier the baby learns to discriminate between and to produce *bu, bu, bu,* as opposed to *mu, mu, mu,* and *pu, pu, pu,* the better off he will be for he will have mastered control of his velum. The difference between *pu, pu,* and *bu, bu* can be visually shown through play use of feathers, etc., as described above, but the prolongation of the "m" may be more difficult for the very deaf child. Practicing with a prolonged hum or (m) in the final position may be most useful, and humming is an easy, natural developmental activity that most babies enjoy.

We cannot deal in detail with all the aspects of articulation here. Intensity has been discussed as attached to the basic vocalizations. Rhythm and accent can be presented at that time, and continued on into the babbling and lalling stages. The closer the physical proximity between child and speaker, the better all these aspects will be felt and heard. Primarily we wish to use any and all input systems to stimulate the child to produce these himself, for the production is vital for his complete perception of all that is involved in speech. Berry (1969, p. 50), in summarizing work in this area, states that, "It is the shift in muscular action (accompanied by proprioceptive feedback) from one series of articulatory sequences to the next which governs our ability to perceive language and to repeat what we have comprehended." Proprioceptive feedback is also vital to the other aspects of speech, (intensity, stress, rhythm, phrasing). One cannot help but think here of the work of Brauckmann (1933), Avondino (1929) and Connery (1935) as being visionary. With their insistence on repetitive babblings in varying rhythmic and pitch patterns they were developing kinesthetic feedback and were teaching children to speak through the act of speaking. Again, separate individual aspects of the speech essentials may have to be dealt with in isolation, but all should be integrated and practiced as a whole as soon as possible.

Vocabulary-syntactic Development

As the baby passes through these stages of developing sensory perception and acquiring the essentials of speech, the need for producing a word will become apparent. On the basis of the child's needs and interests, the parents and teacher can choose several words which will have high valence for him. These words should be repeated again and again in meaningful context and with emphasis on the key word until the youngster perceives that this particular combination of phonemes has special significance. The first words are usually those that do not just name the object, but are words of broader function and meaning. They are words that help the child control his environment. *Up, down, open, more, no, no more, all gone, stop, go, hot, fast, ouch* are all morphemes that frequently appear early in the young child's vocabulary. Once he has uttered one of these, albeit imperfectly, there should be an immediate response. Family, teacher, and all concerned must respond with joy and delight to such extent that the child will repeat and repeat until he has acquired spontaneous mastery. An abstraction has been made by the child. A particular utterance has real meaning, has acquired real value. He will use it again and again, and new words will soon be added. He is beginning to control his world through speech.

As these first words emerge, teacher and parents must begin to pay attention to the importance of expanding the initial vocabulary into kernel sentences. Should the child say, "All gone milk," the parent must, as does the parent of the hearing child, accept the expression and also present new forms immediately, i.e., "Oh. Your milk's all gone. You want more milk? Here's more milk." Via the feedback system, the child will perceive that words are put together, and he will begin to do so himself at the proper developmental time. Parents and family must understand that they are an integral part of the feedback link system and must perform that role. There is no room here for the "no-no" form of teaching that says, "Not that, but this." What is needed is sufficient correct input so that the child can formulate his own principles and gradually learn the code of his language. In the case of profoundly deaf children, the use of graphics at an early age may become most important because these children will need a stable visual form for additional information.

Thus the child must grow, from use of the word, to the kernel sentence, to the complete utterance. This process must be accelerated by parent and teacher. All sorts of devices may have to be invented to provide for maximum input and to ensure that language, as well as speech, develops at the appropriate age; but parents who talk and respond are the prime factor.

Two vital questions remain to be discussed: (1) Can a deaf child acquire speech if he is not enabled to follow the developmental sequence outlined above at the proper chronological age? (2) Can the very few children in whom the auditory channel cannot be made to function at all learn to talk? In both instances they can, given intensive training and teaching with much increased attention paid to the visual and tactile input systems. However, they will do this only if the proprioceptive feedback system can be put in motion and if they live in an environment that stimulates and rewards constant oral effort. Unfortunately, their speech in many instances will be very similar to that described by Hudgins and Numbers (1942): arhythmic, monotonal, lacking in rhythm and pitch, and containing poor phrasing. It can be intelligible to small audiences and can be functional. It seldom is pleasing. This chapter is a plea for facilitating for as many as possible the developmental approach, so aptly named by van Uden (1968) the *Maternal Reflective Method.*

As is always the case, research is needed in many areas. Despite the fact that the value of early auditory training is clearly proven, we are a long way from knowing the best type of auditory input for any given child. Equally important is more information concerning both visual and tactile input instruments. However, the most essential need is provision for making the results of research, along with meaningful interpretation, more readily available to parents and teachers. Only as these things take place can we be confident that we are providing the child with the form of neurosensory stimulation that will be most effective in setting his particular speech cycle in motion.

APPENDIX

A case history supportive of Miss New's philosophy shows that very young deaf children can learn to talk through talking, even if they have a severe hearing loss.

Robert (Reynolds) was first seen by the Speech and Hearing Clinic at Eastern Michigan University at the age of 10 months. His parents suspected a hearing loss. The pediatrician was unsure and referred the child for testing. The first evaluation session confirmed the parents' suspicions, although the extent of the loss was not immediately clear. At this time the child vocalized, but the vocalizations were atypical. They were too loud, too high, and too infrequent. Primarily only vowels were uttered. The paucity of consonants affected rhythmic patterns. Although some intonational patterns were present, these were unattractive and contained far less pitch change than normal. The parents were immediately counseled as to the voice level needed to alert Robert, and they were instructed in the value of "naked ear" auditory training. Robert was enrolled in the Parent Counseling Clinic. Hearing aid fitting (two body aids) soon followed. When Robert was 20 months of age the parents began to keep a diary of progress, recording receptive and expressive language, responses to sounds in the environment, and speech production represented in International Phonetic Symbols. Samples of this child's development are presented here along with his audiogram.

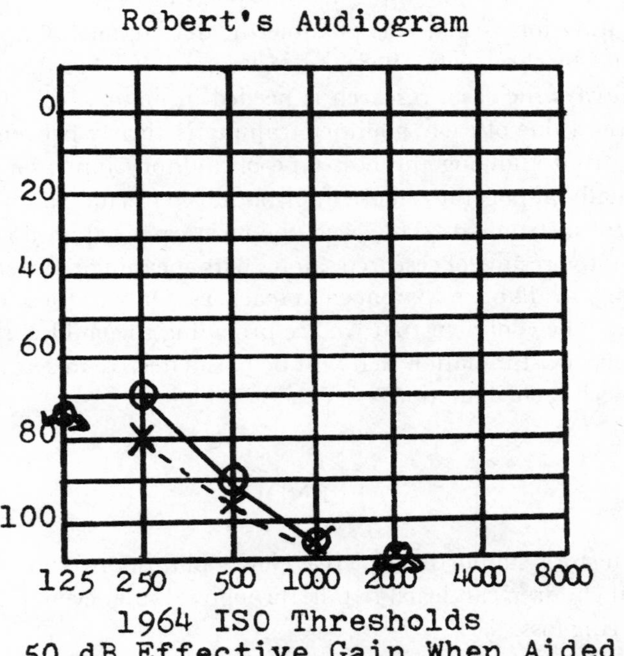

As of Twenty Months:

Expressive Vocabulary in Use:

bye-bye [ba ba]; up [ʌ p], all gone [a: ɔ] more [ba] or [m ɔ]; jump [ʌ p]; round- denoting circular motion [ʊ: ʌ]; rock in chair [ʊ ɔ]; ouch [ɔ pf]; hot - unvoiced [ɔ]

Phonemes in Use:

[a]; [æ]; [ɔ]; [o]; [b]; [p]; [m]; [d]; [f]; [v]; [g]; [k]; [kt]; [j]; [l];

Jargon: Combinations of the above.

Primarily bi-syllabic utterances.

Much use of rising inflection.

Twenty-first Month:

New Expressive Vocabulary:

ball [ba]; banana [balala]; down [ɔun] all gone - g added [ag ɔ]; open [ʌpʌ] fast [fa]; cookie - string of syllables beginning with k [kekaku]; round - shape as well as motion [u ʌ n]; poke [po]; jump - command [um]; walk - command [u ɔ], eye [a]; no [o]

New Phonemes:

[d]; [n]; [ŋ]; [k]; [t]; [r]; [e]; [ɪ]; [i];

Jargon: Much practice with [k]; [g]; and [ŋ]

Tri-syllabic utterances.

Varying inflections

Twenty-second Month:

New Expressive Vocabulary:

hello [ɛ :o]; night-night [aɪ:aɪ]; light [ai]; bear [be]; blanket [blæ]; mama [ama]; bread [be] or [bæ]; bang [ba]; on - opposite of off [ɔ]; bad boy [bæ: b ɔ ɪ]; shoe [eu]; bottle [b ɔ]; blow [blo]; pop - referring to pop beads [p ɔ p]

New Phonemes:

[nj]; [bl]; [ai]

Jargon: Playing with vcv and vcc combinations. [ænja]; [o:gla:o:a]; [ei,pa: ei,pa]

Increased consonantal babbling. Telephone talk in different voice than usual jargon.

Twenty-third Month:

New Expressive Vocabulary:

oh boy [oboi]; off [ɔ f]; strawberry [abe]; juice [ua]; more milk [m ə mɪ]; peach - alternately [pe] and [tiʃ]

New Phonemes:

[ks]; [ʃ], [ʒ]; [tʃ]; [d ʒ]; [θ];

Jargon: Talking in sleep. [ama: ɔ pa: up]

Four syllables commonly used.

Singing with accent on final syllable [a: o:a:o:a:o'ba]; [a:o:a:o:'ba]

Twenty-fourth Month

New Expressive Vocabulary:

go [o]; stop [b ɔ p or ɔp]; bump [bup]; water [a:ua]; what sheep says [baa]; dog says [r ʌ f r ʌ f]; cow says [ma]; shoe [ɛ u]; more [mu]; more bread [m ə bla] or m ə be]; more ice cream [mə baba]; off [baf]; bunny rabbit [baba'bi], hot - now voiced [ɔ]

New Phonemes:

No others noticed.

Jargon: Continues as does singing and talking in sleep. Four and five syllabic utterances common.

Twenty-fifth Month:

New Expressive Vocabulary:

meow [m:aʊ]; flower [au:u]; hello mousie - to toy [eo:mou:ɪ]; uh, uh - for no [ʌ ʌ]; oh oh [ʌ ʔo]; bunny rabbit now four syllables [baba'babe];

New Phonemes:

None noticed.

Jargon: Includes sharp glottal stops. Six syllabic utterances appear.

Twenty-sixth Month:

New Expressive Vocabulary:
cow [au]; fish [fi]; apple [æpu]; open the door [opu]; spoon [pu]; knife [af]; all wet [aʌ] or [aɛ]; dirty - unvoiced [ə]; foot [fu]; two [u:]; one [ba]; three [ɪ]; fly - insect [fæ]; giraffe [daf]; telephone and jello [ɛo:]

New Phonemes:
None noticed. However, initial consonants other than bi-labials appear.

Jargon: Many long phrases. Six syllables are frequent.

Many comments in journal noted that Robert talked all day.

BIBLIOGRAPHY

Avondino, J. *The babbling method.* Washington, D.C.: The Volta Bureau, 1929.

Berry, M. F. *Language disorders of children.* New York: Appleton-Century-Crofts, 1969.

Brauckmann, K. *The conversational ability of the hard-of-hearing.* (Reighard translation), Jena, Germany: Press of Gustav Fischer, 1933.

Bunger, A. M. *Speech reading: Jena method.* Danville, Ill.: Interstate Press, 1952.

Connery, J. M., and Young, I.B. *Voice building.* St. Louis, Mo.: private printing, 1935.

Downs, M. P. Early identification and principles of management. *Proceedings of International Conference on Oral Education of the Deaf.* Washington, D.C.: Alexander Graham Bell Association for the Deaf, 1967, 746–757.

French, S. L. Implications of information theory for speech for the deaf. *Proceedings of International Conference on Oral Education of the Deaf.* Washington, D.C.: Alexander Graham Bell Association for the Deaf, 1967, 614–628.

Gaeth, J. H. *Deafness in childhood.* Nashville, Tenn.: Vanderbilt University Press, 1967. Chapt. 18.

Griffiths, C. *Conquering childhood deafness.* New York: Exposition Press, 1967.

Guberina, P. Verbotonal method and its application to the rehabilitation of the deaf. *Proceedings of the International Congress on Education of the Deaf.* Washington, D.C.: U.S. Government Printing Office, 1964, 279–293.

Hudgins, C. V., and Numbers, F. An investigation of the intelligibility of the speech of the deaf. *Genetic psychology monographs,* 1942, **25,** 289–293.

Krijnen, Br. A. Developing the voices of very young deaf children. *Proceedings of International Conference on Oral Education of the Deaf.* Washington, D.C.: Alexander Graham Bell Association for the Deaf, 1967, 664–671.

Lenneberg, E. H. *Biological foundations of language.* New York: John Wiley and Sons, 1967.

Ling, D. Implications of hearing aid amplification below 300 CPS. *Volta review,* 1964, **66,** 723–729.

New, M. C. Speech for the young deaf child. *Volta review,* 1940, **42,** 592–599.

New, M. C. Speech in our schools for the deaf. *Volta review,* 1949, **51,** 61–64.

Pollack, D. The crucial year: A time to listen. *International audiology,* 1967, **6,** 243–247.

Reynolds, J. A. Assistant Professor of English Language and Literature, Eastern Michigan University, contributed Robert's journal.

van Uden, A. *A world of language for deaf children.* St. Michielsgestel, The Netherlands: The Institute for the Deaf, 1968.

Whetnall, E., and Fry, D. B. *The deaf child.* Springfield, Ill.: Charles C Thomas, 1964.

Wyatt, G. L. *Language learning and communication disorders in children.* New York: The Free Press, 1969.

CHAPTER X

Speech Curriculum

Eleanor Vorce, M.A.

"Curriculum is the educational design of learning experiences for children, youth and adults in school. It is people and their value systems, their beliefs, their philosophy, and their practices regarding education" (Cay, 1966). Applied specifically to speech curriculum, these are the experiences which an educational system must provide its students for the learning and practice of spoken language. Essential to the nature and effectiveness of these experiences is the commitment to and belief in the idea that most deaf individuals can and will learn to acquire functional speech as an effective and habitual means of communication, given adequate and consistent opportunity for the development and practice of skill.

"It [curriculum] is educators and parents working together for the improvement of the educational program" (Cay, 1966). The speech curriculum must be concerned, not only with the student and his learning experiences, but also with an educational plan for parents and others who will consistently influence the student's life.

"The living curriculum is school experiences involving interaction between those who teach and those who learn. As in all enterprises, educational or otherwise, a moving force or personality is necessary to put the design into action. In curriculum the moving force is the classroom teacher. It is in the context of teacher-pupil interaction on a daily basis that life is breathed into a preconceived design we call curriculum" (Cay, 1966). The challenge to the teacher of deaf students is nowhere greater than in the teaching of speech, since the students are "extraordinarily dependent on their teachers for the exact delineation of their linguistic environment" (Hart, 1969), and it is the on-going daily, hourly interaction which energizes the design into a way of life. In this context parents may also be construed as teachers.

"Curriculum includes determining educational goals" (Inlow, 1966), for the way we educate a child ultimately depends on our outlook for him (Silverman, 1968). The development of competency and confidence in the habitual use of good speech as a means of interpersonal communication is the goal of all speech programs. Useful objectives should be stated in terms of behavior or performance, describing what the learner will be *doing* when the objectives have been attained (Mager, 1962). Described in these terms, we should expect our pupils ***to be talking.*** If the goal is habitual use of good speech, the tenuous interrelationships existing between the on-going use of correct speech and the "teaching" of speech (in a specific period set aside for the purpose of developing or practicing some specific aspect of the speech process) must be well delineated and understood by all—by administrators, by classroom and subject matter teachers, by parents, and after-school personnel. Speech as a medium for the exchange of ideas, information, and feelings for all educational and social activities is truly speech as a way of life. By design, the pupils not only acquire the outer manifestations and skills of verbal communication, but through involvement in the process they become interesting individuals with something to talk about.

"Curriculum is translating goals into the substance of learning, the selecting and employing of instructional methods designed to make learning effective or economical" (Inlow, 1966). It also involves the development of processes and materials for achieving the goals (Silverman, 1968). This aspect (e.g., methods of teaching and the selection and sequencing of speech content) have generally comprised the bulk of the speech curriculum, and historically were outlined in specific and arbitrary detail. Recent evidence suggests that speech practices are changing under the influence of current research in psycholinguistics, in acoustic and experimental phonetics, in audiology, and in other related disciplines and that the time expended in international congresses, NDEA workshops, national conferences, and government-sponsored regional and local workshops has been effective.

The final step in the consideration of curriculum building and improvement is "evaluating how well any educational echelon has achieved predetermined goals" (Inlow, 1966). Objective methods of investigation should be employed to establish the basis for modifying, eliminating, or improving our organizational methods and procedures (Silverman, 1968). No evaluative techniques (objective or otherwise) have yet emerged for routine general use in speech programs for the purpose of providing data that will assist us in establishing, eliminating, amending, or modifying our arrangements and practices in teaching speech. Speech evaluation is time-consuming and frequently costly, and consistent routine evaluation is often omitted from the program.

The interrelatedness and interdependence of these aspects of the speech curriculum cannot be overemphasized, for the degree to which we aspire and are committed to the use of speech as a total way of life (our value system) will determine what speech is taught, when it is taught, how it is taught, who teaches it, how students talk, how much they talk, when they talk, to whom they talk, and why they talk. It will determine our evaluative techniques and our satisfactions or dissatisfactions with the end results. It will influence the educational process to include "speech" in the total environment—the classroom, the home, the recreational program. It will concern and be concerned with all those who come in contact with the student.

Speech Curricula—Present Status

"An adequate system for the education of the deaf through secondary school involves programs designed to facilitate language and speech preparation for children, including those as young as one and two years of age" (Education of the Deaf, 1965). This trend for the extension of age to include infants and toddlers at one end of the program and high school students at the other will necessitate change in environment, activities, and methodology in most of the existing speech programs for deaf children. Any program spanning this wide age-range will be concerned with the development, motivation, reinforcement and retention, correction, and expansion of speech at different levels. For speech, as well as other subjects in the total curriculum, we must attempt to introduce a well organized course having large ideas which emerge repeatedly, with cumulative detail devised to develop the ideas in greater depth (Goodlad, 1964).

The area of planning speech curriculum for deaf children is among the most difficult, for, unlike other general areas of study (such as science, social studies, or math where adaptable curricula have been developed and tested on a wide population of hearing children) there has been little or no experimentation in speech content and methodology, and few models exist from which a curriculum might be adapted. Over the years professional journals and conference proceedings have dealt with varying aspects of the speech teaching process. Some have described problems of the speech of the deaf (e.g., voice quality, pitch variations, breath support, durational aspects, abutting consonants, etc.); others have dealt with methodology within educational programs (e.g., speech in the preschool, upper school, etc.) or techniques for the teaching of specific speech concepts (e.g., color coding for breath-voice-nasal concept; Klinghardt Markings or Pike's Intonation notation; speech charts and orthographic systems, etc.); still others have related the teaching of speech to other disciplines (e.g., learning and information theory and audiology). Spectrographic analyses and cinefluorographic studies on small, selected samplings of deaf speech have begun to appear, but no well-controlled studies of deaf speech have been conducted over large populations since the Hudgins-Numbers study of 1942. Only a few books deal with the speech of the deaf and are highly relevant to the planning of speech programs (Ewing and Ewing, 1964; Haycock, 1942; Dale, 1967; Whetnall and Fry, 1964). Speech monographs, demonstrations, and films from this and other countries (Education of the Deaf in Europe and in the U.S. Film Series, U.S. Office of Education; John Tracy Clinic films) are helpful in focusing thought on specific areas of the curriculum.

It remains for the coordinators and teachers of each program, however, to make inferences and effect changes in their own programs. A recent study of speech curricula in schools and programs for the deaf (Vorce, 1970) tabulated 21 responses to questionnaires on this subject.* If the answers in the survey are representative of general speech methods and curricula throughout the United States, there is little indication of agreement, and the range in philosophy and/or methods varies not only from program to program, but often within the programs themselves. Among the 21 responding programs most have written curricula or indicate an "understood sequence or methodology" where it is not written (only two responses were construed to indicate *no* curriculum); most include systematic or routine teaching of speech skills (although speech methods and content vary with the age and individual needs of the children and many indicate that skills "are taught only as needed"); most children of elementary school age have daily speech periods, but at other levels specific daily work is often not provided in the overall plan; most

*Details of the survey are shown in the Appendix A

speech work is group work at least some of the time, with a few programs providing individual tutoring at specific levels; less than half employ special speech teachers (the majority of these being at the upper levels where pupils "rotate" among subjectmatter specialists); no consistent system for planning speech work emerges (some decisions are made jointly by the classroom teacher and the departmental or speech supervisor, others by the teacher or the supervisor without reference to other personnel).

The answers reflect practices in speech programs from a variety of settings, including those where deaf children routinely attend classes with normally hearing children. Since respondents were not asked for rationale, there is nothing to indicate whether these practices are preferences based on philosophical commitment or are arbitrary adjustments to the realities of financial stress and available personnel. It may be significant that programs do vary so greatly, that the range is wide, and that there is sufficient flexibility to make arbitrary and unqualified statements a difficult task.

Another questionnaire (Vorce, 1970) sampled the attitudes of 80 upper and high school deaf students toward their own speech and the speech program. These students attend a metropolitan school for the deaf committed to an oral philosophy and have daily speech classes with speech teachers. The total population sampled included pupils with a wide range of academic and speech abilities.* In general, the pupils' answers indicated a positive attitude toward speech, a desire to improve their speech, and confidence in talking to strangers with a general expectancy of being understood. Most pupils indicated that their speech improved when wearing a hearing aid (although opinion was less than unanimous); most liked their speech classes, even though a small number indicated that classwork did not bring about speech improvement. Nearly all agreed that teachers should correct their speech, but were less enthusiastic about correction from parents. More than half considered their own speech "good," and rated their speech and language abilities equal (which was in agreement with independent ratings of teachers), but most were not realistic in diagnosing their own speech problems. Preferences for tutoring or classroom speech work were nearly equally divided, with some pupils liking a combination. Checks of those areas of the speech program liked best, liked least, and thought most helpful correlated positively.

*See Appendix B

While studies of spontaneous vocalizations of young deaf children have been reported over the years (Sykes, 1940, 4–7-year-olds; Carr, 1953, 5-year-olds; Neas, 1953, 3–4-year-olds; McCarty and Houchins, 1954, 4–5-year-olds; Fort, 1955, 2-year-olds; Lenneberg, Rebelsky and Nicholl, 1965, infants; Mavilya, 1969, 3–4-month-old infants), little is known of the developing phonological system of deaf children as it relates to the syntactic and semantic aspects of language. "Modern linguistics teaches that language is a structured system of arbitrary vocal sounds and sequences of sounds which is used in interpersonal communication and which rather exhaustively catalogs the things, events, and processes of human experiences" (Carroll, 1966). It is this sound system with which linguists are first concerned in the normal development of language, yet few studies concerned with the language of the deaf have dealt with *spoken* language analysis (Simmons and associates from Central Institute) and studies concerned with the speech of the deaf rarely utilize the spontaneous communicative language of the children. Little is known of the assimilative quality of their voluntary speech. What does appear to be emerging from the application of the principles of normal linguistic development to the speech-language process of the deaf is a "new kind" of speech program for the young deaf child. These programs closely resemble that advocated by Groht (1958) and New (1954) at the Lexington School, but have gone further by making application of data only recently compiled from psycholinguistic research. These programs have developed in conjunction with increased interest in the deaf infant, in the beginnings of linguistic research on the speech and language processes of the deaf, and with the improvement and wider use of amplification systems, especially at an early age. The programs are few in number and have existed only in the recent past. While there is as yet no widespread adoption of their philosophy and/or methodology, the limited information available reports effective results with the developing language-speech processes of the young deaf child. It remains for time and continued study to ascertain the long-range effect on the speech and the speech curriculum for older children.

Essentials in Speech Curriculum Planning

Environment. "Throughout language development the child learns what verbal gestural responses will get what he wants or fend off what he dislikes and what responses on the part of others are the cues for what he wants or does not want. He is learning the 'semantics' of language" (Carroll, 1966). Deaf children, too, can learn to manipulate their environments through vocalizations and verbal gestures, and the more consistently their vocal utterances can be patterned into common linguistic sequences with conventional intonation and stress patterns, the more effective the speech will become. The early linguistic environment is, then, one of the most important factors affecting the rate of spoken language development. It is important that verbal experiences be conducted in a meaningful and happy environment, for "when a child is absorbed happily in learning he seems to be a part of what he is discovering. We need to organize environments so that children can't wait to succeed" (*The Learning Child,* 1969). This is no less true of the verbal environment. It may well be that the richness and stimulation of the environment will have greater influence on what the child will learn (even about speech) than the number of repetitions it provides, for the child chooses from his environment those events to which he wants to give his attention (Kagan, 1969). It is essential that the educators and the family plan together for a consistently stimulating environment that will "teach children to love to talk" (Bentzhen and Williams, 1961), where they will find someone to help them talk, and in which they will find speech the natural mode of communication. It is not enough that children acquire a number of vocal skills which they are able to produce on demand; they must have something to talk about and they must be interested in communicating their ideas and feelings to others.

The "large ideas" recurrent in the speech curriculum in its continuum from infancy through high school involve the content for and the extent of speech practice; the sequencing of material and experiences; the degree and kind of ongoing support for the use of speech; and the expectancies at any level. Educators should be aware of the total process and know what has preceded so that they can utilize the cumulative effect of the program. While no curriculum will be able to itemize and specify all that is to be taught at any specific level, guidelines for the above may be found in many areas and should be utilized in planning the total speech curriculum, in planning the speech work for any level, or for setting goals for daily speech practice and expectations.

Curriculum Correlation

Correlation with other aspects of the total curriculum will strengthen the total educational process. Among these, two stand out as essentials within the speech teaching-learning process for the child, and another as an adjunct to the school curriculum.

Speech-Language. It is important not only that speech (especially in its early stages) be considered spoken language, but that the language and speech curricula within any one program agree and be mutually reinforcing. Consistent patterning of complete spoken phrases and sentences as essential to language will permit children to abstract their own rules and construct a more complete and meaningful language system. Application of speech skills to the ongoing language of classroom activities will reinforce and solidify phonological principles within the framework of interpersonal communication.

Use of Hearing. The exercise of the auditory channel is a prerequisite for the acquisition of language, an auditory vocal system. Critically important are the early experiences in the first year of life (Chase, 1969). "The evidence strongly suggests that it is not merely a truism that the critical difficulty for the deaf in learning language is their inability to hear large amounts of language *spoken* . . . the grammatical patterns of printed words cannot express themselves on the mind as in spoken language" (Carroll, 1964). Early amplification and the exploitation of the auditory channel for the intake of language and the monitoring of vocal utterances for the output of language thus becomes a second curriculum corollary: "The problem with the education of the deaf child is essentially in giving him enough listening and speaking experiences so that he can build up a knowledge of the sound system and of the statistics of the language" (Fry, 1963). Opportunities for meaningful listening experiences must be provided, not only during the early years, but as an integrated aspect of all areas of the curriculum.

Parent Education. In the past "speech at any price" has often been considered a commendable goal for a positive speech program. Current research data in the developing phonological systems now indicate that this is no longer necessary or defensible. Emphasis has shifted from speech as an entity that is the goal of oral education, to speech as a mode through which deaf children may be educated more successfully. The importance of the climate in which speech develops and is used and the necessity for consistency within all phases of this climate emerge as crucial. Under optimum conditions (early appropriate amplification, a linguistically stimulating environment, adults who are aware of the emerging speech-language process and who can utilize every opportunity for its enhancement) and at the appropriate age (especially the first two years of life, during which time the normally hearing child is developing his language system) a more nearly complete spoken language system will emerge along with a favorable self-image and pride in learning. Consistency and cooperation in the total environment is the keystone upon which the success of this process depends. A curriculum for parent education in the communication process is desirable.

Inter-disciplinary Cooperation

Information from other disciplines enhances the planning of the content of the speech curriculum and in guiding the judgments that are the continual accompaniment to speech teaching. Educators should seek and incorporate into the curriculum guidelines from other disciplines such information as:

1. Social, Intellectual, Emotional Maturity

While it is entirely possible, even probable, that "work" on a particular speech principle will recur from level to level, at each stage, the activities and expectations must be appropriate to the interests and maturity of the children at that level. Young children, for instance, are interested in and react to the here and now, and speech activities for them must be personal, short in duration, active and concrete in nature. Older children dealing with other aspects of the same principles may generalize, abstract, and apply them to activities or experiences less concrete. Older children should develop responsibility for correct speech habits and for applying the known to new and more difficult speech concepts. While young children are ego-centered and not always motivated by the need of good speech for social life, the social aspects of speech may be emphasized to reinforce speech for older pupils.

2. General Spoken Language Development

Although there is much still to be known about the developing language system in normally hearing children, generalizations such as those listed below are of value to the speech teacher of deaf pupils:

a. Young children learn the stress and intonational patterns of their native language before they master the phonemic content. Fundamental pitch of the voice and meaningful pitch variations are within the hearing range of many young deaf children. We must teach them to listen, and we must aspire to their unconscious use of pitch to convey meaning through their consistent associations in listening to those patterns in their own environment. While it may be necessary to deal with pitch levels more directly at a later stage, it would be more meaningful for the deaf child to learn these through usage at an early age.

b. Early language is usually reflective of the egocentric child (Piaget, 1959) and is often heavily overlaid with emotional content—frequently negative. One-word sentences emerge before connected language. The young deaf child's early vocabulary should reflect these principles.

c. "Vocal production of language is dependent upon the understanding of language/but not vice versa" (Lenneberg, 1962). Parents and educators must be aware of the receptive language level of the child in order to know the level of speech to teach or encourage.

d. Syntactical rules are learned before morphological rules. The varying forms are not acquired simultaneously, but do follow a known sequence (e.g., phonological affixes (/s//z/ or / ə z)) for the third person singular, plurals and possessives are learned in that order and the rules for past tense (/t//d// ə d/) in similar order. Children learn the simple consonant before the syllabic form is used (Berko, 1958). Our expectations for deaf children may not be realistic—and we may not be giving them sufficient practice in processing the material to extract their own rules.

3. Phonetic-Phonemic Development

Norms and sequences, wherever they have been established, should be utilized as relative guides for our teaching, especially for the selection of material for articulation practice. The following are significant:

a. *Articulatory levels:* Seven-year-old children produce nearly all the sounds correctly, with vowels developing more accurately at an earlier age than consonants (even short vowels are accurately developed by age 3). In general, voiceless consonants develop before voiced cognates (Templin, 1959). Experience has shown that determination and practice can produce most of the consonant and vowel sounds even in young deaf children and, given sufficient practice under the surveillance of a skilled and enthusiastic teacher, that they can be articulated correctly in words. With studies such as the above for guidelines, one might question the practice of expecting and practicing for accuracy of phonemic production at an early age, especially when these practices automatically limit vocabulary and linguistic expansion. It is in no way suggested, however, that educators go to the opposite extreme and make no effort for accuracy of articulation. The establishment of realistic goals based on objective data and the pursuance of plans for their consistent development are recommended.

b. *Consonant positions in words:* Consonant production varies with the position in the word or phrase. According to Hall (1963) children of 3–4–5 years of age use sounds in initial positions in words with more accuracy than they use the same sounds in medial or final positions; the ability to produce consonant blends increases with age, but does not keep pace with the acquisition of articulatory skill for single consonant sounds used post-, inter- or pre-vocalically in words; and sound substitution seems to have some phonetic consistency. Teachers of the deaf should be aware of such variations and gauge both their speech practices and their expectancies for accurate speech accordingly.

c. *Rank order of features:* (Menyuk, 1968) While studies applying distinctive features to the developing speech of children are still preliminary, there is some evidence that features for consonants mastered and maintained early appear to be articulatory gestures with clear-cut on-off characteristics (e.g., voice-voiceless; nasal- non nasal etc.) Later consonants have varying degrees of such definition. Voicing and nasality appear to rank high, gravity and diffuseness rank low in feature maintenance. Consonant features ranked in order of use by adult speakers are: nasal, grave, voice, diffuse, continuant, strident. As yet, little attempt has been made to apply distinctive feature analysis to the speech of the deaf. Studies such as Menyuk's are interesting and can suggest comparative guidelines.

d. *Phonemic systems: (Fry, 1968) and Assessment (Beresford and Crady, 1968)* Closely associated with distinctive feature analysis is the suggestion by these authors that the inventory of the child's speech be generalized to ascertain the "system" rather than the number and kinds of errors produced. "The child's language at any stage is not an imperfect version of adult language; it is itself a complete functional system which is capable of expansion. At the phonological level the child begins with a restricted system of two or three units and the framework of the system expands until by the age of about five years or more the child has developed the complete adult system of about 40 units. Development of the phonemic system implies also the development of acoustic cues which are used in both the decoding and the encoding of speech" (Fry, 1968). Little is known of the phonemic system of deaf speakers, and while it may be the task of researchers to extend these studies to the deaf (at least for the present), there are implications for educators and for the planned development, correction, and reinforcement of the phonemes of English in the curriculum.

e. *Sequencing:* In planning for the development of the phonemic repertoire of deaf children it should be remembered that combinations of sounds and the more difficult sounds should follow and be built upon the simple sounds already acquired. (e.g., /t/ and /ʃ/ are usually established before /tʃ/, and /tʃ/ usually precedes /dʒ/).

f. *Sound categories:* Attention should be focused on sound categories rather than on specific phonemes. While this is implied in the studies cited above, it is an important concept for the teacher, for "coarser contrasts appear first" (Leopold, 1966).

g. *Precise Articulation Age:* (Hirsh, 1969) According to Hirsh the precision in the child's speech is a function of his age—a fixed habit does not appear until adolescence. The imprecision in motor behavior causes speech variability so that the normally hearing child does not achieve in individual speech sounds anything resembling a fixed habit before early adolescence. This establishes the target date for precise articulation later than has previously been thought. Since we do not have information regarding the target age for deaf individuals, we must assume that it does not occur earlier than this. It is, therefore, unrealistic to become discouraged or to "give up" when consistency of articulation has not been achieved before this age. Our curricula do not incorporate into their philosophies an expectancy for practice at least equal to that of the hearing child.

4. Acoustic Information

Information from acoustic analysis is valuable in guiding the selection of those aspects of speech which can be emphasized and reinforced through audition. The relative intensity, temporal dimensions, and frequency spectrum of phonemes and morphemes seen in relation to a child's (aided) audiogram should provide additional cues for choices of linguistic samples for classroom use. When it is possible to structure favorably for use of hearing (without limiting linguistic content) it is wise to do so. Useful guides for vocabulary and/or language input include: (Head, 1969)

a. *Phoneme arrangement in order of average length*—longest to shortest: 1) stressed vowels 2) unstressed vowels 3) voiceless continuants 4) voiced continuants 5) voiced plosives 6) voiceless plosives 7) voiced stops 8) voiceless stops

b. *Effect of consonant environment on vowels:* 1) power greater when between voiced consonants or nasals than between voiceless consonants 2) nasals provide greater power for the contained vowel than is the corresponding voice homophenous sounds.

c. *Effect of syllable accent on power of vowel:* the vowel in an accented syllable has three or four times as much phonetic power as one in an unaccented syllable.

5. Interaction with other Disciplines

Contributions from specialists in the behavioral and scientific fields (including those of early childhood, elementary and secondary curriculum) should facilitate planning for motivation and enhance the appropriateness of the content and experience.

Interaction with other areas of the curriculum will both strengthen the use of speech and give to the content area an additional "conversational" dimension when pupils are able to discuss their interests with others. For example:

A recent upper school social studies project involved an investigation of pollution which included excursions into many areas of the community. The culmination of the project was a class-made movie which traced a discarded piece of paper from the time it left the classroom to its final disposal in a large city incinerator. In the process of the project many opportunities arose for the enhancement of spoken language (e.g., new vocabulary needed to be studied for pronunciation; the language of film-making arose and was used in discussion; oral reports from newspaper clippings emphasized syntactic and semantic aspects of speech; interviews with employees of the various areas visited gave practice in using the language of the project as well as in building confidence in asking questions of and conversing with strangers; the knowledge gained and the ability to talk about it put these pupils in the mainstream of current topical conversation. The social studies teacher had many opportunities to "correct" and implement spoken language and to increase speech vocabulary within the framework of a social studies unit.

These opportunities for application of speech principles and abilities occur continuously and it is their consistent use that establishes speech as a way of life rather than as an exercise.

6. Group *vs.* Individual Teaching

At any level the decision for group or individual speech work must be made on the basis of the pupils' age and maturity as well as the nature of the specific material being presented.

Certain processes and problems lend themselves more readily to individual work (e.g., correction of individual speech problems) while others may be more effectively learned in social situations (e.g., dramatization applying speech principles). The degree to which electronic visual and tactual instrumentation (e.g., Visible Speech, S-Indicator, Pitch-Period Indicator, etc.) can be utilized in the curriculum will both determine and be determined by the availability of individual speech tutoring and/or the teachers' skill in using these displays for group practice.

7. Speech Intelligibility

Judgments must be made and priorities assigned in correcting or patterning the speech of the deaf and in setting the model (the teacher's own speech).

Studies of speech intelligibility give priorities to consonant articulation, rhythm and phrasing (Hudgins and Numbers, 1942), time dimensions (Fry, 1964) and to pitch variations.

8. Methods of Development

While speech may best be taught to deaf pupils by methods generally paralleling normal speech development, it is simplistic to expect full competency without the careful guidance and intervention of skilled teachers.

Approximations must not be continued indefinitely, plans must be made for the development of more precision in articulation. It is essential that teachers know when additional practice is needed and how to provide for it and that the methodology is consistent with the philosophy of the entire educational program. Speech curricula can provide guidelines for the "what" and the "how" more efficiently than the "when".

9. Evaluative Procedures and Techniques

Since educators and curriculum builders readily agree that routine objective assessment and diagnostic techniques are necessary for the evaluation of progress and for the planning of individual programs in all areas of the curriculum, it then follows that evaluative procedures and techniques appropriate to the varying age levels should be built into the speech curriculum. Ongoing diagnostic teaching is also an essential to speech correction within the framework of communicative spoken language.

As has been suggested earlier, a system for generalizing either the abilities or the difficulties of individual children and of groups of children should provide the teacher with guides for teaching. Rating scales may be utilized to indicate profiles in which the child's speech abilities in intelligibility, rhythm and phrasing, breath control and voice quality can be seen at a glance. Together with articulation tests for specific phonemic abilities and general cumulative notations of the teacher (Greatest Improvement This Year; Greatest Problems This Year) they form the basis for future planning. Audio taping at regular intervals provides longitudinal records of individual speech which is of value in assessing programs as well as individual progress.

10. Motor Aspects of Speech

While the explanation of how man learns to generate original sentences cannot be fully provided by the associative connection between muscular responses and physical stimuli (Bruner, 1961), the motor aspects of speech must not be ignored.

In acquiring speech some of the most intricate classes of motor learning are involved, usually without conscious intervention. Speech is a "comprehensive set of motor gestures" acquired through the auditory pathways in the first years of life (Chase, 1969).

In the beginning stages it may be desirable to recapitulate or enhance the babbling stage, for at this time the child perfects the motor skill necessary for all speech by building up a permanent memory store of various kinds of motor experiences (Whetnall and Fry, 1964).

"The most important aspect of this activity, however, is that during babbling a child develops the circuitry which links auditory feedback and auditory memory with proprioception and kinesthetic memory" (Fry, 1968).

Important factors in the infant's ability to develop sensorimotor coordination are voluntary movement and accompanying sensory feedback (Held, 1968).

"Speech sounds are not put together like letters; articulation is not simple sequences of movement where each movement is the invariant representative of one 'standard' sound. Programming the muscles for the utterances of sentences requires knowledge of all the rules that are required for completion of that sentence. There is an active interplay between muscular activity, articulatory movement, production of speech sounds, of morphemes, words, syntactic categories and sentence constituents" (Lenneberg, 1968).

While repetitions of meaningless syllables (drills) will not produce speech, it is possible that when the motor system has not been "programmed" to perform some of the necessary activities for the production of speech, special practice may be needed.

Need for Research

As has been noted, objective study of the speech of the deaf has only recently begun and the samplings are as yet small in number and scope. As a result, existing curricula for teaching speech to the deaf have been based upon experiences in widely different settings—hence they vary greatly. The relationship between the resulting speech and any particular curriculum is not yet known. With the advent of infant programs, the application of linguistic studies to the language and speech development of the deaf and of a general expansion and enrichment of the total academic curriculum, a renewed interest in speech development has emerged and the need for further data seems imperative. The following kinds of research study are suggested as being vital to the ongoing process of speech teaching:

1. Present status

Status studies (both qualitative and quantitative) of speech of the deaf should be conducted over a large population and wide age range, with implications for phonemic development and for identifying critical aspects.

2. Speech as Language

Studies of spontaneous spoken language to give insight into the developing language system of the deaf child and to indicate the degree to which the syntactical and semantic aspects of the language of deaf speakers influence the phonological system, both for the development of phonemic levels and for the assessment of the prosodic and assimilative features of speech.

3. Diagnostic Testing

The development of objective techniques for the assessment of speech of the deaf.

4. Voice Quality

A large-scale investigation of the voices of deaf speakers with implications for the development or retention of pleasant appropriate voice quality.

5. Instrumentation
Studies leading to the practical application of instrumentation, including optimum age levels for their use. Speech laboratories have only recently begun to be a function of educational programs for the deaf.

6. Individualizing Instruction
Development of self-monitored and/or programmed work for individual and independent speech work.

7. Causal Factors
An investigation of causal factors together with strategies for reversal of what Rosenstein has described as "lack of improvement with age."

8. Longitudinal Studies
Longitudinal studies of the speech of deaf children from infancy through later years with emphasis on maintenance of linguistic competencies accrued from early intervention in infant programs.

9. Professional Preparation
Improved instruction for speech teaching at the professional preparation level which will enable all classroom teachers to be more effective in enhancing the speech of the deaf at all levels.

10. Sensory Modalities
Further investigations into the role of the sensory modalities and sensory integration in the development of spoken language in the deaf child.

Summary

It is possible that the knowledge of spoken language development in the normally hearing child and the past experiences in teaching speech to the deaf child can be combined to indicate optimum methodology and guidelines in the curriculum for teaching speech to the deaf. It is probable, however, that no curriculum will be able to provide precise information that can universally be applied at a given level. As reflected in the 1970 questionnaires, speech principles are extracted for practice as needed for individuals at any level rather than as detailed by the curriculum.

While speech and language processes must not be grossly dichotomized in our educational curricula, it will be necessary to provide a plan for specific speech practice and/or development of specific aspects of speech that will lead to independence in the learning and use of "good" speech. Awareness of current research and application of this knowledge to the individual within the broad framework of the speech curriculum, planning to avoid known difficulties and to enhance strengths is the responsibility of educators of deaf children. As the chief motivating force in translating the values and goals of the curriculum into action and experiences with the child, the teacher must be well informed, skilled in the application of her knowledge, and committed to her assignment, for we must be sure that the spoken language of the student keeps pace with the social, intellectual, and emotional growth of the students. A consistent philosophy among all areas of the educational and social program is crucial, as is the complete cooperation and consistency of all those responsible for the environment of deaf pupils.

APPENDIX

Tabulation of questionnaires sent to schools and educational programs.

Table I. Geographical Distribution

Number	Type of School	Location
6	Large residential school	Eastern Pennsylvania Northern California Iowa New York State Utah New Jersey
7	Large Public Day School	Boston, Mass. Cleveland, Ohio Los Angeles, Calif. New York City Washington, D.C. Highland Hts., Ohio Montreal, Quebec.
6	Private Residential-Day schools	Northampton, Mass. Portland, Oregon Mystic, Conn. St. Louis, Mo. University City, Mo. New York City
2	Day Classes	Ida, Michigan Las Vegas, Nevada

Table II

	Yes	No	No Ans.
1. Do you have a written curriculum?	15	6	
2. Is your speech always taught in groups?	1		
individually	4		
combinations of above	16		
3. Do your pupils have daily speech periods?	11	8	
2 qualified answers			
4. Who decides the content for speech work?			
Teacher	4		3
Department sup.	1		
Speech supervisor	1		
Combinations of above	12		
5. How are speech skills taught?			
Formally	17		
Only indirectly	2		
Only as needed	1		
6. Do you have a speech supervisor?	9	12	
7. Do you have routine evaluation?	9	9	3
8. What kinds of tests do you use?			
Standard Artic. Tests	3	17	1
"Your own" Artic. Tests	8	12	1
9. Do you routinely tape your children's speech?	6	14	1
Do you use audio tape?	6		
Do you use video tape?	2		
10. On what do you principally rely for speech correction and reinforcement?			
Printed or written form	15		
Oral-aural patterning	6		

Table III. Table III Indicates Those Aspects of Speech Receiving "Routine" Attention and Those That Are Taught Only as Needed.

Speech	Routinely Taught	Taught Only as Needed
Monitoring of voice	15	6
Development of pleasant voice quality	16	5
Development of appropriate pitch levels	13	6
Development of suitable rhythm	19	2
Development of appropriate accent and stress	18	3
Pronunciation of new or difficult words	18	3
Development of conventional intonation patterns	17	3
Improving the rate of speech	16	5
Practice for special speech motor skills	14	7
Improved breath control for speech	14	7
Articulation of Consonants and Vowels	19	2
Orthographic system used consistently in program	18	2

Table IV

Aspect of Speech	Rank (Median)	Range
Development of pleasant voice quality	3	1–8
Articulation of consonant sounds	3	1–7
Articulation of vowel sounds	3	1–6
Orthographic system	4	1–13
Appropriate pronunciation	4	1–10
Monitoring of voice	6	1–13
Development of suitable rhythm	6	1–13
Conventional intonation patterns	6	1–12
Improvement of breath control	6	1–11
Appropriate stress and accent	7	1–10
Suitable variety in pitch levels	8/9	1–13
Improve rate of speaking	9	3–13
Practice for speech motor skills	11/12	1/13

Table IV indicates the median rank order of priority given to 13 arbitrarily selected aspects of speech and the range of the individual ranking. The exceedingly wide range is especially interesting.

Additional Comments:

1. "We do not 'teach' anything per se but rather create an atmosphere in which an attitude where both use of hearing and speech is of prime importance. For the most part the initial speech development is an on-going part of the teacher's daily involvement."
2. "We look on speech as an attitude rather than a methodology."
3. "No formal work 4–8. Primary follows normal linguistic development. Feed in normal language, ask for vocalizing, babbling, jargon with inflection, intonation, rhythm and on to more precise articulation, depending on the level."
4. "Age and ability determine the aspects of speech to be taught and the manner and setting in which it is taught. There are priorities at different levels."
5. "Sustained motivation, both for teachers and pupils is necessary."
6. "Daily maintenance drill on basic speech skills, syllable drills, reference words, phrases, expressions incorporate key skills as daily warm-ups."
7. "Saturate with written material as early as possible. Establish language which in turn should really precipitate spontaneous speech."
8. "Singing at all levels is helpful, using teacher-made songs and appropriate commonly used songs."
9. "Use any and all—that which works for the particular child and teacher."
10. "We have moved away from pronunciation stress to include rhythm and accent and intonation."
11. "We have been using the oral-aural linguistic approach with approximation of sounds and only a limited amount of speech skill work as required within the material. We have recently decided to add a formal speech period for 3–8 range and are writing a developmental sequence into the curriculum."
12. "Our weakest suite is speech."
13. "All schools should evaluate speech programs."
14. "Suggested materials, equipment and activities for speech practice included: assemblies with skits and plays; audio flashcards and tape recorders; teacher-prepared phonic work and therapy materials; dictionary work; speech notebooks for individual basis; speech lab; playground games, chants, and songs of normal school children; rhythm bands; speech through rhythm and movement."

Perhaps the most interesting in the above is the complete diversity of opinion and practice.

PUPIL QUESTIONNAIRES
(Total number 80)

Table I

	Yes	No	Some-times	No Ans.	Other
1. Do you like to talk?	76	4			
2. Do you talk to your friends?	72	5	3		
3. Do you talk to your parents?	70	9	1		
4. Do you talk to people whom you do not know well?	46	22	9	3	
5. Do you think speech is important?	72	8			
6. Would you like to improve your speech?	69	7	3	1	
7. Are you ever afraid to talk to strangers?	6	64	10		
8. Do people usually understand you when you talk to them?	47	8	25		
9. Do they understand you better when you wear a hearing aid?	46	27	7		
10. Do you like your speech class?	59	16	5		
11. Do you think your speech class helps your speech?	52	24	4		
12. Do you like to have your teachers correct your speech?	72	5	3		
13. Do you like to have your parents correct your speech?	60	12	8		
14. Do you think you have good speech? (* don't know 6 fair 2)	45	12	12	3	8*

Table II. Pupils' and Teachers' Ratings of Language-Speech Quality

Pupils' Ratings of Their Own Speech		Teachers' Ratings				
		Agree	Language is better	Speech is better	Language & Speech the same	Not rated
Speech is better than language	9	1	1	—	3	4
Language is better than speech	18	8	—	—	1	9
Speech and language are about the same	53	23	5	2		23

Table III

Rank	Best liked	Least liked	Most helpful	Rank
1	Pronunciation of new or difficult words	Accent and Stress	Pronunciation of new or difficult words	1
2	Voice work	Songs & Singing	Developing pitch levels	2
3	Developing pitch levels	Work on common phrases	Voice work	3
4	Listening for Speech improvement	Poetry reading	Articulation	4
5	Articulation and Dramatics	Dramatics	Poetry reading	5
6	Work on common phrases	Articulation	Listening for Improvement	6
7	Poetry reading	Developing pitch levels	Songs and Singing	7
8	Songs and Singing	Voice work	Dramatics, Phrases Accent and Stress	8
9	Accent and Stress	Listening for Improvement		

Table indicates pupils' preferences for an arbitrary selection of speech principles according to those liked best, liked least, and those thought most helpful. Pupils' answers have been combined and ranked on the basis of number.

Table IV. Years in Attendance at This School

Under 5	less than one	8	36 pupils
	less than two	9	
	less than three	13	
	less than four	4	
	less than five	2	
Five to Ten years in the present school			15
More than ten years in present school			28
Intermittent attendance in present school			1

BIBLIOGRAPHY

Bentzen, Ole, and Williams. Speech development in hard of hearing children. In H. Huizing (Ed.), *Proceedings of 2nd International Course in Paedo-Audiology.* The Netherlands: Gronigen University, 1961.

Beresford, R., and Grady, P. Some aspects of assessment. *The British journal of communication disorders,* 1968, **3,** 28–35.

Berko, J. The child's learning of English morphology. *Word,* 1958, **14,** 150–177.

Bruner, J. *On knowing, essays for the left hand.* New York: Atheneum, 1966; Cambridge: Harvard University Press, 1962.

Carroll, J. *Language and thought.* Englewood Cliffs, N.J.: Prentice-Hall, 1964.

Carroll, J. Language development in children. In S. Saporta (Ed.), *Psycholinguistics.* New York: Holt, Rinehart and Winston, 1966.

Cay, D. *Curriculum: design for living.* Indianapolis: Bobbs-Merrill, 1966.

Chase, R. Sensory feedback, the family, society. *Horace Mann Symposium, The World of Learning and Deafness.* Boston, Mass., 1969.

Dale, D. *Deaf children at home and at school.* London: University of London Press, 1967.

Education of the Deaf, a report to the Secretary of Health, Education and Welfare by his Advisory Committee on the Education of the Deaf. Washington, D.C.: U.S. Dept. of H.E.W., 1965.

Ewing, A. W. G., and Ewing, E. C. *Teaching deaf children to talk.* Washington, D.C.: The Volta Bureau, 1964.

Fry, D. B. Speech. *Report of the Proceedings of the International Congress on Education of the Deaf.* Washington, D.C.: U.S. Government Printing Office, 1964, 183–191.

Fry, D. B. The phonemic system in children's speech. *British journal of communication disorders,* 1968, **3,** 13–19.

Goodlad, J. *School curriculum reform in the United States.* New York: The Fund for Advancement of Education, 1964.

Groht, M. *Natural language for deaf children.* Washington, D.C.: Alexander Graham Bell Association for the Deaf, 1958.

Hall, W. A study of articulatory skills in children from three to six years of age. *Speech Monographs.* Columbia: University of Missouri, August 1963.

Hart, B. Comments by an educator of the deaf. *Verbal behavior of the deaf child: studies of word meanings and associations.* New York: Teachers College Press, 1969.

Haycock, G. S. *The teaching of speech.* Washington, D.C.: The Volta Bureau, 1942.

Head, J. Teaching guide (adapted from Hoops, Ladefogged, Singh and others). New York: Lexington School for the Deaf, 1969 (unpublished).

Held, R. Experiments in how we learn to coordinate. *Mental Health Program Reports—2,* HEW Public Health Service, Feb. 1968.

Hirsh, I. Precision of articulation. *International Education of the Hearing Impaired Film Series,* Programs in U.S. Washington, D.C.: Office of Education, H.R.E. Project, 1969.

Hudgins, C. V., and Numbers, F. C. An investigation of the intelligibility of the speech of the deaf. *Genetic psychology monographs,* 1942, **25,** 289–392.

Inlow, Gail. *The emergent in curriculum.* New York: John Wiley and Sons, 1966.

Kagan, J. Child development, the family, society. *Horace Mann Symposium, The World of Learning and Deafness.* Boston, Mass., 1969.

The learning child. Englewood Cliffs, N.J. Learning Materials Division, Responsive Environment Corporation.

Lenneberg, E. Prerequisites for language acquisition. *Proceedings of International Conference on Oral Education of the Deaf.* Washington, D.C.: Alexander Graham Bell Association for the Deaf, 1967, 1302–1362.

Leopold, W. Patterning in children's language learning. In S. Saporta (Ed.), *Psycholinguistics.* New York: Holt, Rinehart & Winston, 1966.

Mager, R. *Preparing objectives for programmed instruction.* San Francisco: Fearon Publishers, 1962.

Menyuk, P. The role of distinctive features in children's acquisitions of phonology. *Journal of speech and hearing research,* 1968, **11,** 138–146.

New, M. The deaf child's speech vocabulary. *Volta review,* 1954, **56,** 105–108.

Piaget, J. *The language and thought of children.* New York: Humanities Press, 1959.

Silverman, S. R. Some thoughts on curriculum improvement. Curriculum: Cognition and Content, *Volta review,* 1968, **70,** 372–375.

Simmons, A. A. Teaching aural language. *Volta review,* 1968, **70,** 26–30.

Simmons, A. A. Audio-lingual approach to the teaching of very young children. Workshop, New York, 1969.

Templin, M. *Certain language skills in children: Their development and interrelationships.* Minneapolis: University of Minnesota Press, 1957.

Whetnall, E., and Fry, D. B. *The deaf child.* London: William Heinemann Medical Books, Ltd., 1964.

CHAPTER XI

Techniques of Teaching

Marjorie E. Magner, M.E.D.

Recognizing that the auditory modality is of primary importance in the development of speech in hearing children, it is necessary in this discussion of techniques in teaching deaf children to talk, that emphasis be placed upon a multisensory approach. An appreciation of the psychological as well as the physiological development of children also must be a vital concern. Although the teaching of speech to the deaf is essentially a matter of teaching motor skills (Hudgins and Numbers, 1942), psychological factors, including the attitudes of the children, of members of their families, and of their teachers, are fundamental to the adequate achievement of those skills.

The techniques in teaching speech must be geared to meet the particular needs of the individual child. Numerous variables affect the development of speech including type and extent of the hearing impairment, cause, and age of onset of deafness, as well as many of the same social, intellectual, physical, and emotional problems that cause delayed and faulty speech in hearing children.

A survey of the literature indicates that the speech of the deaf cannot be categorized as a singular process or pattern of vocalization (DiCarlo, 1964). Deaf students exhibit wide variations in the degree of intelligibility. Large numbers of the deaf population today can and do speak intelligibly, but techniques in teaching speech must continue to be improved if deaf citizens are to assume their full roles in modern society. Every deaf person should be given an opportunity to acquire oral communication skills and should be helped to gain a feeling of security in utilizing speech as a means of conveying his ideas to the minds of those who hear it, which as Haycock has noted is the chief purpose of speech (Haycock, 1933).

Special techniques are required in a program designed to help deaf children develop speech in both informal situations and in more formalized analytic lessons. The skills of the instructors and their experiences in utilizing techniques of teaching contribute greatly to the degrees of success in which the deaf person learns to talk. The attitudes of the teachers and their abilities to offer a consistent and continuous program are equally important. The child's teachers, parents, and associates must recognize the intrinsic fact that successful achievement of speech depends as much upon the consistent and continuous functional use of speech as upon the particular techniques utilized to help children to develop skills needed to articulate words and thoughts orally.

An informal approach to speech should be introduced as early as possible in the child's life and should never be terminated. The child's natural vocalizations and speech approximations should be encouraged, and emphasis should be placed upon spontaneous, natural, meaningful oral communication. The time when more formal or analytic techniques in teaching should begin varies according to the readiness and needs of the individual child. Educators of the deaf are not in complete agreement as to the specific time when more structured, analytic techniques should begin. This discrepancy is due to the fact that some children exhibit the readiness to understand and benefit from a carefully planned analytic program in the early primary years; other children do not appear to be ready until they reach the upper primary level; and still others continue to indicate a poor speech readiness level when they reach the intermediate grades. When a child is able to understand speech through his hearing and sight, when he indicates a desire to communicate to the extent that he vocalizes, and attempts to approximate words spontaneously and meaningfully, he can then begin to benefit from more structured teaching techniques in an analytic speech program (Ewing and Ewing, 1964). It appears that the extent and effectiveness of the techniques utilized in the informal approach often have as much or more influence upon the time when children are prepared to begin an analytic speech program as do the physical and other innate characteristics of individual deaf children.

The two general approaches, the informal and the analytic, each require techniques of teaching consistent with the approach. Skilled professional instructors are required in pursuing special teaching procedures in both approaches. Along the informal avenue of teaching, the instructor must place as much emphasis upon guiding the parents of deaf children, especially at the preschool level, as upon teaching the child himself. Along the more structured, analytic road the emphasis of the teacher must be placed directly upon helping the child establish goals and acquire skills for developing, improving, and utilizing his speech as a communication tool.

Excellent techniques in the informal approach in helping deaf children develop and use speech are being utilized in preschool centers throughout the world. Those units that are parent-centered, however, are especially valuable. In such programs children can reap continuous benefit at home as well as in school (Ewing, 1958, Rotter, 1961, Simmons, 1966, Harris, 1964, Luterman, 1967). Parents of deaf children must be given assistance in acquiring techniques which will help them learn to talk effectively with their deaf children. They must be guided in the important task of establishing a rich oral environment in their homes. They must be given guidance in where they can seek medical, audiological, and special educational assistance. They must be guided in learning techniques to help their children utilize their remnants of hearing to the maximum, along with their sight for perceiving speech. They must be given guidance in providing their children with opportunities to participate socially and to assume reasonable responsibilities in daily family and community activities. As children hear and see meaningful sentences which relate to them spoken within their immediate interest range and feel the interaction of communication in their homes, they gradually develop a desire to understand and participate in oral communication. Through their experimental vocalizations and approximated speech children begin to attempt to express their own feelings and thoughts orally in a functional manner.

The importance of introducing functional sentences before deaf children are expected to perceive selected, isolated words is emphasized in the literature and must be taken into consideration in the techniques of teaching. Research studies have proven that speech perception, that is, the understanding of speech through a multisensory approach, language development, and the production of intelligible speech are substantially influenced by the meaningful expression and rhythmic movement of the whole thought. Hudgins, the Ewings, and others have stressed in their studies that sentences are easier to lipread than are single words, and that auditory cues, even when only faintly perceptible, have a positive influence upon the student's ability to perceive speech. The utilization of the child's remnant of hearing, regardless of how limited, combined with his sight, have proved to be of greater value in speech perception than the use of either lipreading alone or of hearing alone (Ewing, 1954, Hudgins, 1934). Simmons has noted in her studies that one hears, speaks, and responds to language in totality. Certain words which she terms "function words" can never be taught in isolation for they take on meaning only as they relate to other words or serve to structure the sentence (Simmons, 1968). Hudgins emphasized that the speech mechanism as a whole influences the production of speech as much as, and in fact more than, the accuracy of the articulation or movement of each component of speech (Hudgins and Numbers, 1942).

Parents' Role

Guiding parents along the informal road of the speech program requires skill and flexibility if their own individual needs and the needs of their children are to be met adequately. Conferences with teachers and other professional staff members, observations of teaching techniques through one-way vision mirrors, discussions with other parents, attending lectures and films, and the dissemination of appropriate literature are procedures that are being successfully utilized today. Probably the most effective techniques are those in which the parents can gain information and self-confidence through a) practice in talking, playing, and working with their own children under skillful professional guidance and b) participation in a planned guidance program wherein they can learn through their own experimentation and evaluation (Ewing, 1956). The technique of utilizing a one-way vision mirror in a sound-treated booth for the purpose of giving parents experience in lipreading with and without benefit of sound has proved effective.

Through actual experimentation parents discover for themselves that: a) Simple sentences are easier to lipread and/or hear than are single words. b) Words of two or more syllables are easier to understand than are monosyllabic words. c) Lipreading is less difficult when one can see something concrete that is being discussed. d) Proper lighting and auditory clues, no matter how limited, influence one's ability to lipread speech (Ewing, 1964).

The utilization of audio and video tape recorders offers parents as well as teachers objective means of acquiring effective techniques in communication. The use of these recorders gives parents opportunities to gain through experience a better appreciation of the extent and limitations of the child's hearing aid and other amplifying equipment. Often parents discover through video recordings that gross exaggerations, over-articulations, and other strange mannerisms which their children appear to be developing in their speech, are the result of imitation of abnormalities in their own speech patterns which can often be easily corrected. By playing back the audio tape of speech that is recorded when spoken at various distances from the microphone—approximately six inches, one foot, and six or eight feet, one can discover for himself the importance of speaking within a few inches of the microphone and utilizing a pleasant clear voice quality and normal speech rhythm patterns. Parents should be encouraged to put on and wear their child's hearing aid for brief periods so as to experience ways in which they can help their children care for and use the instruments most effectively as an aid to speech.

At this stage of the child's development the techniques of teaching must continue to be informal and should be similar to those used in guiding hearing children to develop and use speech. No effort should be made to "teach" the child a particular sound, to "force" him to give or to repeat a sound, or to "correct" a specific sound or word.

The deaf child must be an integral part of the daily activities of his family and preschool program. His parents, preschool teachers, and other associates, including his hearing peers, must utilize meaningful natural speech during informal situations throughout each day and expect him to participate as an active, responsible member of the family and school. They must recognize and encourage the child's own vocalizations by personal and positive attention. The satisfaction that the deaf child enjoys kinesthetically and auditorily from his vocalizations, plus the pleasure and encouragement that he receives from the effect that his vocalizations and attempts to communicate have upon others, bring positive and favorable results. In this way deaf children develop an interest in expressing their thoughts orally, and gradually begin to make an initial effort to approximate meaningful words and phrases to express their thoughts in a natural rhythmic flow of voice and breath. The child's environment must continue to provide him with constant opportunities for the reception and expression of functional, spontaneous oral conversation that offer him personal satisfaction and stimulation. The techniques which the child, his parents, and his teachers acquire for the promotion of spontaneous oral expression of language must never be terminated or neglected as the child moves along the informal road and on throughout the entire speech program.

Introducing the Structured Approach

Structured, analytic teaching techniques are introduced when a deaf child has indicated an interest in expressing his thoughts orally and has begun to approximate meaningful words and phrases spontaneously in an effort to express his thought in a rhythmic flow of breath and voice. The informal and the analytic approaches move along simultaneously. The two general systems can be alluded to as parallel avenues which converge gradually into a major thoroughfare of intelligible speech.

Teachers must listen to and analyze the child's approximated spontaneous speech. Limitations and problems in the child's ability to produce speech need to be detected and studied. Then, carefully planned, systematic techniques must be utilized to help the child develop special skills which will improve specific areas of his speech production. As the child is guided along the parallel roads of speech development, all aspects of speech must be included if the roads are to merge into a free flow of spontaneous, fluent, intelligible speech. Deaf students must be helped to acquire skill in appreciating and utilizing techniques for developing and improving the three general aspects of their speech production: *voice quality* (intensity, pitch, resonance, breath and voice control, intonation), *articulation* (vowel sounds; voiced, breath, and nasal-voice consonants which function to release or arrest a syllable, abutting consonants, consonant blends or compound consonants, syllabification, and accent), *rhythm* (rate of syllable utterance, breath and voice control, phrasing, accentuation, and emphasis).

Physical and social readiness, together with the child's need to develop a particular skill for the production of better speech, are factors which must determine the specific analytic work which is presented at any given point. Special care must be taken to select and explain to the pupil according to his need, understanding, and ability the particular speech problem and ways in which to solve the difficulty. Only a single problem involving one of the three general aspects of speech should be introduced or called to a child's attention at any given time. The pupil must be helped to understand the aim of the lesson and the techniques for reaching the desired goal. The instructor must be able to establish good rapport with the child. He must be encouraging, systematic, and honest in his effort to help him. The periods of work must be meaningful, relatively short, and as frequent as possible. Young children benefit more from two or more short speech sessions daily than from a single period of longer duration. Children need to be held to their best efforts, and to feel the importance of and responsibility for improving each area of speech. The instruction must be consistent and the program must be continuous if good results are to be realized.

Adding Phonetic Orthography

A phonetic system of orthography must be established and followed throughout the program. Northampton Consonant and Vowel charts, Thorndike's markings, Webster's markings, International Teaching Alphabet, and other phonic systems have been used with varying degrees of success throughout school programs. It appears that continuity of the use of the technique rather than the system itself has the stronger influence upon the extent in which children are able to succeed in any particular phonetic system. Cooperating teachers must utilize a single phonetic system, follow similar general techniques of approach, utilize systematic means of improving speech, and encourage and expect deaf children and adults to utilize speech as the functional tool for communication. In this discussion the Northampton Charts will be utilized whenever there is a need to use phonetic reference.

When a child achieves reasonable success in a particular area of any of the three aspects of speech, it must be reinforced through further practice in the analytic program. Then, the pupil must be encouraged to apply that newly developed skill in his spontaneous speech. This procedure is applicable throughout the analytic approach.

Each of the fundamental aspects of speech—*voice, articulation,* and *speech rhythm*—need to be considered independently in this discussion of techniques in teaching. Pupils must be helped to improve one of these areas of speech at a time, but it is recognized that all three aspects must overlap and fuse in order for speech to be intelligible.

Pleasant Voice Quality Essential

A pleasant *voice* can sometimes be established satisfactorily through the informal approach to speech, but most deaf pupils require special work in this area at some point in their lives. Children sometimes develop pleasant, clear voices with satisfactory pitch and resonant qualities when they are young, but unfortunately the quality of their voices occasionally deteriorates as the result of strain, health factors, faulty teaching, and other causes. It is essential that the child's instructor possess a keen ear which is sensitive to fine shades of differences in vocal tones. The teacher must be able to detect almost imperceptibly any note of strain, abnormal pitch variations, problems of resonance, intensity, and intonation. Specific work must be done to relieve the problem and to help the child understand how he might improve the particular area of speech in question (Haycock, 1933).

Correct habits of breathing and control of breath along with appropriate use of resonators (chest, larynx, pharynx, nasal chambers, mouth, and sinuses of the head) for reinforcement of vocal tones are essential to adequate voice production (Eisenson, 1965, Haycock, 1933). Speech breathing exercises prepared by Dr. C. V. Hudgins have proven to be of special value in helping profoundly deaf children improve the quality of their voices. It is recommended that the literature explaining his recommendations be studied in detail and applied in classrooms in schools for the deaf (Hudgins, 1937).

Undue tension must be avoided when the pupil is developing speech breathing skills. Games appropriate to the age and interests of the child have proven effective. For example, the instructor and child using the tips of their fingers might hold a large colorful balloon. The balloon should be held approximately one or two inches from the teacher's mouth and placed so that the child can view her face. As the instructor babbles freely, the child can see her lips move, feel the vibration of the balloon with his fingers and listen to her voice through his hearing aid. The child should be encouraged to babble using a variety of syllables and levels of pitch, as he feels his own voice cause the balloon to vibrate. His hearing aid should, of course, be utilized to the maximum extent. This technique has served to help children improve the intensity of their voices, to hold a steady pitch with a sustained vowel, to improve speech breathing skills, and to begin to group syllables utilizing a variety of rhythm patterns. Creative teachers have utilized sound-level-meters and numerous other vibrating and visual aids in similar ways most effectively.

A piece of string or the drawing of straight line on the blackboard can be utilized to help children realize that in speech breathing the inhalation must be quick and the exhalation extended. The child should be directed to take a breath. Then, as he or the instructor begins to move along the line he should be encouraged to produce voice on a single exhalation. Through this simple technique he can practice giving an open vowel, a series of syllables, a series of groups of syllables, and eventually meaningful phrases and full sentences on a single slow breath exhalation. Visual aids ranging from the simple feather and strip of paper to the use of audio-video tape recordings, pitch indicators, spectrographs, and others can be utilized effectively by skilled, creative teachers as they develop and apply techniques for helping students to improve their voices.

Pitch and intonation patterns can be indicated through visual aids, but if the child is able to perceive sound in the speech range, the hearing aid will be the most valuable immediate and continuous tool. Stories wherein pitch can be dramatized are often effective. For example, in the child's story of *The Three Bears,* the voice of each bear can be given dramatically and reinforced throughout the story. Teachers have utilized musical instruments, measuring rods, stair steps, and other devices as they apply techniques in helping children gain an understanding of pitch differences.

To help children develop and improve the resonance in their speech requires that the teacher have a very keen ear for speech as well as being able to utilize techniques for teaching. Special methods that are recommended to be used with hearing children should be studied and applied when believed to be appropriate. Valuable information concerning the production and correction of speech in hearing children can be acquired by studying the texts of numerous authorities who have successfully developed techniques for improving speech. In addition, instructors of the deaf should familiarize themselves with the work in the area of voice production and quality that is included in the literature prepared by educators of the deaf and researchers in the field of audiology and speech of the deaf.

Children who have minor problems of resonance often can be helped through special exercises for controlling the breath, the tongue, and the muscles of the soft palate. Frequently the improvement of the articulation of the nasal consonant sounds *m, n* and *ng* within the syllable is required. The duration of those nasal-voiced sounds when serving as the releasing and arresting function of syllables, and when functioning to join two syllables influences greatly the resonating quality of the voice. For example, the stopping of voice and breath between the article and noun *a man* should be discouraged. The child should be required to arrest the first unaccented syllable with the consonant *m* and continue it into the accented second syllable in the function of a releasing nasal voice consonant. In the words *some men,* the arresting *m* in *some* must continue to resonate and smoothly release the second syllable or word *men.* Thus, the consonant *m* must be one continuous resonating movement serving as the arresting and releasing functions of the two syllables. It is important that children develop the habit of lengthening the nasal sounds giving an adequate amount of resonance. The practice of giving *m, n* and *ng* reasonable duration in connected speech must be continuously reinforced.

When students exhibit minor problems of excessive use of resonance, it often helps to encourage them to lower the pitch of their voices. The muscular act of doing this sometimes causes the back of the tongue to separate from the soft palate. The greater opening makes it possible for air to be expelled through the mouth rather than directly into the nasal passages. Holding the child's hand or a visual aid in front of his mouth so that he can feel his breath as he produces whispered vowel sounds is helpful. The child should then be encouraged to produce voice while permitting some breath to escape through the mouth. It is essential that children be helped to gain a kinesthetic appreciation as to how to keep the voice and breath from going up into the nasal chambers. Syllable drills in which vowels are released and arrested by breath consonants is a technique that has proven helpful. For example: fa(r) f fa(r)f. A variety of breath consonants and vowel sounds should be utilized in this practice. The use of the aspirate *h-* which is the breath formation of the vowel which immediately follows it is helpful for some children in solving their problem of excessive nasality. Writing the vowel with broken lines to indicate breath, and with firm lines to note voice, is often beneficial in helping children to understand this technique. For example:

a(r) a(r) ha(r)

ee ee hee

Throughout all informal and analytic speech work, pleasant vocalizations should be accepted and responded to immediately. Poor vocal productions should be ignored in so far as possible. Honest and sincere encouragement in a positive direction on the part of the instructor is essential in helping the student recognize and gain an appreciation of the auditory and kinesthetic patterns needed to produce a good voice quality.

Articulation

Techniques for developing and improving *articulation*, the second aspect of speech in this discussion, require skillful listening, analyzing, and teaching. Consonants and vowels must always be associated in the manner in which they appear in normal speech, and must be taught as vital parts of an integrated whole. Although the formation of vowels and consonant sounds must be taken into consideration, the syllable is the indivisible speech unit (Numbers, M.E., 1942). Every syllable must contain a vowel, but it need not contain a consonant. It is possible, however, for a syllable to contain as many as three consonants functioning to release it and three consonants functioning to arrest it, as in the monosyllabic word, *splints*. The omission or faulty articulation of any of the numerous complicated motor skills required to produce a syllable or a group of syllables affect the intelligibility of speech. In a study of the speech of the deaf, Hudgins and Numbers noted that consonants are of greater importance than vowels in determining speech intelligibility. They found seven general types of consonant errors including: 1. non-functioning of releasing consonants; 2. non-functioning of arresting consonants; 3. failure to distinguish between surd and sonant consonants; 4. consonant substitution; 5. malarticulation of abutting consonants; 6. malarticulation of compound consonants; 7. excessive nasality (Hudgins and Numbers, 1942).

Specific techniques which might be utilized in any one area of articulation are numerous and the application of each varies with the child, the instructor, and the situation. It is essential, however, that the child be required to try to improve only one articulation problem at any given time. A number of techniques will be described in this discussion to exemplify procedures for resolving a common articulation problem. Continuity as well as the use of specific techniques will be taken into consideration.

When a child indicates that he cannot produce a syllable with a releasing consonant *k* or *c* in his spontaneous speech, he must be given special help in the analytic program to enable him to develop and use the sound. The instructor should call the child's attention to meaningful words and simple syllables in which the sound of *k* functions as a releasing consonant, i.e., *c*ar, *c*ow, *k*ey. If the child is unable to articulate the sound naturally, his attention must be called to the normal, unexaggerated production of the sound as it releases into the vowel. The teacher's production must be clear and natural. Over-articulation should be avoided. Neither the teacher's mouth as she produces the syllable, nor the child's mouth as he imitates the syllable, should ever be opened wider than to allow one finger to be inserted between the upper and lower teeth.

Should the child's attempts to imitate the sound fail, the instructor might refer to other releasing consonant plosive sounds in syllables that are familiar to the child. She might then work through the use of analogy of the articulation of these sounds, such as: pa(r), ta(r), ka(r); or po͝o, to͝o ko͝o or pee, tee, kee. It should be noted here that the formation of the lips in these syllables is influenced by the vowels. When presenting the syllable ko͝o, for example, the lips should be slightly rounded for the vowel *o͝o* before the consonant *k* is released into that vowel. When the mid to back section of the tongue makes a brief contact with the roof of the mouth in the area at which the hard and soft palate join, the lips assume the formation needed for the vowel before the tongue releases, causing a plosion of breath into the vowel. The vowel itself affects the specific point of contact of the tongue and palate. Because the consonant is a movement, the lips must not assume any exact single formation for that consonant, but rather should serve to complete the smooth releasing function of the consonant as a part of the movement into the vowel. The use of a mirror, video tape recorders, and television have sometimes proved helpful in the utilization of further techniques of imitation and analogy.

Some children are better able to understand the technique of producing a releasing *k* sound through the use of a personalized diagram. As the child stands in front of a blackboard the teacher might dramatically draw his profile. The instructor might suggest that the child stick out his tongue as she draws around his nose and mouth so that the diagram shows the tongue protruding beyond the front teeth. This movement adds humor and also establishes the child's comprehension of the drawing. Then the teacher should erase the tongue and draw the tongue in the formation of the consonant *t* before it releases into the vowel. She should write the vowel in front of the lips. The child should then be encouraged to say the syllable, *ta(r)*. When he can do this successfully, the teacher should erase the tongue marking again and draw the formation of the *k* before it releases into the vowel. Here

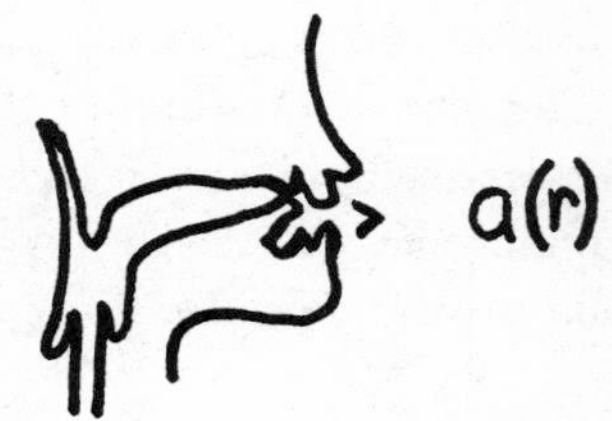

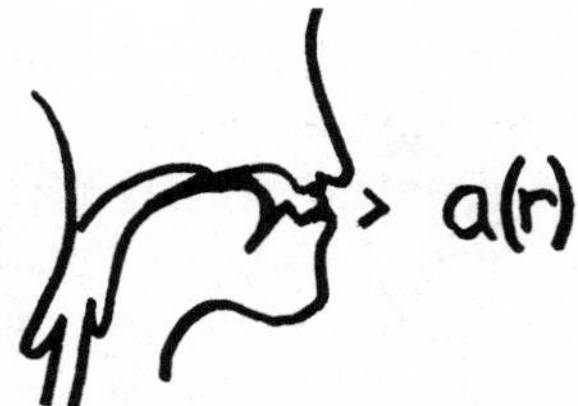

again she should write the vowel before the lips. The child should be reminded if necessary that his lips must not be more than the distance of one finger apart. Special care must be given to avoid a strained plosive sound causing a throaty cough.

A technique of using the fingers to exemply the "flick" movement in the front of the tongue for the releasing *t* and back part of the tongue for the releasing *k* was developed by the Ewings. It has brought successful results in innumerable cases. It is recommended that the reader refer directly to the text prepared by the Ewings for a complete description of this technique (Ewing, 1964).

If the child is able to give the nasal voice sounds in syllables it is sometimes possible to help him learn to produce the releasing *k* by utilizing such syllable practice as:

a(r)m ——— pa(r) o'om ——— po'o eem ——— pee
a(r)n ——— ta(r) o'on ——— to'o een ——— tee
a(r)ng ——— ka(r) o'ong ——— ko'o eeng ——— kee

The use of a very small lollipop or tongue blade stick that has been soaked overnight in a sugar water solution to make it more palatable might be used as a last resort. The teacher and child seated before a large mirror should take time to examine their manipulators (lollipop or sweetened tongue blade). The teacher then should encourage the child to watch and imitate her as she says ta(r), ta(r), ta(r). She then should carefully place the manipulator on the very tip of *her* tongue and close her jaw easily so that her teeth are nearly touching the tongue blade. Then she and the child should place *his* tongue manipulator on the *tip* of his tongue in the same way. With the manipulator holding the tip of the child's tongue down, the teacher should proceed to give good strong clear syllables using a releasing consonant *t* as: ta(r), ta(r), ta(r). The child should be encouraged to imitate this, but the tip of his tongue should be securely held down with the manipulator. His effort to give a releasing consonant *t* should force the mid to back section of his tongue to rise. A quick plosive sound should result as contact is made with the palate, thus causing a releasing *k* into a syllable ka(r). Each successful attempt should be awarded with an expression of pleasure on the part of the teacher so that the child can realize what he is doing and can recognize the kinesthetic sensation when the releasing consonant *k* is produced correctly. Gradually the child should be encouraged to produce the sound without the manipulator. He must be given further practice in producing this sound in syllables and words. When a child has learned to give the *k* sound in a variety of syllables, his teacher and members of his family must help him learn to apply it. Only his best functional usage of that sound should be accepted. No longer should he be permitted to omit or use a careless, approximated releasing *k* sound in his spontaneous speech.

When the child is able to produce the releasing consonant sound, he is then introduced to the arresting *k*. He must be taught to produce the *k* as an arresting function in two ways. First, he must learn to follow the arresting consonant movement with a quick, voiceless expulsion of breath such as a(r)k as it is given in normal speech as the end of a thought phrase. Then he must be taught to arrest the syllable by utilizing the same consonant movement but holding the breath rather than producing a breath plosive immediately following the *k;* such as a(r)k o͝ok. This second technique is required for the smooth articulation of consonant blends within syllables and in abutting consonants within groups of syllables used in connected speech. For example, the consonant blend in the word boo*ks* requires that the breath of the *k* be given through the *s* rather than immediately after the *k;* in the word *fact* the *c* or arresting consonant *k* is formed, but the expulsion of breath follows the *t;* in the phrase, *a black cat,* the breath is held as the consonant arrests the first syllable and is expelled through the releasing consonant in the word *cat;* similarly in the phrase, *a black dog,* the breath in the consonant *k* is expelled through the syllable or monosyllabic word *dog* rather than immediately following the *k* in the syllable *black.* Practice in the articulation of nonsense syllables, such as: a(r)k, o͝ok, eek, wherein the child is required to hold the arresting air plosion, is sometimes helpful. Excessive practice in giving isolated syllables wherein breath is not released naturally through the following sound or syllable, however, has been known to cause the child to "swallow" the *k* and develop poor articulation habits which later require correction. Children often find it easier to acquire the technique of holding the plosion when their attention is called to specific meaningful examples. The child must be given further practice and encouragement until he can use the consonant *k* to serve as the releasing or arresting function of the syllable in his spontaneous speech.

The child has now reached the point in the analytic program where he is ready to begin to learn techniques for articulating blends with *k* as both releasing and arresting functions of the syllable. These include combinations of two or three consonants, each of which has its own identity, but fuses with the other consonants to serve as a releasing or arresting function in the syllable, such as *cr*eam, *scr*eam, mi*lk*, mil*ked*.

The pupil must always be helped to realize his problem and to understand how he can solve it. He himself must be held responsible, but he must be guided one step at a time and encouraged all the way. Never should the child be subjected to lengthy sessions in which the teacher repeats the sound again and again. It is the pupil rather than the teacher who should receive the practice and reinforcement. From the moment that the child has acquired the ability to use the sound, he must be required to utilize it in his speech functionally and to the best of his ability. As each articulation need is noted, the child must be given special, consistent help. Appropriate techniques can be utilized similar to those discussed in the development of the consonant *k* as it functions in fluent speech. Each technique requires initiative, judgment, and perseverance on the part of the teacher.

Speech Rhythm

Speech rhythm, the third fundamental aspect of speech, contributes as much to the intelligibility of speech as do the two other aspects in this discussion, and requires skillful techniques of teaching. Speech rhythm is a specific form of rhythm and is dependent upon a high degree of coordination between the several parts which make up the speech mechanism. The rate of syllable utterance, proper grouping, accentuating, and phrasing of syllables are basic components of speech rhythm. Musical rhythm patterns are different from speech rhythm patterns. Deaf children should not be deprived the knowledge and pleasure of musical rhythms, but the learning of those rhythms appears to be of little or no value in speech (Hudgins and Numbers, 1942).

Poetry should be included in speech work. Deaf children, as well as hearing pupils, can gain much from the use of poetry to express feeling in words. The extended use of poetry as a technique in teaching speech rhythm at any level in a school program, however, is questionable. When poetry is utilized in a speech program, the aim of the lesson should be upon the development and improvement of some aspect of speech rather than upon the literary analysis or memory of a particular poem.

Along the informal spontaneous road of speech development pupils must be encouraged to speak at a reasonable rate of speech and to use natural groupings of syllables. Like their hearing peers, deaf children imitate and use the speech rhythm patterns that they perceive through their sight and remnants of hearing. Teachers and parents must continually set good patterns by speaking naturally and fluently to their children.

The use of audio tape recordings of library books at the reading and interest level of children has proved to be a valuable technique in this area of speech development. Recordings should be carefully prepared by adult readers. In the beginning, children should be required to follow the printed page noting the speaker's phrasing and pausing throughout the stories. Later, children should learn to follow the print with their eyes alone as they listen to the amplified, recorded speech. Gradually children begin to read orally along with the reader and attempt to imitate the speech rhythm as they read and speak independently.

From the beginning, children should be encouraged to speak two or more syllables on a single breath exhalation and utilize natural accentuation of syllables. For example, the child should be encouraged to say the word *mother* in his approximated speech as a whole with stress upon the first syllable as soon as he begins to vocalize it meaningfully. Later, should analytic work be needed to help the child develop or improve sounds within that word, specific help should be given utilizing techniques previously discussed as part of aspects of articulation. Immediately following the work on articulation, the whole word *mother* with accent on the first of the two syllable beats should be presented again. The child should be expected to utilize the rhythm pattern and produce the word as a whole. The child should not be permitted to lengthen the second syllable or to place equal stress on the two syllables.

The familiar technique of clapping loudly for the accented syllable and softly for the unaccented syllable frequently leads to punchy, arrhythmic speech. The act of clapping softly for the unaccented syllables tends to decrease intensity of voice but often allows the same duration of time to be given to those syllables as to the accented syllables. By clapping only on the accented syllable some children have shown marked improvement in the rate of utterance, duration of vowel within single syllables, intensity, and pitch of unaccented syllables. The lengthening of the unstressed beat in words and phrases must be avoided even at the cost of affecting the articulation of the consonant and vowel components of that word. Articles and other meaningful but unstressed utterances must be fused with releasing and arresting consonant sounds of the accented syllable or word rather than be treated as isolated beats. For example, in the words *a man,* the unaccented syllable has a quick beat which moves and blends into the accented syllable. The article *a* must not be separated by an inhalation of breath, exhalation or extended duration of time. The child must be helped to say: ŭ mán.

Grouping of syllables for analytic practice is a technique that can offer valuable dividends, but it is important that children be helped to associate this practice work with functional speech. As an example, one might begin by utilizing two syllables. The child must be encouraged to speak two syllables on a single exhalation of breath:

dá(r)	dă(r)
dŭ-	dá(r)
dá(r)	dŭ-

Meaningful words should be associated with this practice from the beginning such as:

básebáll	footbáll
tŏdáy	ă mán
Móthĕr	báby̆

Gradually groups of three and four syllables should be introduced and practiced. From the beginning, the child must be taught to inhale quickly and quietly, using good speech breathing patterns. He must avoid taking an excessive amount of breath, but he must have enough breath to produce the number of syllables within the group. Children should be encouraged to suggest words and phrases illustrating the following rhythm patterns:

fŭ- fŭ- fá(r)	ă bă̆llóon	ĭn ă bóx
fŭ- fá(r) fŭ-	tŏmórrŏw̆	ă báby̆
fá(r) fŭ- fŭ-	yéstĕrdăy	Wáshĭngtŏn
fŭ- fŭ́- fá(r) fŭ- fá(r)	thĕ Ŭnítĕd Státes	ĭn ă cómĭc bóok
fŭ- fá(r) fŭ- fŭ- fá(r)	ă tríp tŏ thĕ móon	the náme ŏf thĕ gáme

Rules for grouping syllables and phrasing speech which Haycock lists in his text have proved helpful to teachers in this area of work (Haycock, 1933). In addition to phrasing or grouping of syllables, children should be taught that they can stress a syllable in three ways: 1) by slightly lifting the pitch, 2) by slightly lengthening the vowel of the syllable, and 3) by extending the length of the syllable.

As accent gives prominence to a syllable in subordination to other syllables, emphasis gives prominence to one word in subordination to other words in much the same manner (Haycock, 1933). Changes of duration in the time given to the production of speech sounds and the time intervals between phrases, allow the speaker to show feeling and to emphasize and subordinate meaning (Eisenson, 1965). Because emphasis requires understanding of the thought or situation, it cannot be learned mechanically. Special work must be given in helping children to understand that words which are important and those that express differences must be emphasized. Children must be taught that words can be stressed just as syllables can be accented by lengthening, intensifying, lifting the pitch level of the voice, and briefly pausing immediately after the emphasized word is given.

The utilization of the child's remnant of hearing to help him gain an appreciation of speech rhythm and in reinforcing his use of normal speech patterns is of utmost importance. Auditory cues, visual and tactile references associated with the pupil's understanding of the goals to be achieved, continue to be basic factors in the techniques of teaching speech rhythm as well as in other aspects of speech.

Summary

In summary, techniques in teaching deaf children must be founded on a multisensory approach and be based upon the psychological and physiological growth and development of children. They should follow as closely as possible the linguistic developmental patterns of hearing children. The child's parents, teachers, and peers must share in establishing an environment wherein the child might gain a desire and receive adequate practice in the utilization of speech as his chief means of communication.

Two general avenues of approach are recommended in teaching deaf children to talk. Both avenues require skilled, professional teachers and special techniques appropriate to the approach. The first avenue is informal and continues from the time when deafness is suspected in a child throughout his life. The second avenue, a structured, analytic approach, is begun when the child is equipped to understand and to give his full cooperation. The avenues parallel each other as techniques are presented to help the children develop and improve their skills in each of the three fundamental complex aspects of speech—*voice, articulation,* and *speech rhythm.*

The techniques in teaching speech must be geared to meet the particular needs of individual children at specific times and under widely varying circumstances. Skilled instructors who are experienced in utilizing techniques in all areas of a speech program can help deaf students develop speech. The utilization of intelligible fluent speech and the achievement of a feeling of security in the functional use of oral communication skills continue to be the responsibility of the deaf person and his associates.

BIBLIOGRAPHY

DiCarlo, L. M. *The deaf.* Englewood Cliffs, N.J.: Prentice-Hall, 1964.

Eisenson, J. *The improvement of voice and diction.* New York: Macmillan Company, 1965.

Ewing, A. W. G. (Ed.) *Educational guidance and the deaf child.* Manchester, England: Manchester University Press, 1957.

Ewing, A. W. G., and Ewing, E. C. *Teaching deaf children to talk.* Washington, D.C.: The Volta Bureau, 1964.

Ewing, E. C. Some psychological variables in the training of young deaf children. *Volta review,* 1963, **65,** 68–73.

Ewing, I. R., and Ewing, A. W. G. *New opportunities for deaf children.* London: C. Tinling & Company, Ltd., 1958.

Ewing, I. R., and Ewing, A. W. G. Speech and the deaf child. *Volta review,* 1954, **56,** 222–223.

Green, M. C. L. *The voice and its disorders.* Aylesbury, Bucks, England: Hazell Watson and Viney, Ltd., 1964.

Harris, G. M. For parents of very young deaf children. *Volta review,* 1964, **66,** 19–26.

Haycock, G. S. *The teaching of speech.* Stoke-on-Kent, England: Hill & Ainsworth, Ltd., 1933.

Hudgins, C. V. A comparison of deaf and normal hearing subjects in the production of motor rhythms. *Proceedings of the 38th Meeting of the Convention of American Instructors of the Deaf,* Senate Document No. 66, 85th Congress, 1st session. Washington, D.C.: Government Printing Office, 1958.

Hudgins, C. V. A comparative study of the speech coordination of deaf and normal subjects. *Journal of genetic psychology,* 1934, **44,** 3–48.

Hudgins, C. V. Speech breathing and speech intelligibility. *Volta review,* 1946, **48,** 642–644.

Hudgins, C. V. Voice production and breath control in the speech of the deaf. *American annals of the deaf,* 1937, **82,** 338–363.

Hudgins, C. V., and Numbers, F. C. An investigation of the intelligibility of the speech of the deaf. *Genetic psychology monographs,* 1942, **25,** 289–392.

Luterman, D. A parent-oriented nursery program for preschool deaf children. *Volta review,* 1967, **69,** 515–520.

Numbers, M. E. The place of elements teaching in speech development: Is the cart before the horse? *Volta review,* 1942, **44,** 261–265.
Rotter, P. The parents' role in encouraging speech growth. *Volta review,* 1961, **63,** 12–15; 46.
Simmons, A. A. Language growth for the pre-nursery deaf child. *Volta review,* 1966, **68,** 201–205.
Simmons, A. A. Teaching aural language. *Volta review,* 1968, **70,** 26–30.
Stone, L. J., and Church, J. *Childhood and adolescence.* New York: Random House, 1968.
Van Riper, C. *Speech correction.* Englewood Cliffs, N.J.: Prentice-Hall, 1954.
Van Riper, C., and Irwin, J. V. *Voice articulation.* Englewood Cliffs, N.J.: Prentice-Hall, 1958.
Yale, C. A. *Formation and development of elementary English sounds.* Northampton, Mass.: The Clarke School for the Deaf, 1929.

CHAPTER XII

The Relationship of Speechreading and Speech

PAULINE M. JENSON, PH.D.

Speech and speechreading may be viewed as complements: the encoding and decoding of spoken messages. Such a view, however, is somewhat simplistic, since speechreading involves much more than the decoding of speech-motor configurations. It suggests a visual process by which congenitally, profoundly deaf persons learn to decode messages by combining clues from their environment, the sender, and language itself.

The Need for Operational Definitions

Research has shown that in addition to these variables, the ability of the receiver is a significant factor acting upon the quality of the spoken message (O'Neill and Oyer, 1961). The oral receptive language experience of an eight-year-old congenitally deaf child differs considerably from that which confronts an eight-year-old recently become deaf. One child has a vast store of heard language from which to make trial and error deductions and inferences concerning spoken messages. For the congenitally deaf child, speechreading is, instead, a developing language process (Costello, 1957).

Historically termed lipreading, speechreading has also been called visual hearing and visual communication. The former suggests that the visual receptive language process is similar to the acoustic one; the latter suggests a full range of visual communication systems, including manual types. Indiscriminate use and interchange of terms impedes the development of a taxonomy and operational definitions for the unique set of tasks involved in the oral education of congenitally deaf persons.

Lipreading, which developed as an aid to the hard of hearing, best suggests the extraction of speech-motor behaviors from those highly integrated sensory and perceptual processes called upon by all persons for oral communication purposes. This isolation of a part from the whole for practice purposes is a basic teaching strategy which implies that gains as a result of practice will ultimately contribute to increased efficiency in the unrestricted processing of all information available in the original stimulus item, the spoken word.

Like teachers, researchers also isolate parts from the whole, but for different purposes. In-depth studies and the intractable nature of research designs require that the speech-motor aspects of speechreading be studied in isolation. Findings, then, contribute to basic knowledge of certain of the characteristics and properties of an isolated visual process; they do not apply directly to the teaching situation, nor can they be intelligently considered or used without informed interpretation. And here lies a dilemma current in all of education, a lack of persons knowledgeable in both teaching and research to recommend classroom applications of research findings.

Many concerned with the education of profoundly deaf persons have noted the limitations of speechreading as a comprehensive language system, inferring from research findings with hearing subjects that fewer than 50 percent of English speech sounds are available on the lips. From this stems the generalization that less than 50 percent of all spoken messages are available to the speechreader, without consideration of his additional sensory capacities or life experiences.

Linguists and speech scientists have shown that spoken messages are comprised of far more clues than the sum of the individual phonemes composing each word (Miller, 1951; Jakobson, Halle, and Fant, 1952). In speechreading, as in reading, the gestalt or sum of all the variables establishes for the reader the content of the message. In purely visual terms, a speechreader processes situational clues, kinesic information (the body language of posture and the supportive gestures of face and upper extremeties), time features, and emphases, in addition to the entire range and redundant combinations of articulatory gesture. All these visual elements and others not yet known or herein stated, combined with the most limited auditory information—stress and rhythmic patterns—provide the profoundly deaf child with far more information than critics of speechreading have identified.

Schools for the deaf include speechreading in the concept of aural-oral communication, considering it a natural complement to the input of amplified speech. It has not been customary, however, to isolate its various aspects for practice purposes. This is unfortunate, as speechreading is known to be learned behavior. It has been aptly described as a successive discrimination task (Brehman, 1965). Research has consistently shown that discrimination tasks produce practice effects (Mussen, 1960). Many oral deaf adults testify to the value of speechreading practice regimens, enrolling in adult lipreading classes for the purpose of improving their speechreading skills. The longstanding misconception that speechreading is an art and therefore not responsive to formal instruction has deprived large numbers of congenitally deaf people of the opportunity to practice the receptive language skill most useful in their communication with hearing persons. For in spite of the fact that it is not formally taught in schools for the deaf, it becomes for many deaf adults their primary symbol system (Myklebust, 1964).

Descriptions, Properties, and Characteristics

Whether the deaf infant is born to deaf or hearing parents, he is heavily dependent on his visual system to carry information necessary to his survival and comfort. Prelingually deaf children very early come to employ gross visual cues for gaining information about their environment. Some never learn or are too late made aware of the correspondences between their own articulatory movements and the message-bearing movements on the lips of others.

Alich has identified 11 "optically seizable mark-like shapes of movements of the speech organs" which he termed kinemes. He proposed that these shapes correspond to phonemes in their "capacity as bearers of lingual elements," and pointed out that opening and closing, rounding and narrowing the lips are "lingual optic characteristics" that must be discriminated (Alich, 1967).

In a study using hard of hearing and hearing adults, Brannon and Kodman investigated the experimental variables of visibility of selected PB words, word frequency defined by Thorndike counts, degree of vertical mouth opening, and values assigned to phonetic units. Only one interrelation was significant, that of visibility and vertical mouth opening. They concluded that the total-movement of the word is the best cue a lipreader has (Brannon and Kodman, 1959).

Seeking to define the units of visual perception active in oral-visual communication, Woodward and Barber tested perceptual differences among English initial consonants. Stimuli were presented to university undergraduates by means of a silent film. Analysis revealed only four visually contrastive units:

Unit I	p,b,m	bi-labial
Unit II	W,w,r	rounded bi-labial
Unit III	f,v	labio-dental
Unit IV	t,d,n,l	and all other non-labials

Members of each unit were homophenous to the hearing subjects taking part in the experiment (Woodward and Barber, 1960).

In a study of visually perceived consonant confusions, Fisher determined ten mutually exclusive consonant groupings which he called visemes. Five groups resulted from confusions of initial consonants, five from final consonants. Fisher concluded that the results of his test, administered to hearing college students, supported the linguistic groupings of Woodward and Barber, rather than classical listings (Fisher, 1968).

In a study to determine the visibility of English sounds, teachers on the staff of a lipreading project gave scrupulous attention to the formation and evidence of each sound. A chart of Visibility Values for the Sounds of English was established and each sound placed into one of four categories:

1.00 represents .75 to 1.00 (perfect visibility)
.75 represents .50 to .75
.50 represents .25 to .50
.00 represents .00 to .25

Visibility values for each sound in a sentence were recorded and the percentage visibility of the sentence derived by formula. Minimum acceptable visibility for useful practice sentences was set at 65%.

Experiments using trained and untrained lipreaders were conducted to determine the reliability of the visibility values. Findings revealed that the correlation between computed and observed visibility was directly proportional to the amount of lipreading training (American Hearing Society, 1943).

Interestingly, teachers' ratings of visibility designated /th/ as perfectly visible to trained lipreaders, while researchers found it is not differentiated by hearing adults. This discrepancy suggests that visibility values differ as a function of the training of the receiver. Teachers of the deaf, by exaggerating tongue and lip movements, may be strengthening the perceptual characteristics of some speech sounds, making them more readily identifiable by deaf persons, even in normally delivered conversational speech. The possibility that other such discrepancies exist between deaf and hearing groups is implied in Myklebust's statement that the "deaf person is dependent on visual cues which are irrelevant when hearing is normal" (Myklebust, 1964).

Current summaries of the literature in speechreading as it applies to school-age deaf children are contained in studies by researchers in education of the deaf (Simmons, 1959; Guilfoyle, 1968). These studies investigate the psycho-social and cognitive variables in speechreading. The discussion which follows will be directed to prerequisites for speechreading in preschool and infancy. We shall see that these may continue to be lacking in some children throughout their school life.

Examining Prerequisites for Speechreading

In a pioneering study which followed the development of speechreading in a profoundly deaf child of 14 months, timed samples were made of the number and duration of the child's eye contacts with the therapist's face. Mean duration of contact was compared with mean number of speaker utterances delivered in the same time periods. From the data, an estimate of visual linguistic input was derived (Mulholland, 1967).

Forty-five orally trained profoundly deaf children were examined in a study of the effects of age, distance, and practice on their visual discrimination and response to articulatory movement. The children, ranging in age from 3 to 12 years, were equally proficient in processing nonsense syllables at three teaching distances. In addition, the expected practice effect was found. A hearing sample, matched except for a simulated nonhearing condition, revealed poorly developed visual discrimination for speech-motor movement. Even at 11 years of age, hearing subjects' performance was inferior to the 3-to 5-year-old deaf group (Jenson, 1969).

In this orally trained sample of deaf children, screened for normal visual acuity, some important prerequisites for speechreading had been developed. They could use deferred imitation as a response mode and as a learning strategy, suggesting they had already completed earlier stages of discrimination, differentiation, and direct imitation.

Piaget has identified six stages of imitation, closely approximating his sensory motor stages of the infant. He reports that imitation appears by the fourth month, and that soon after, the child will imitate any gesture made by an adult, provided that at some time, it has been performed by the child himself. Soon, the child is able to copy gestures that are new to him, so long as they can be performed by visible parts of his own body. Regarding facial movements:

> The difficulty is then that the child's own face is known to him only by touch and the face of the other person by sight, except for a few rare tactile explorations of the other person's face. Such explorations are very interesting to note at this level, when the child is forming correspondences between the visual and tactile-kinesthetic sensations in order to extend imitation to the nonvisible parts of his body. Until these correspondences are elaborated, imitation of facial movements remains impossible or accidental" (Piaget, 1969)

When, at last, the child begins to imitate facial movements, he has learned to accommodate himself to the displacement of other faces. While watching the movement, he accommodates only his eye movements, but after observation, accommodation becomes direct imitation. Piaget has observed that a condition requisite for imitation is the capability of differentiation. He has stated that a child will not imitate a movement he has not differentiated (Piaget, 1962).

Roger Brown, discussing the perception of speech, reasons that differentiation is preceded by discrimination. The child who fails to discriminate cannot differentiate, and so must continue to generalize common qualities (Brown, 1964).

Gibson notes that consistent repetition not only assists the child to differentiate, but may even sharpen discrimination of critical attributes. She states that phonemic constituents of sound may be discriminated prior to the association of sound with object (Gibson, 1966).

For purposes of discussion, let us assume that there exist visual counterparts of the phonemic constituents of language, and that these kinemic (or visemic) constituents must be discriminated before the association of articulatory movement to object can occur. It would appear, then, that the infant's ability to discriminate is the foundation stone upon which visual-oral development rests. Infant vision cannot and need not bear the burden alone. Not only must audition be nurtured at the very earliest age, but every effort must be made to establish for the infant the visual to tactile-kinesthetic correspondence that is prerequisite for the imitation of facial movements. Cessation of babbling has been noted in some infants fitted with hearing aids before the critical sixth month.

Perhaps this need not have happened if these babies had internalized pleasurable tactile-kinesthetic experiences in the exchange of vocal play with others, and had been motivated to continue this kind of game. Increased tactile-kinesthetic experience may well be a critical missing ingredient in the oral education of some deaf children (Vivian, 1966). Only well-documented studies of the effects of such teaching on deaf infants will reveal whether this approach, so useful in teaching the deaf-blind, may be equally effective in the early oral education of deaf children.

The finding that distance is not a factor in deaf children's visual discrimination of speech-motor movements, challenges the practice of speaking close to the face, a behavior sometimes employed by teachers of the deaf with the assumption that decreasing distance increases visibility. It is not only unnecessary to speak to deaf children at close distances, it is undesirable. Close distances are fatiguing for all persons, but especially for the young child who is operating under maximum accommodation, taxing his eye muscles in order to bring the image onto the fovea of each eye simultaneously (Fonda, 1965; Pirenne, 1967). Also, research with hearing persons reveals that acuity decreases significantly with decrease in distance. In persons with uncorrected errors of refraction, significant differences in acuity can occur from one distance to another (Sloan, 1951).

The high incidence of visual defect in deaf children has been periodically documented (Braly, 1937; Stockwell, 1952; Suchman, 1967). The effects of specific visual deficits on the speechreading performance of deaf children have yet to be explored. Studies of the relationship of visual deficit to speechreading in hearing adults have shown that minor acuity problems result in significantly lower scores on tests of lipreading (Lovering and Hardick, 1969; Hardick, Oyer, and Irion, 1970). Early vision care must be considered a prerequisite to successful visual-oral functioning.

In summary, the literature and current studies suggest a number of prerequisites for success in beginning speechreading: adequate visual functioning; a knowledge of the correspondences between visual and tactile-kinesthetic sensations; the ability to discriminate speech-motor movements, through whatever sensory systems prove to be the most effective for the particular child; the ability to differentiate speech-motor movements, made possible through consistent repetitions and however much practice a particular child requires; the ability to imitate the visual components of oral language, first directly, in the manner of simultaneous speaking; then the critical ability to defer imitation, revealing that visual images of language can be stored and recalled, that the stage of representation has been achieved.

Issues and Trends

In addition to the fact that routine visual screening is still not instituted in every school and agency serving deaf children, there are other problems which bear on the effectiveness of the developing speechreading process.

Ten years have passed since Myklebust noted that speechreading diagnostics have not been developed (Myklebust, 1960). School records still show teacher ratings from very poor to very good, based on subjective judgment. And though the judgments be reliable, teachers have no common referent, and therefore no valid measure of individual gains. Too often, ratings stand as final statements of performance, rather than starting points for remediation.

Myklebust, pioneer in educational diagnostics, has reported the condition of speechreading aphasia, a receptive language disorder seen in many deaf children. He notes that one of the outstanding symptoms is "the marked incapacity to imitate speech positions and to speak." Many of these children show speech progress after they begin to read. He explains that the internalization of the printed form serves as the necessary referent upon which the spoken word depends (Myklebust, 1964).*

Early speechreading diagnostics would serve to identify these children and provide them sooner with remedial programs to better suit their needs. But surely, all the deaf children who are considered poor speechreaders do not also suffer the central nervous system damage which results in language disorder. What can early speechreading diagnostics tell us about the "normal deaf child"?

At the Lexington School for the Deaf, the recently developed Speechreading Test for Young Children (Butt and Chreist, 1968) was administered to a group of 20 four-and five-year-old profoundly deaf children. Employed as a measure of speechreading achievement, it revealed among the children a variety of oral-visual behaviors, making it a useful tool in the discovery of children who require special speechreading instruction. One child spontaneously responded to the pictures by naming the objects, yet was unable to identify the same words on the examiner's lips. In the nursery, such a child may be a master at reading situational clues and mirroring the speech behaviors of teacher and peers. Such a child

*Myklebust, Helmer, *The psychology of deafness*, (2nd edition), 1964, Grune & Stratton, Publishers, pp. 81, 366.

may be among the most oral, and even exhibit some of the best speech. But in fact, he has only overlearned direct imitation. Well-informed teachers, testing at intervals, will catch this condition and apply remedial techniques. If this does not happen, teachers may be chagrined to find that a prize pupil in the nursery becomes a slow learner in a classroom setting. The critical period for speechreading diagnostics and remediation is during the preschool experience. Hopefully, in not too many years, experience and experiment will result in our instituting them during infancy. The test provided by Butt and Chreist, applicable to children under 3 years of age, offers a sound beginning.

The following screening procedures were developed at the Lexington School for the Deaf and employed for the purposes of sample selection in a research study (Jenson, 1969). They are readily adapted for the testing of prerequisites for speechreading in four-and five-year-old deaf children.

Testing a young child's ability to imitate nonsense syllables is a relatively easy matter, and a good starting place in speechreading diagnostics. Success implies that the child has accomplished visual discrimination and differentiation of the sounds presented. One may begin with gross motor movements of the upper extremities. Seated on eye level with the child, initiate clapping, hands on shoulders, forefinger to ear, eye, nose, and finally to mouth. From here, the imitation of tongue gymnastics is useful, for it reveals not only the ability to imitate speech-motor movements, but offers opportunity to examine, in an informal way, the condition and functioning of the parts of the oral mechanism. Raising and protruding the tongue reveals the length of the frenum, the ligament under the tongue. A short frenum restricts the production of all alveolar sounds: *t, d, n,* and *l,* as well as *r.* The length of the uvula, the flap at the end of the soft palate, can be observed during the production of the vowel *ah,* as in the word *father.* Sometimes a deaf child's hypernasality is due to malformation rather than malfunctioning. Malformations may be observed or hidden, as in the case of sub-mucosa clefts. Ideally, oral examinations should be carried out by qualified medical personnel, made familiar with the speech problems of profoundly deaf children.

Testing for deferred imitation requires two examiners. Condition the child as for tongue gymnastics, only this time require that he watch, make a half-turn, and repeat what he saw to the second examiner. Do not expect or hold the child to perfect sound production. More important, for speechreading purposes, is his ability to repeat speech movements in correct sequence.

Nonsense Syllable	Distinctive Movements
1. wa	widening action
2. ah oo	narrowing action
3. ahl	raised tongue
4. shah	lips forward and back
5. ahp (explode)	widen, close, explode
6. poo	plosive burst, narrow, round
7. eef	lips wide, teeth to lip
8. foo	teeth to lip, narrow, round
9. eeth	lips wide, tongue to teeth
10. thaw	tongue to teeth, lips narrow

It is essential that stimuli be nonsense syllables devoid of meaningful associations. Children who fail to perform all items may do so for various reasons, but undoubtedly have not developed skills prerequisite to speechreading. Any child who fails more than two items should be checked for visual acuity, and the ability to discriminate sounds in isolation at different teaching distances: 12 inches (face-to-face); two and one-half feet (tutoring distance); and 10 feet (blackboard to desk).

The ability to differentiate can be assessed by constructing and presenting phoneme pairs, asking the child to identify them as "same" or "different."

In the course of testing, some children will consistently reverse the order of movements, suggesting poorly developed skill in visual sequencing of speech-motor movements. Some children, if tested in the corner of a classroom, will restrict their own visual field by cupping their hands around their eyes to shut out distracting stimuli. All these reactive behaviors give us additional information about children's needs, and suggest teaching strategies and extended educational programs to bring about more successful functioning and efficient learning in young deaf children.

Hopefully, other testing procedures will come to light, and new measures of achievement will be devised.

Two factors which influence all sensory processing are rate and repetition. Children differ in their requirements for number of repetitions before a referent is sufficiently established for retention and recall. In order to cope with the temporal nature of speechreading, some children require reduced rates of presentation in order to "catch up" and "get the idea."

An encouraging trend to aid children along these lines is the increased use of practice films for the improvement of speechreading skills. Under the auspices of Captioned Films for the Deaf, Dr. Frank B. Withrow developed a series of continuous loop cartridge films for deaf children's self-instruction. The films have been made available in schools and classes for the deaf throughout the United States (Withrow, 1965). The ease with which children can load the projector fosters independence, and the opportunity to manipulate equipment provides continuing motivation.

Like all instructional materials, the films' effectiveness depends to some extent on the context provided by the teachers. The films constitute practice regimens, and as such, present single words. (Ideally, these would be later incorporated by the teacher into longer linguistic units, related to the children's language experiences.) Such strategies not only strengthen perceptual characteristics of movement features, but aid the child in recognition of word boundaries in running speech. To become a skillful speechreader, the deaf child must come to acknowledge the correspondences of speech-motor form to printed form. Until he does, many familiar words remain embedded in strings of syllable configurations and their junctures.

We look forward to follow-ups to these initial films, and expansion of this independent practice approach. Promoting self-help skills in deaf children is among our major educational goals.

New Directions from Old

The most widely discussed attempts to augment speechreading are the Rochester Method and Cued Speech. Developed almost a century ago by Westervelt, the Rochester Method consists of the simultaneous use of spoken language and fingerspelling. A comprehensive discussion of the method can be found in the literature (Scouten, 1964). Critics of the method claim that deaf persons are presented with two conflicting coding systems: speech, as the oral code, and fingerspelling as the written code (a secondary symbol system). When presented with both, the tendency is to focus on the one designed for "reading," to the detriment of speechreading practice. Also, it has been noted by deaf and hearing persons alike, that the rhythms of the two systems differ, causing the spoken message to be rendered as a stylized version of English with unique patterns of stress and flow, evident in the spoken language of deaf children educated by the method. Research has not investigated these claims.

Cued speech, on the other hand, deals directly with speechreading, attacking its greatest weakness, the homophenous nature of some speech sounds. By providing unique visual-motor identities for the units of written language, it allows differentiation of these on the lips. Its creator, R. Orin Cornett, discusses its value as a total communication system (Cornett, 1967).

A reasonable question is, could these differentiations be made with existing techniques, more easily faded in later life than a total communication system? And, does an additional system ease or add to the burden of learning socially useful coding systems when hearing is impaired?

The differentation of homophenous sounds on the lips can be approached in other ways, perhaps more in keeping with oral communication goals.

Speechreading, as a developing language process, brings new insights to the decoding of spoken messages as the child continues to internalize more and more spoken and written messages, the correspondences of their unique units and strings, their shared syntactical clues for recognition of meanings, sentence types, and transformations. For the most part, the context of spoken language provides ample clues for differentiation. "Mom lost her sweater" versus "Bob lost his sweater" is a case in point. And since there is no Pop in our family, Dad never enters the picture. The opportunity for a child to make deductions, to act on the information presented, greatly assists cognitive growth. In attempting to ease the burden of learning for deaf children, we constantly run the risk of depriving them of self-help and discovery.

What if the context did not differentiate Mom and Bob? Some persons would have the family change the name of the child. Such psychologically loaded impositions on the family's intactness and emotional strength are ill-advised. What then?

In the interest of exploring more efficient practices of fostering oral communication in young deaf children, an identification and synthesis of existing methodologies is called for. In the vast repertoire of teaching techniques special to teachers of the deaf are many practices, undocumented, sporadically seen, passed on through demonstration from one talented teacher to another. Among these is one I have identified and termed Place Cueing.

Place Cueing is used by teachers of the deaf to cue the speech production of their pupils with hand signals designating the place and manner of articulation. The finger to the nose to evoke a nasalized /n/; the open hand under the chin to signal the emission of breath, reduced to a thumb when suggesting a thin stream of air for the production of /s/; a forefinger to the throat to evoke a /g/, the addition of the hand under chin to demonstrate the breath correlate /k/. These signals are reminders of tactile-kinesthetic and proprioceptive experiences attached to speech sound production. It is possible, though often not advisable, to signal every English phoneme with a place cue. To differentiate Mom and Bob, a teacher need only apply a place cue to one initial sound. Either will do. To cue more than a child requires is to make him unnecessarily dependent on the help of teachers.

Place Cueing not only evokes improved speech from deaf children, it aids in the differentiation of homophenous sounds in speechreading. Information offered for speech correction carries over to speechreading, one oral activity reinforcing the other.

Place Cueing is an integral part of a cueing hierarchy. It will be recalled that place cues have as referents early moto-kinesthetic sensations. The child whose /n/ has been corrected through tactile-kinesthetic technique recognizes the teacher's finger-to-nose placement as a cue for him to nasalize. He also recognizes that cue when she uses it to differentiate *not* from *lot,* or *night* from *tight,* when she speaks to him. He uses it himself to monitor his own speech production, placing a finger on his nose as he articulates. When his teacher believes he can differentiate a printed *n* from other graphemes (particularly *r*), she attaches the place cue to the written symbol. Now she may cue correct speech by underlining the faultily produced sound as he reads from blackboard or paper.

At this point, the child may respond in several ways, depending on the strength of the original moto-kinesthetic image. He may produce the word intelligibily by correcting himself by written cue, a major landmark in his oral communication development. Or, he may raise a finger to his nose to monitor a cautious rendering of the faulty sound. Or, he may be so low on the cueing hierarchy that he stretches a hand toward the teacher for more of the tactile-kinesthetic information he has not yet fully internalized. Observation of each child's responses offers a complete history of his speech sound development, as well as his progress in learning self-help skills for speech correction.

In summary, the cueing hierarchy may be initiated with the child's earliest acceptable speech sound productions. Once a sound is mastered, it can be called forth again and again by a place cue as the teacher monitors the child's spoken language. The method is especially useful during the pre-reading period. When differentiation of graphemes is established, place cues are attached to written symbols, keeping in mind that they must be gradually faded, as self-help through phonetics is assured.

Obviously, this method is but a part of a total speech program, but it can serve as a construct upon which other speech teaching activities can be attached. The concept of Place Cueing may encompass all visualizations of speech teaching information conveyed by the teacher's hands. These include indicating pitch changes by altering the height of the moving hand, beating out patterns of stress and rhythm; evoking improved voice quality by touching areas of teacher throat and diaphragm. And not least, the entire range of that speech analog called hand analogies (Ewing and Ewing, 1964).

For example, it is speech analog to simulate palate and tongue by tapping thumb to forefinger to illustrate /t/; to "jump" the thumb away from the forefinger for /ch/ (while forming the sound with the articulators); by clenching and abruptly releasing the fingers to express the pressure and tension in /j/. It has been noted that children, slow to respond to other speech teaching techniques, respond well to these hand analogies, perhaps because the critical speech information is isolated and enlarged. The technique is readily expanded to illustrate longer speech units: blends, syllables, and words and their junctures. When speech is stimulated and supported in this manner, the child is spontaneous in his response, unfettered by symbol systems, and operating entirely on an oral level. Such speech practice is a rewarding experience.

Place Cueing is currently in use in oral schools and day classes. As a potentially powerful system, it suffers from lack of identification, standardization, consistency of application, and a curricular framework which offers continuity from preschool throughout the grades. As a totally visual-oral system compatible with aural-oral philosophy, it exemplifies the relationship of speech and speechreading. It deserves to be adopted for wider and wiser use.

BIBLIOGRAPHY

Alich, G. Language communication by lipreading. *Proceedings of International Conference on Oral Education of the Deaf.* Washington, D.C.: Alexander Graham Bell Association for the Deaf, 1967, 465–482.

American Hearing Society. *New aids and materials for teaching lipreading.* Washington, D.C.: American Hearing Society, 1943.

Braly, K. W. Incidence of defective vision among the deaf. New Jersey School for the Deaf Technical Series No. 4. West Trenton, N.J.: 1937.

Brannon, J. B., Jr., and Kodman, F., Jr. The perceptual process in speechreading. *AMA archives of otolaryngology*. 1959, **70,** 114–119.

Brehman, G. E., Jr. Programmed discrimination training for lipreaders. *Symposium on research and utilization of educational media for teaching the hearing impaired.* Washington, D.C.: Department of Health, Education and Welfare, 1965.

Brown, R. *Words and things.* New York: The Free Press of Glencoe, 1964.

Butt, D. S., and Chreist, F. M. A speechreading test for young children. *Volta review,* 1968, **70,** 225–239.

Cornett, R. Cued speech. *American annals of the deaf,* 1967, **112,** 3–13.

Costello, M. R. A study of speechreading as a developing language process in deaf and hard of hearing children. Unpublished doctoral dissertation, Northwestern University, 1957.

Ewing, A. W. G., and Ewing, E. C. *Teaching deaf children to talk.* Manchester, England: University Press, 1964.

Fisher, C. G. Confusions among visually perceived consonants. *Journal of speech and hearing research,* 1968, **11,** 796–804.

Fonda, G. *Management of the patient with subnormal vision.* St. Louis: C. V. Mosby Co., 1965.

Gibson, E. J. Association and differentiation in perceptual learning. Paper read at a meeting of the Society for Research in Child Development, State College,.Pennsylvania, March 1961.

Guilfoyle, G. R. An investigation of the process of speech reading in deaf adolescents. Unpublished doctoral dissertation, New York University, 1968.

Hardick, E. J., Oyer, H. J., and Irion, P. E. Lipreading performance as related to measurement of vision. *Journal of speech and hearing research,* 1970, **13,** 92–100.

Jakobson, R., Halle, M., and Fant, C. G. *Preliminaries to speech analysis.* Cambridge, Mass.: M.I.T. Press, 1952.

Jenson, P. M. Age and distance factors in deaf children's visual discrimination and response to articulatory movement. Unpublished doctoral dissertation, Columbia University, 1969.

Lovering, L. J., and Hardick, E. J. Lipreading performance as a function of visual acuity. East Lansing: Michigan State University, 1969 (mimeographed).

Miller, G. A. *Language and communication.* New York: McGraw-Hill, 1951.

Mulholland, A. M. Receptive language development in the deaf infant. Paper read at the Fifth World Congress of the Deaf, Warsaw, August 1967.

Mussen, P. H. (Ed.) *Handbook of research methods in child development.* New York: John Wiley and Sons, 1960.

Myklebust, H. R. *The psychology of deafness* (2d ed.). New York: Grune and Stratton, 1964.

O'Neill, J. J., and Oyer, H. J. *Visual communication for the hard of hearing.* Englewood Cliffs, N.J.: Prentice-Hall, 1961.

Piaget, J. *Play, dreams and imitation in childhood.* New York: W. W. Norton and Co., 1962.

Piaget, J., and Inhelder, B. *The psychology of the child.* New York: Basic Books, 1969.

Pirenne, M. H. *Vision and the eye.* London: Chapman and Hall, 1967.

Scouten, E. L. The place of the Rochester Method in American education of the deaf. *Report of the Proceedings of the International Congress on Education of the Deaf.* Washington, D.C.: Government Printing Office, 1964, 429–433.

Simmons, A. A. Factors related to lipreading. *Journal of speech and hearing research.* 1959, **2,** 340–352.

Sloan, L. L. Measurement of visual acuity: A critical review. *Archives of Ophthalmology,* 1951, **45,** 704–725.

Stockwell, E. Visual defects in the deaf child. *Archives of Ophthalmology,* 1952, **48,** 428–432.

Suchman, R. G. Visual impairment among deaf children. *Archives of Ophthalmology,* 1967, **77,** 18–21.

Vivian, R. M. The Tadoma Method: A tactual approach to speech and speechreading. *Volta review,* 1966, **68,** 733–737.

Withrow, F. B. The use of audiovisual techniques to expand lipreading and auditory experiences of young deaf children. *Symposium on Research and Utilization of Educational Media for Teaching the Hearing Impaired.* Conference supported by a grant from Captioned Films for the Deaf. Washington, D.C.: Department of Health, Education and Welfare, 1965.

Woodward, M. F., and Barber, C. G. Phoneme perception in lipreading. In Edgar L. Lowell (Ed.), *John Tracy Clinic Research Papers, No. 11.* Los Angeles: John Tracy Clinic, 1960.

CHAPTER XIII

Language and Hearing

Audrey A. Simmons, Ed.D.

Speech is generally a highly efficient and convenient way for an idea of one person to become that of another. Man's thinking is fostered through the process of verbal communication which is a basic ability of man that sets him apart from the animal kingdom. While there are means of communication other than speech, they tend to be abstractions of the spoken form.

The fundamental task of a speaker is to arrange his thoughts, decide what he wants to say, and then put it into linguistic form. This requires selecting the correct words to express the precise meaning, placing the words in proper order required by the grammatical rules of the language, and utilizing pauses to clarify the meaning, while applying appropriate pitch, stress, and inflection to articulated phonation.

Language Code

Linguistic form is dictated by the language being spoken in the home, and it is actually a code understood only by those familiar with that particular language. Spoken language is not a simple code, although it has much in common with other code systems, such as the Morse code. It is a highly elaborate form, structurally complex, and it involves a number of dimensions.

Phonemes: The speaker of the language uses a variety of sounds in an exceedingly varied manner to communicate meaning. For instance, the speaker can produce isolated speech sounds, such as *b,* which then can be combined with other speech sounds into a meaningful word such as *boy*. The phoneme *b* of itself has no meaning. It is only when combined with a vowel and possibly another consonant that it has distinctive features. It is then that it makes a difference whether the word is *book* or *look, rib* or *rip*.

Morphemes: The speaker can also produce sound combinations, such as the suffixes *ed, ing,* and *ly,* which by themselves have independent meanings. It is only in combinations with words that this meaning can be obtained. To tell about "Mary danc*ing*" is quite different from saying that "Mary danc*ed* last week." To do something *happily* may differ quite dramatically from being *happy*.

Syntax: Still more complex is the manner in which the speaker can arrange words to obtain certain meanings. For instance, a speaker who can produce the words *leaves, rake,* and *yard* still must decide whether "leave the rake in the yard" or "rake the leaves in the yard" is correct according to the meaning he wishes to signal. When one realizes that each sentence a speaker uses is unique, the task does seem great.

In addition to word order, the speaker needs to use certain words which, unlike nouns, verbs, adjectives, and adverbs, have little or no lexical meaning. Rather, they serve only to communicate structural meaning. To give the instruction, "Take the medicine *in an* hour," would call for different action than almost the same words in, "Take the medicine *on the* hour." The words which could be filled in the blanks "__Make__People__Buy" could aid or lose a sale for the company who used the paradigm in their advertising, e.g., *The* make *all* people *will* buy, or *A* make *few* people *ever* buy.

Intonation: Further complicating the spoken language is the way it is stressed or accented. Meaning is conveyed not only by what is said, but also by *how* it is said. For instance, the sound patterns of "Isn't Tom great?" appear to have a rather definite and complimentary meaning for Tom, but it is possible for the speaker's voice inflection to turn that simple statement into a sarcastic comment.

A speaker may also employ pitch and stress to communicate still further meanings. For instance, if the speaker says, "Where are you going tomorrow?" you can derive a variety of messages from the words, depending upon the speaker's manipulation of pitch. If his voice rises and falls on the word "going" as in: "Where are you *going* tomorrow?" then he is primarily concerned with someone's destination. However, if his voice rises on the second syllable of "tomorrow" and then falls on the third, as "Where are you going to*mo*rrow?" then he is primarily concerned with the day on which the person is going.

The meaning-carrying value of stress can be dramatized by noting the changes which occur in the meaning of a phrase such as "The white house" when voice inflections change. In the following example, the stress on "white" is relatively weak: "It is the white house." However, the stress changes when the speaker wants to say the house belongs to a person named White. Here, "White" receives a relatively heavy stress to ensure communication of the message: "It is the White house." Similarly, the stress changes when the speaker wants to refer to the house of the President of the United States. Then the speaker would place relatively heavy stress on both "White" and "House" to deliver his message.

Stress helps to emphasize certain parts of spoken communication. However, the usefulness of stress and pitch does not end there. The degree of loudness of the voice, together with pitch, is also used to distinguish between statements and questions. For instance, note the differences in stress and pitch in the following sentences:

She is a good student.
She is a good student?

Finally, accent is also used in language to distinguish between two forms of the same word. For instance, the meaning of the words *present* and *refuse* is dramatically changed by the stress patterns. The two words in, "Never refuse a present" change parts of speech in the next sentence, "Present it to me or throw it in the refuse container." This is strictly an auditory-vocal process because the words do not change in their spellings.

Oralism—Auralism

Speech teaching, then, must include code teaching in order for the rules to become habitual and intuitive. Unlike those people described by Silverman (1954) who look upon speech (or carry on their programs in such a way) as a separate subject to be taught like a foreign language to only those who can "benefit" from it, teachers who instruct orally should endorse the proposition that speech is a multifaceted process which is a basic means of communication. It should be a mechanism of adjustment to the communicating world around the child. Hence, the stage should be set for the deaf child so that speech is meaningful, significant, purposeful, and worthwhile for him at all times.

For too many teachers *oralism,* however, means teaching speech and excluding the language of signs or the manual alphabet. In light of today's knowledge *auralism* would be a more appropriate term to use. Considering all of the phonologic information that is crucial to linguistic understanding, it becomes readily apparent that full exploitation of hearing as implied in the term *auralism* is essential. Along with Hirsh (1966) I believe that for deaf children, auralism is the best route to oralism.

Recent literature on the acquisition of language by hearing children emphasizes the necessity of hearing language sounds, almost incidentally but nevertheless very frequently, imitating the audible pattern of others, and inducing the rules of the language code from such fragments as are perceived. Reduced even further, these necessary conditions are: an environment in which people are talking to the child, listening skill, and at least limited ability to derive the rules of language. Impoverishment in any one of these three areas can result in language retardation.

Environment

Sociologists, psychologists, and educators engaged in developing compensatory programs for deprived children have been particularly concerned with environmental stimulation and its effect upon children's language of her social group to her child. They thereby serve as temporary interpreters for the permanent code. Thus the learning of the cannot exist practically in isolation from the economic, social, and emotional climate in which the young child lives.

In real life it is the mother or her teacher-substitute who brings the language of her social group to her child. They thereby serve as temporary interpreters for the permanent code. Thus the learning of the "mother tongue" is an intensely emotional experience for the young child. Like all emotional learning, it is achieved through the processes of conscious imitation and unconscious identification. Learning to speak, like all primary learning, is influenced, therefore, by the child's relation to the mother or her substitute (Wyatt, 1969). The acquisition of speech, though influenced by maturation, is a learning process dependent upon input and feedback from adult to child. During the early stages the mother-figure serves as the primary model for the child's attempts at imitation of the language patterns (Brown & Bellugi, 1964).

The optimum condition for successful speech learning is a continuous, undisrupted, and affectionate relation between the adult and child manifested in frequent and appropriate communication. It is appropriate if the model takes her cues from the child's behavior and attempts at verbalizations. She thereby provides the child with a corrective feedback.

Language learning goes through a series of interrelated stages. Each new and higher stage of development represents fundamentally an innovation, not merely an addition of certain characteristics to those of the previous level. With increasing mastery of language the child needs the model less often. Eventually, he will achieve autonomy of function to such a point that he no longer needs the original model.

Hearing

How sound is delivered and perceived by children and the acoustics of speech are beyond the scope of this chapter. Nevertheless, some attention must be given to hearing. Until recently it was far too prevalent an idea that the hearing of children born deaf was of little value in enabling them to talk. This idea led to the disregard of the possibilities of using what hearing they had. Now it is known that very few, if any, of these children have no hearing at all (Elliott, 1967). While there are differences in the amount of residual hearing among children who are deaf, these children are likely to range from those who hear only at the low frequencies to those with hearing for more or higher frequencies. These differences have not been sufficiently exploited. Hirsh's (1966) comment recognizes this: Since the distinction between deaf and partially deaf is fuzzy anyway, perhaps we would best serve them by treating them all as partially deaf, at least for a time (p. 626).

Much of the phonologic code, particularly phonation, duration, and prosody of speech, is frequently audible. Even to those children with minimal amounts of hearing we can communicate much about the linguistic form. Temporal aspects of speech are available, giving them the rhythm of spoken thoughts. Strong patterns can be differentiated from weak ones. Certainly variations in sentence lengths are distinguishable (Silverman, 1949).

The process of learning to hear consists of learning to recognize sound and interpret it. It has been rightly said that the brain is in series with the ear. The child should be exposed to sounds of the linguistic code he will speak and he should receive feedback not only from the mother or her substitute, but also from his own voice as he is encouraged to match the mother's model. The essential conditions for learning to hear language are: that the speech to be "heard" is amplified, it is given often, and it is associated with the meaning. Learning to hear requires not just a lot of sound but sound that is patterned, discriminated, and utilized actively. It is listening to speech which is meaningful language, because the child himself experienced it at the sensorimotor level. In this way the child develops a deep structure of understanding for the linguistic code.

Fine discrimination among speech sounds requires the hearing for high frequencies, therefore deaf children should not be expected to use their ears to perform this task. Certainly those discriminations that depend upon high frequencies will not often be available to these children, but the rhythmic structure of speech, the pulsings, and the stresses that give information about the speech sounds themselves can be perceptible. Continuing efforts to make the acoustical features of speech available should enhance the appreciation of speech and its development in the child.

It is imperative that teachers apply basic principles of amplification, acoustics, and phonetics to the classroom situation in order for the total language code to take on significance.

Stages

There are necessary environmental and auditory conditions for language learning. Sensory experiences must be constantly mediated with the appropriate language code. The child must be given the model to imitate and from it to receive sensorimotor feedback, providing these conditions allow the hearing impaired child to follow stages of speech development described for hearing children. Unfortunately the hearing deprivation forces the development at a later chronological age than normal hearing allows. Nevertheless, it has been my experience that when children have learned to make maximum use of their hearing and when the teacher takes on the role of mother models, hearing impaired children approach the stages linguists consider to be universal.

Along with Lenneberg (1967) and Chomsky (1965), I believe that the capacity for the development of certain phases of language *is* biologically determined. When the child receives data, he can eventually induce the principles of our grammar. The data, however, must be programmed into him.

McNeill (1966) once referred to the child as a computer and labeled the device for this important learning LAD, (Language Acquisition

Device), if the child is a boy, and LAS, (Language Acquisition System), if a girl. Using this analogy, I would like to present models of this acquisition process derived from my experience.

Before we discuss the stages, however, I emphasize that the hearing impaired child does not accomplish the stages at the ages a child with normal hearing does. For the former it comes later and each of the stages is longer in duration. Nevertheless, the stages do seem to apply to these children.

Stage I

The first illustration represents that early stage. LAD is merely vocalizing and Mother is giving him somewhat meaningless language. The focus at the time is on *intonation,* not meaning. Note the variety of the input, e.g. "That's a good baby." "Aren't you a cute baby?" "Come to Mummy." "Smile pretty for Mummy." The meaning is not the critical factor but the intonation is.

LAD at this stage is just making his wants known and he vocalizes to communicate these wants. Mother, being the teacher that she is, reinforces the vocal activity. By responding with vocal-play to vocal-play, and with a bottle to the whimpering, Mother shows LAD the value of vocalization.

The prompt reward for using his voice to communicate his needs starts LAD on the way to shaping that voice for other uses of language.

Implications for Teachers: Essentially I am proposing that we do two things. First we should provide a model for the deaf child to imitate and secondly that we reinforce his first attempts at vocalization. He needs to find that he too can manipulate people through his phonation. Just using his natural pleasant voice *must gain* some strong reinforcers, such as attention and positive reaction, for the child at the first stage.

Furthermore, the teacher should contrive situations and present the code of language in its entire sentence form for processing through the child's motor-sensory mechanism. The child's attention is on the idea, but the teacher is aware of his capabilities and knows the effect his imitation of her model can elicit. The teacher's expectations vary depending upon the child's ability at the time. Critical to this procedure is the child's reception of feedback from his own attempts at imitating and the teacher's acceptance of his best efforts.

Contrived experiences should be appropriate to the child's chronological, social, and cognitive age. To these experiences the complete code needs to be given, not just the lexical vocabulary or any other abortive portion of the linguistic form. Because the children and the teacher together have performed the activities, the linguistic form has significance and takes on meaning. The child senses the deep structure and stores it in his computer.

Stage II

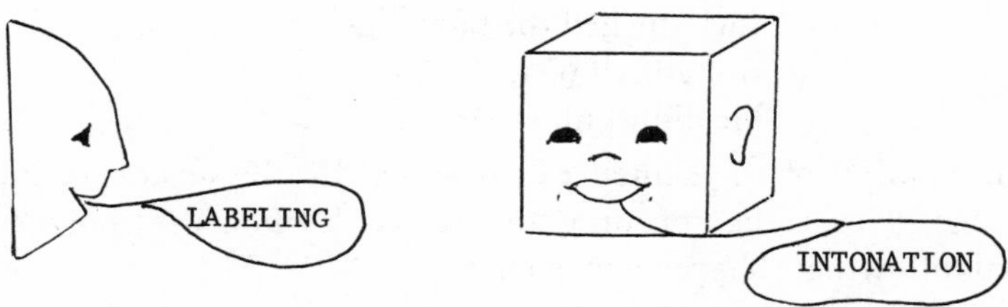

The second illustration shows LAD grown a little larger. Now mother is labeling things in his environment. These are things that he sees, tastes, feels, smells, hears, and does. The samples contain such things as "There's a puppy." "Look at the puppy dog." "Look at the airplane." "The airplane is in the sky." "Oh, it smells so good." or "Umm, the cookie tastes good."

The objects are very much the here and now. They are all within LAD's perceptual range, but he still isn't saying the words. LAD seems to be trying out intonation patterns instead. Linguists, who are interested in syntax, feel that this is an important step. The prosodic pattern does give us the grammar of sentences and punctuations. Whether this is what LAD is beginning, I can't say with confidence at this time, but he does chatter in units with emphasis. When Mother makes an effort to interpret the chatter, LAD learns that intonation is a part of communication.

Like Lewis' hearing children (1963) the hearing impaired children I have studied respond and imitate affective patterns first. Sentences which relate to the child's feelings of surprise, happiness, or dissatisfaction if they are captured and recorded usually can be easily imitated.

Implication: The teacher must be sensitive to what it is that the child wishes to express. She must give vocal form to the child's feelings. Through her the child gets his orientation to the linguistic stereotyped simple declarative sentence work.

We went to the store.
Tom bought a balloon.
Jane bought a comic book.
Bill bought some bubble gum.

Sentence groups such as the following are better:

Jane found a penny.
Oh, she was happy.

Tom bought a balloon.
It popped.

Jack pushed the boat.
Bill got all wet.
He didn't like that!

The intonation of the sentences presented by the teacher stands the best chance of carrying meaning to the child when the sentences are presented following a shared experience.

To get the child to attend to the sounds he cannot hear, the sentences should be printed. He can learn that something goes into those empty auditory spaces this way. However at this stage the children, like hearing children, attend to the intonation pattern rather than the words, and this is expected.

The reward for imitation of intonation is acceptance of the imitation. The reward for spontaneous use of intonation is understanding by the adult.

Stage III

Mother moves on then to giving sentences that focus more on the idea than on the object. She tells about what will happen. She talks about things past. "Daddy will take you to Grandmother's this weekend." "We had fun at the park yesterday, didn't we?"

In all of this input, the child is receiving information about the notion of time and how we express it. He is learning how Mother feels about things from the intonation in her voice. He is being exposed to pronouns with their abstractness. He is getting vocabulary, not just words, *park, daddy,* and *Grandmother,* but also structure words. He is seeing how these thought-connectors are used. The function words, like *will, to, this,* and *at,* have meaning only in structure. Therefore it is important that complete structure is used at all times and that the meaning of the total sentence grows out of shared experience.

The exposure LAD receives to lexical and structural vocabulary ordinarily comes in the form of simplified, repetitive, and idealized dialect. It is always and forever in sentence style. Further, not only is the language said frequently, but usually it is also very much about LAD, himself.

LAD, though, is only beginning to name things and activities. He uses more nouns, and verbs and adjectives also occur. These are the words that had primary stress patterns in Mother's model. Sometimes he clothes these words in chatter, e.g., "ummm*car*," "ummm*grandmother*," but adult language structure has yet to develop.

While his efforts sound like jargon, LAD is employing another linguistic form, that of rhythm, to his utterances. Imbedded in the jargon are words, but obvious to the listener is the prosody of his utterance.

Implication: Children should be asked to match the "time envelope" of the teacher's model. As Hudgins and Numbers (1942) pointed out, the intelligibility of the speech of deaf children is reduced because of its arhythmic characteristics. They reported that phrasing was slow and labored. Calvert (1962) found that the deaf take three to four times as long to articulate each phoneme and the relative duration between phonemes was distorted.

As the child works to match the "time envelope" of the teacher's model he is limiting breath and articulatory motion and, as a result, gives better articulation. If he needs units shorter than a complex sentence, the teacher needs to break the utterance into thought units, not word units. The total sentence naturally will be repeated once more for the child to perceive the rhythm and the intonation of the whole.

Stage IV

The efforts of LAD are picked up by his mother, and by this time, if he is hearing impaired, by his classroom teacher also. They take his offerings and expand them. LAD's "Ummmtruck, UmmmMummy," is expanded to "Yes, there's a truck," or the mother/teacher may model new sentences as, "Yes, Mummy sees the big truck. It is carrying furniture, I believe."

The teacher's and the mother's language to LAD differ from that which adults use to one another in many ways. Their sentences are shorter and more simple. For the most part they are the kinds of sentences that LAD will produce a year or two later. Mother and teacher follow the topic LAD initiated and keep the integrity of his idea. Imitation by adults with appropriate expansions have been reported to occur about 30 percent of the time in hearing children's utterances (Brown & Fraser, 1964). This apparently is a powerful learning device.

Implications: It has been proposed that the reason the hearing child has difficulty with the little words of English, the structure words, and leaves them out of his telegraphic speech is because these words have secondary stress patterns. He, therefore, does not hear them. Certainly the hearing impaired child will have similar difficulty. For him, the printed form of the total sentence must be available so that he can see the words which occur in his auditory blank spaces.

When the hearing impaired children reduce their imitations of the teacher's model or when they telegraph their own spontaneous language, the teacher must expand and fit in the appropriate little words, the *in, of, but, so,* etc. She is thereby "programing in" the use of these structural words with their meaning.

In addition to the little words, the teacher's instruction should be structured in such a manner that the children begin to see that the phonemes are the basic signals of the language code. It is here that the teacher puts emphasis upon production of the sounds, remembering to keep the light touch. Rhythm, stress, and duration must constantly be monitored, however, as they enhance even poorly articulated speech. Well-articulated speech that lacks good rhythm, stress, and intonation can be unintelligible.

Stage V:

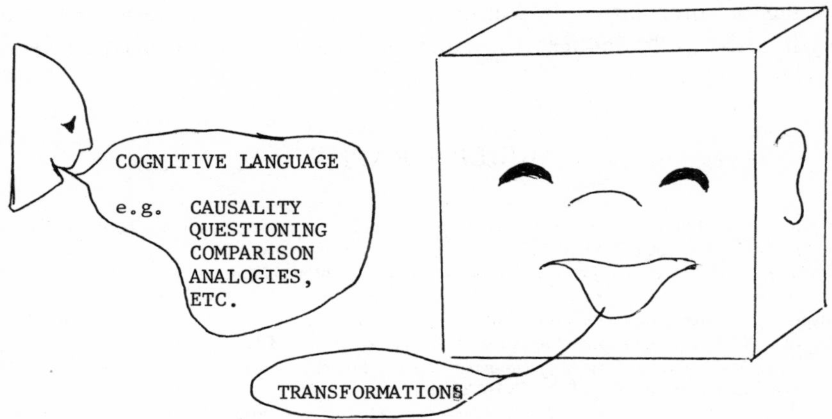

By the fifth stage the teacher is now feeding into the computer, LAD, causal relations, contingencies, time, and other ideas clothed in language. LAD begins to use longer sentences, employ questions, and gain control of a multitude of transformations (Menyuk, 1969). There seems to be a latency connected with phonemic understanding and he reproduces phrases with some indication of his faulty perception. He sings, "Stanley, the cross-eyed bear" for ". . . sadly the cross I bear," and says "For Richard stands" for ". . . for which it stands," in our Pledge of Allegiance.

While the speech and time of phoneme acquisition varies enormously between deaf and hearing children, the sequence in categories, nevertheless, is similar. It has been my experience that hearing impaired children learn coarse contrasts first and move gradually to greater refinement following the pattern described by Jakobson and Halle (1961). The hearing impaired child, while older, seems to follow the same universal developmental steps to linguistic competence.

Summary

In summary, the complex language code has many dimensions which all need to be built into a hearing impaired child's speech. Some of these are distinctively auditory. These phonologic features must be processed through the child's auditory and speech mechanism in order for him to benefit from the sensorimotor feedback. As with a hearing child, the hearing impaired child needs the opportunity to imitate linguistic form when he is aware of the meaning transmitted by the form. From the storage of information including phonologic, syntactic, and semantic features the child induces the rules of language, and consequently of speech.

BIBLIOGRAPHY

Brown, R., and Bellugi, U. Three processes in the child's acquisition of syntax. *Harvard Educational Review,* 1964, **34,** 131–151.

Brown, R., and Fraser, C. The acquisition of syntax. *Child development monograph,* 1964, **29,** 43–79.

Calvert, D. R. Speech sound duration and the surd-sonant error. *Volta review,* 1962, **64,** 401–402.

Chomsky, N. *Aspects of the theory of syntax.* Cambridge, Mass.: M.I.T. Press, 1965.

Elliott, L. Descriptive analysis of audiometric and psychometric scores of deaf students. *Journal of speech and hearing research,* 1967, **10,** 21–40.

Hess, R. D., and Shipman, V. C. Early experience and the socialization of cognitive modes in children. *Child development,* 1965, **36,** 869–886.

Hirsh, I. J. The ears of the deaf unstopped. *Volta review,* 1966, **68,** 623–634.

Hudgins, C. V., and Numbers, F. C. An investigation of the intelligibility of the speech of the deaf. *Genetic psychology monographs,* 1942, **25,** 289–392.

Jakobson, R., and Halle, M. Phonemic patterning. In S. Saporta (Ed.), *Psycholinguistics,* New York: Holt, Rinehart and Winston, 1961.

Lenneberg, E. H. *Biological foundations of language.* New York: John Wiley and Sons, 1967.

Lewis, M. M. *Language, thought and personality in infancy and childhood.* New York: Humanities Press, 1963.

McNeill, D. Developmental psycholinguistics. In F. Smith and G. A. Miller (Eds.), *The genesis of language.* Cambridge, Mass.: M.I.T. Press, 1966, 15–85.

Menyuk, P. *Sentences children use.* M.I.T. Res. Monograph #52. Cambridge, Mass.: M.I.T. Press, 1969.

Silverman, S. R. Teaching speech to the deaf—the issues. *Volta review,* 1954, **56,** 385–389; 417.

Silverman, S. R. The implications for schools for the deaf of recent research on hearing aids. *American annals of the deaf,* 1949, **94,** 325–339.

Wyatt, G. *Language learning and communication disorders in children.* New York: The Free Press, 1969.

Part IV. Organizational Patterns

CHAPTER XIV

Teacher Education

PATRICIA A. SCHERER

What is a teacher? A teacher is one of the most important of all people to pass through a child's life. The physician may care for the child's body, but it is the role of the teacher to awaken the child's mind, set thoughts astir, and set him on an unending quest for knowledge. This is the most exciting and rewarding task imaginable.

Is a teacher born or can the art of teaching be imparted to individuals desirous of attaining this art? It may well be that one of the greatest failures of our contemporary teacher preparation programs is that they train mere technicians. The student teachers do not learn the major goals and values for which the classroom should exist. When teaching is reduced to the level of instruction, the inspiration is missing and the classroom becomes a dull, static place where rigid, boring drills are practiced and basic skills are drudgingly acquired. The mind is deadened, for individual thinking is not encouraged in such a class. The instructor decides what facts the class should learn, imparts the knowledge, and requires the class to dutifully memorize the material. It is little wonder that children seek to escape such classes. They are eager to rejoin the outside world which is a natural and dynamic learning environment.

It has often been wisely said, first a child—then a deaf child. The same statement can apply to the teacher. First a teacher—then a teacher of the deaf. The roles are similar, the goals the same: the individual development of an independent socially mature adult capable of fulfilling himself. However, the relationship between the child and the teacher of the deaf is unique and particulary rewarding as the teacher is one of the few people in this child's life with whom he can communicate. This act of communication establishes a deep bond between child and teacher. Because the deaf child has a tendency to accept statements from his teacher at face value, it is her responsibility to avoid the role of "feeder of facts" and to move with assurance toward the role of catalyst in the learning process.

How can a teacher learn the art of stimulating minds? How can she bring the exciting world of ideas into the classroom? Hers is the joy of offering to young and avid minds the capacity to think creatively. Children can live fuller and happier lives because they have spent time with such a teacher.

What can be done to assist the student interested in the profession of teaching to understand the true goals of the educational process? It seems almost elementary to suggest that her own college education should embody all those attributes which enable learning to occur. And yet as simple as this solution might be it is the rare university program that practices what it preaches. The student cannot analyze effective learning techniques without experiencing them. How can a future teacher weigh the merits of a suggested type of learning when she has experienced no feedback from such a system? It might therefore be proposed that the most critical aspect of any teacher preparation program is the model learning environment offered to the student as she acquires the knowledge and skills basic to teaching.

This chapter will attempt to describe such a model. The reader is asked to remember that this suggested model can serve at any level from preschool up through the university. The model will be divided into three basic sections:

I. The teacher-child relationship
II. The acquisition of knowledge:
— goal orientation
— analysis of subject content
— presentation of material
III. Practicum

The first section will discuss the teacher-child relationship that should exist in the classroom if effective learning is to occur. It will try to show how to establish the warm accepting environment in which learning is a joy rather than a burden.

The second section will describe the process for the selection and presentation of the material to be learned. It is designed to make the teacher aware of the cognitive steps she must follow to create an appropriate learning plan for her class. The development of such skills should enable her to acquire greater insight into the process of learning in children. If a student in training only experiences the rigid classroom lecture approach to learning it is difficult for her to be creative in planning for new and stimulating ways of teaching.

The third section will set forth a plan of practical experience which will provide the student with the training needed for internalization of classroom learning.

In summary, it is hoped that such a schema can be of help to the university professor, the teacher in the classroom, and the student preparing to teach.

The primary goal of any teacher is to provide a warm, accepting classroom environment which fosters within the child the desire to learn. The development of this environment is a prerequisite which must be met if effective learning is to occur. The question raised is twofold: 1) what comprises a learning environment? and 2) what is the university's role in helping the student teacher understand how she can best create such an environment in her classroom?

The Teacher-Child Relationship

The most important aspect of the learning environment is the interpersonal relationship between the teacher and each child within the class. Dewey has written that education is a continuum of experience. However, in order that any experience be meaningful there must be a real encounter between the teacher and the child. The teachers must be themselves and not play roles. They must teach the children and not teach the subject. The child wants to know about life and its realities. The deaf child is often compelled to turn to the teacher for the answers he needs for everyday living. If the learning environment is to continue, the teacher must respond to this request as a real person and not as a dispenser of facts.

Teachers of the deaf are often guilty of becoming overly involved in teaching a series of facts or skills to the child. At first the teacher may feel that these acquired skills mean a job well done, but she gradually becomes disillusioned when the child fails to integrate the facts or to make meaningful application to new learning situations. The disappointment felt by the teacher when the children fail to generalize learned material permeates the classroom, affecting both herself and her pupils.

The effects of this type of teaching are best described by John Holt in his book *How Children Fail* (1970). Holt indicates that children who store up facts and parrot answers suffer a great deal of anxiety. They fail to find themselves adequate for the world in which they must live. This feeling of inadequacy leads to failure after failure, eventually ending in serious educational deficiencies.

When the teacher sees herself as a mere instructor and when she relates to the children as receptacles into which she can pour information, she creates an environment which stifles and destroys growth. Leonard (1969) attempted to explain the learning process when he wrote; "To learn is to change. Education is a process that changes the learner. . . . Learning involves interaction between the learner and his environment, and its effectiveness relates to the frequency, variety, and intensity of the interaction."

Therefore, the task of the teacher is to provide meaningful experiences through which children can learn. Meaningful experience requires in-depth interaction between child and teacher. The relationship cannot be instructor-to-child but rather human being-to-human being. Such a relationship implies mutual respect, concern, and honesty. In order that such interaction can occur, the teacher must know each child as an individual. She must be aware of individual learning processes, but she must first be aware of the child as a child. A child will not reveal himself to his teacher unless the environment is warm, honest, and conducive to complete expression. The work of the teacher is like that of the artist: it is a shaping of something that is given, and no serious artist will say in advance that he knows what will be given.

An effective learning environment can occur anywhere. It is helpful if it occurs in beautiful surroundings, but the surroundings are trimmings and are not a guarantee that learning will occur. Within this environment are people—children and a teacher. *Caring* is the underlying principle within the classroom. The teacher *cares* for her children and they in turn *care* for her. The people interacting within this environment are honest with each other. The atmosphere is open and accepting so that the children can be honest without fear. Evaluation is self-imposed and the child is freed from the inhibiting fear that his every act is subject to the stamp of *Good* or *Bad* by the teacher. In this room there are no failures. There is mutual respect for all members, and each child responds in his unique way. The teacher understands the uniqueness of each child, respecting and fostering the individuality rather than forcing it into her preconceived mold.

Some authorities have indicated that children often fulfill the role that they conceive as theirs. Teachers can subconsciously set goals which the children in turn will also subconsciously fulfill. The teacher of the deaf is well acquainted with the educational retardation of the deaf child. She has studied the statistics that tell her over and over of the educational problems of the deaf. It is frightening to wonder how this knowledge may cause her to establish preconceived achievement levels and how this in turn affects the teaching of deaf children. It may be that the establishment of a true learning environment in which preconceived levels do not exist is the best way to reduce the present-day educational retardation of the deaf.

Can the university teach its students to create a learning environment? Are there specific techniques and rules to follow? If we accept the fact that the environment in each class is unique because it is comprised of unique individuals, the answer must be an emphatic *no.* When children apply previously learned material and discover for themselves new principles of knowledge, the teacher can be sure the environment is positive. These are measures of success as well as the major rewards of teaching.

The teacher can learn to evaluate the classroom atmosphere. She can be sensitive to the daily drama played within the room. Her measure of success lies within the development of every child in her class.

When the children are free to expose their feelings to their teacher without fear of judgment, this is a measure of success. This can happen when the child understands that all people (teacher and children alike) are subject to good and bad feelings. The child must learn that it is what we do with our feelings that counts. He must feel freedom of expression, but also he must know there are helpful limits in the class which will enable him to gain inner control of his behavior.

When children enter the room willingly and express an eagerness to learn, this too is a measure of success.

When the children in the class are not afraid to make a mistake as they perform tasks, this is a measure of success. The teacher has realized that failure on a task is not failure of the total child or failure of herself as a person. She has transmitted her feelings of confidence to the children and they are freed to learn without fear of failure.

The only way in which a teacher can acquire an understanding of the true nature of learning is to be exposed to an environment as described above. She must first experience a model. It is impossible to provide a relationship such as has been suggested without first experiencing such a relationship. A reevaluation of the manner in which we prepare teachers is therefore in order. What is the understanding and relationship between professor and student? How actively engaged in the learning experience is the student? Or does she become the victim of the university lecture system?

In addition to participation in a good learning environment within the university, it is critical that the student teacher become aware of herself as a person. The teacher must know and understand self before she can hope to understand others. Knowing self can be a painful experience. Awareness of attitudes toward the teaching profession is necessary. In-depth knowledge of attitudes toward children, specifically deaf children, is essential. Each individual coming into the profession is a person subject to the human weaknesses of us all. Anxiety and vanity are often the underlying reason that the teacher becomes overly involved in method and techniques. The teacher of the deaf has a particular fear of failure based on hundreds of years of failure of educational programs to help deaf children achieve their potential. Is it any wonder that teachers of the deaf cling tenaciously to a method, certain that only through following this method they can survive? If we are to truly *teach* deaf children, teachers must be freed from restricting methodology. They must feel secure in trying new ideas. This can come only when they have confidence in themselves and in the children they teach.

The teacher preparation program can help foster such attitudes by providing group experiences for the students allowing them to explore their feelings about themselves and the children they plan to teach. Such groups, properly directed, can provide the student with the understanding necessary to excellent teaching.

It would therefore appear that the university's role is to provide a learning environment which serves as an appropriate model and to make small student-faculty groups available where feelings and ideas can be freely exchanged. Such a plan suggests radical changes within most university training programs. However, if we in fact are truly dedicated to the educational process, such changes are not merely desirable but mandatory.

The Acquisition of Knowledge

Banathy (1968) has described the teaching-learning activity in terms of an educational system, which can be delineated for any learning task. The system can best be understood if its purpose is clearly stated. That is, we must know why a particular task is important, how the teaching-learning system will operate, and the specifics of the environment in which this learning will occur. To the student preparing to be a teacher of the deaf it is vital that her course work include development of such a system. In this way, she is afforded a model to assist her in developing her own educational system for use in her own future classroom.

At the university level, a statement of purpose may often be found in the specific course descriptions listed in the college catalog. Keeping our criteria of a statement of purpose in mind, a course in Speech Development in the Deaf might be described in the catalog as follows: "The purpose of this course is to develop in the student teacher an understanding of the process of speech development in deaf children. As a result of this course the student will be expected to identify speech problems in deaf children and develop appropriate programs of remediation."

In some courses the student is handed an outline of course content. This is most desirable. However, such an outline should not consist solely of topics to be covered but should include a list of expected competencies that should develop as a result of this course. To continue our previous example such an outline might read:

1. develop an understanding of the process of speech development in normal children which can serve as a basis of comparison for deviant speech development;
2. develop skills in listening to normal and abnormal speech patterns. This skill should enable the student to analyze problems in articulation, nasality, voice quality, stress, rhythm, etc.
3. develop an understanding of appropriate remediation techniques for these problems;
4. demonstrate the effectiveness of these techniques through videotaped presentations of speech lessons with deaf children.

As a final aspect of the course description a statement concerning the environment for learning should be included. "This course is one of a required curriculum core for students training to be teachers of the deaf. It will meet four times a week for 50-minute periods. Laboratory work will be included as an integral part of the work. Tape recorders and tapes will be provided to enable the student to develop good listening skills. The final aspect of this course will take place in the clinic setting. The student will be expected to develop and apply remediation procedures on children with hearing impairment. Video tapes will be made of these sessions."

When the student in training has received all this information, she has before her all the material necessary to plan for the most efficient use of her time in order to derive maximum benefit from the course. Although this same written form cannot be used with small children, the principles are the same. The children need to know:

1. what they are learning;
2. why it is important to learn it;
3. what the necessary skills are;
4. how and where this learning will occur.

The security provided by this information permits the child to give his full attention to the learning task. Energy is not wasted on unnecessary fears of the unknown.

However, statements of purpose are only the beginning. It is then up to the teacher to prepare for herself and her students statements of objectives and goals.

Goal Orientation. One of the first and foremost principles of good lesson preparation should be the principle of goal orientation. This is the first task of the teacher, in that she must decide what learning she expects to achieve by the end of a given period of time. Goals can be established for the school year, the semester, the month, the week, and/or the day. There is value in having both long-term and short-term goals fully in mind before initiating a learning event. Mager (1962) states that in order to prepare instruction that will help the teacher attain her objectives, the objectives must first be clearly and unequivocally stated. Only after the destination is known can the problem of choosing the most satisfactory route to this destination be faced.

There is a skill involved in writing clearly stated goals and the teacher in preparation should acquire this skill. The teacher must be basically concerned with the change in behavior she expects to see achieved by the pupil whom she is teaching. In other words, the teacher must be able to specifically describe the behavior she will accept as the indication that what she was teaching has been learned. For instance, in the area of rhythm and its relationship to speech development, an example of clearly stated goals for a deaf children of varying ages might be:

4 years—the child will demonstrate his understanding of rhythmic patterns by running, walking, hopping, etc. to varying rhythms.

6 years—the child will demonstrate his understanding of rhythmic patterns by imitating patterns played on a drum.

8 years—the child will demonstrate his understanding of the rhythmic patterns of speech by playing rhythmic patterns for simple spoken phrases on a drum.

10 years—the child will demonstrate his understanding of rhythmic patterns by playing rhythmic patterns on a drum and incorporating the appropriate rhythm into his speech.

As you will observe, these statements are useful because they explain or identify what the child must be able to do to show that he has achieved the educational goal. The teaching-learning situation comes into focus clearly. Contrast the above with the rather nebulous goal: the child must understand rhythm. The person stating such a vague goal has no clear picture of what the learning process will be. What does it mean to understand rhythm? Where does one start teaching with such poorly defined objectives? Therefore, the goal serves two major purposes. It helps the teacher to specify to herself the behaviors and understandings she expects to create and it specifies for the child what is expected of him.

It is not only important that the goal be stated clearly but that it also specifies the minimum acceptable standard of performance. Depending upon the activity, standards of performance can be stated in terms of time, accuracy, etc. A goal so stated might read: The child will indicate his awareness of rhythmic patterns by imitating patterns accurately 80 percent of the time.

In stating the goal in this way, the child and the teacher have invested themselves in a learning task which is clearly understood and with learning and proficiency as its component parts. The teacher must now turn her attention to devising techniques and systems for teaching to bring about her stated goal. How much easier this task becomes when she has her purposes clearly in focus! It is difficult at first to be specific, for specificity implies that the teacher understands what she is teaching and can break it down into its logical and sequential steps. This is one of the most difficult tasks for an educator, and yet it is one of the skills with generalizing effects on all areas of teaching.

Analysis of the Learning Task. It is now necessary for the teacher to ask a series of very important questions:

1. what must the child learn in order to reach the desired goal?
2. is there an order in learning these skills?

3. what are the human capabilities necessary to achieve each step, i.e., skills, knowledge, attitudes, etc.?

We might identify two types of tasks at this point: the receptive task and the expressive task. The expressive task specifies the output expected of the learner, while the receptive task specifies the input which is necessary for performance to occur. It might seem that a carefully delineated expressive task will have built into it the receptive task. This may be true when the output is basically imitative and motoric in nature. However, that learning which we are most anxious to develop is basically cognitive in nature. Even though speech production contains elements of imitation and motor function, the most effective teacher of the deaf is vitally interested in the input of language and its effect on cognitive development. She knows that speech for speech's sake is a meaningless effort and waste of valuable learning time. Therefore, the expressive task for a class of ten-year-old deaf children can be stated as follows: The class as a group will be able to say the poem *Trees* in an intelligible manner—good articulation and proper use of intensity, pitch, and duration will be demonstrated. It is evident that the learning tasks which are necessary for this task to be accomplished are many. Now the teacher must specify in an inventory those tasks which must be learned in order that the performance criteria be met. In the beginning it is wise to list all tasks involved in order that the teacher can analyze the point at which any individual child is having trouble. Such a list might contain some of the following items:

1. each child will comprehend the significant ideas incorporated in the poem;
2. each child will demonstrate recall of the poem, its elements, relationships, order, etc.
3. each child will imitate the rhythmic patterns found in the poem;
4. each child will perceive the correct articulation of the words;
5. each child will perceive changes in pitch, intensity and duration;
6. each child will transduce these perceptions into spoken output.

In order for the child to attain these stated learning tasks, it is necessary for him to learn to:

1. understand why it is necessary for him to participate;
2. pay close attention;
3. follow directions;
4. respond to certain cues;
5. recognize internal feedback cues;

6. respond at appropriate times.

If any one of these learning tasks breaks down, the quality of the expressive task will suffer accordingly.

When the teacher has before her the entire range of receptive learning tasks she can subtract from them the tasks in which the children have already attained competence. Banathy diagrams it as follows:

INVENTORY OF RECEPTIVE LEARNING TASKS	MINUS —	INPUT COMPE-TENCE	EQUALS =	ACTUAL RECEP-TIVE LEARNING TASKS

We have now specified the expected behavior and delineated the tasks to be learned in order to achieve terminal behavior. We can now turn our attention to the content or the material to be learned.

The Content. This chapter is not designed to present the material to be taught in a speech course for students training to be teachers of the deaf. Rather it is written to delineate the type of program that will produce the most effective teacher possible. Further, it is an attempt to outline the type of university program which gives the student the necessary theoretical knowledge and also help her to make practical application of her knowledge to the everyday world of teaching.

However, since good teaching is based on sound philosophy, these thoughts cannot be complete without a brief discussion of the philosophical foundation of the content matter—speech development in deaf children.

Speech is an oral verbal output used by most members of our society to communicate thoughts, ideas, and feelings. Unless the deaf child can use speech as such a means of expression, we are bogged down in the senseless task of teaching him a mechanical act. Therefore, for our consideration we will separate the study of speech development into two areas:

1. speech as a conveyor of thought;
2. speech in terms of production and intelligibility.

The first aspect—speech as a conveyor of thought—implies that the teacher is basically concerned with input. It is therefore the task of the teacher preparation program to present the student with thorough background knowledge concerning the development of speech in hearing children. Current work in linguistics (Menyuck, Brown, Bellugi) provides invaluable insight into the process of development. The student must understand the role that audition plays in providing the hearing child with receptive language, i.e., input. When a firm foundation of understanding of normal language acquisition has been laid, it is time to understand the perplexities and difficulties imposed by deafness. The acquisition process is changed. Vision becomes an alternate channel for learning. Is it an effective channel? Myklebust (1960) describes the difficulties that accrue when the child must receive language through a visual channel and transduce the experience to the auditory output—speech. What cues does he use for this transduction? How can he best learn these cues? Myriads of questions come to mind which must be answered to the satisfaction of the student training to teach deaf children.

When input is our primary concern many educators of the deaf (Ewings, Groht, Myklebust) tell us that output will follow in a more meaningful and natural manner. However, again deafness takes its toll, for the output is distorted. Rhythm is poor, timing is off, breathing patterns incorrect, articulation in error. These items cannot be ignored if the child is to develop a spoken language which can be comprehended by others.

This instruction is also an ongoing process. It cannot be isolated to a series of repetitive drills which have little meaning to the child and as a result are poorly incorporated into his daily speech.

Speech production is a motor act. It involves the entire motor system of the body. If we are to remediate these aspects of the speech production, it is desirable to begin at a very early age and incorporate the total motoric development of the child into the program. Skills of listening and feeling must be evolved. Van Uden (1968) has given some insight into the aspect of speech production and its relationship to motor development in the deaf child.

In summary, speech can be viewed as a complex learning task. As it is an integral part of the input-mediation-output-process of oral language, it cannot be taught isolated from its component parts. Good teaching will give basic consideration to input, i.e., receptive language, to the act of cognition when the spoken word is used as the vehicle of thought as well as to the produced word, i.e., spoken output. Intelligibility is a vital aspect of this process because good intelligibility provides the deaf child with the positive feedback which encourages him to try harder in this most difficult task of learning to speak.

The acquisition of basic theoretical constructs implies that the curriculum must contain courses and practicum to this end. It has already been suggested that linguistics is an area necessary to the understanding of input. In addition, courses and practical experiences incorporating the following basic knowledge are necessary to the development of good teachers of the deaf:

child development
language development (normal and deaf)
psychology of learning
psychology of children (normal and deaf)
speech development (normal and deaf)
speech science
anatomy of the speech and hearing mechanisms
basic audiology
amplification (wearable and auditory training units)
media and its application to teaching the deaf
organization and presentation of content material.

These ideas represent only the basic core of understanding necessary in the development of a teacher of the deaf.

Presentation of the Content. Another series of questions now faces the teacher:

What must be done to help the learner achieve success?
Who is the most capable person to perform this task?
What exactly will this person do?
How will she do it?
When and where will it be done?

Banathy (1968) incorporates these ideas into four basic strategies:

1. functions analysis (what has to be done and how)
2. component analysis (who or what has the potential to do it)
3. distribution of functions among components (who and/or what will do exactly what)
4. scheduling (when and where will it be done)

The first strategy suggests that we carefully analyze the nature of the content. When content has been specified it must be organized. The teacher must concern herself with the sequence, the arranging and combining of content. She must be aware of the nature of the learning tasks within the content. She must know if one learning task is a prerequisite to another learning task. She must know how much information can be offered at a given time in order for understanding to occur as well as how much time is necessary for the mastery of a skill.

The presentation of the material is critical. Herein lies the motivating force for the students. Should it be teacher-taught? Are there teaching machines capable of doing as good or better job? Does the teacher need visual, tactile, or auditory aids? Can she use electronic equipment as an adjunct to learning?

The teacher of the deaf must give special attention to these matters. Not only must she specify what aids she intends to use, but she must develop skills in manipulating the materials easily with little or no confusion. Hers is an audience of visual learners who are easily distracted by visual stimuli. Therefore, the teacher must develop the art of incorporating the aids she uses into a smooth plan of content presentation. As the student moves through a preparatory program it is essential that she become acquainted with the content to be taught as well as the various aids and devices she may use to enhance learning. This awareness must include some practical knowledge concerning the operation of the equipment. Many teachers of the deaf are provided with excellent equipment in their classrooms, equipment which sits and gathers dust. This is not due to the teacher's refusal to accept new teaching systems but due to her lack of facility with the equipment. Only with ongoing instruction can she gain the needed ease to incorporate the aid into her daily teaching.

Practicum

This brings us to the third and final stage of the preparation of a good teacher—practical experience. This practical application of theory must permeate the student's entire program. We have previously suggested that the student in training needs practical experience with the equipment and aids that she will use in the classroom setting. Further, it has been suggested that without this practicum such aids will remain of little or no value to her as she takes her place in the teaching world.

It is invalid to say that as the teacher talks the child learns, which raises the question as to whether learning occurs in listening to lectures and reading books or whether the individual must find an active part in some experiences if the ideas gained in the classrooms are to be meaningful. Experience can be created in many ways, but until the student has mentally engaged herself in some form of experience the question as to the internalization of the material she has committed to memory can be raised.

Such learning theories mandate radical changes in teacher preparation programs. We can no longer be content to analyze the deaf child in a clinical, microscopic fashion, but we must be involved with him as a total child—aware of his thoughts, his needs, his feelings, and his goals. We must know him as a child; we must know him as an adult. We cannot help him in realizing his potential if we ourselves have no awareness of realistic goals and attainments. Such knowledge can be gained only through close contact with the deaf in all aspects of their lives—educational, vocational, and social. If such is our goal, the practicum center for students in training moves from the campus and the school into the world.

This is an exciting concept, but one which demands careful planning and implementation. Practicum therefore should serve four major purposes for the student teacher:

1. provide experiences which enable her to understand herself and others;
2. provide the experiences necessary to develop understanding of deaf people of all ages;
3. provide the experiences necessary to develop her own philosophy of teaching;
4. provide experiences which will enable her to develop skills in the use of teaching aids.

With such a broad perspective concerning the nature of the practicum, one could hardly envision an effective teacher preparation program not giving careful consideration to this aspect of its curriculum. It is this aspect of the preparation that allows the student to make use of the theory she acquires in the more formal classroom aspects of learning.

To summarize, it might be said that the preparation of a teacher is also an art. Heretofore we have taught her about subject matter, shown her a few skills, given her a little supervised experience, and sent her forth, her teacher's certificate in hand, with our blessing.

This chapter has suggested that this process is totally unacceptable and all too often produces an insecure, unhappy dispenser of facts. The responsibility lies at the feet of the university. Teacher preparation programs must be reorganized. A plan has been presented here which would expose the teacher in training to a model learning environment in which she would acquire the knowledge and attitudes necessary to good learning. The teacher preparation center would incorporate in its program all those attributes discussed in this chapter as comprising an effective learning environment. The student would no longer be told what to do but would experience first hand the feedback from a model educational system.

BIBLIOGRAPHY

Banathy, B. *Instructional system.* Palo Alto, Calif.: Fearon Publishing Co., 1968.
Holt, J. *How children fail.* New York: Dell Publishing Co., 1970.
Leonard, G. B. *Education and ecstasy.* New York: Dell Publishing Co., 1969.
Mager, E. *Preparing instructional objectives.* Palo Alto, Calif.: Fearon Publishing Co., 1962.
Myklebust, H. R. *The psychology of deafness.* New York: Grune & Stratton, 1960.
van Uden, A. *A world of language for deaf children.* St. Michielsgestel, The Netherlands: The Institute for the Deaf, 1968.

CHAPTER XV

Infant Education and Home Training

WINIFRED N. NORTHCOTT, PH.D.

An individually prescriptive oral and aural program for the hearing impaired child, from birth to three years of age, and his family is the hallmark of infant education models today.

Spontaneous speechreading and the dynamic use of residual hearing and speech for communication receive their maximum encouragement in association with daily activities in the home. If one accepts this premise, interaction of family, interdisciplinary professional team, and hearing impaired infant is central to the educational design. The amount and type of professional intervention depend upon the intellectual ability of the child and his functional use of residual hearing, the quality of parent-child relationships, and the resources within the child, his family, and the community.

An examination of current educational practices described in professional journals, national conferences (Colorado, 1967; Nashville, 1968) and international meetings (Toronto, 1964; New York, 1967; Warsaw, 1967) indicate that the infant's home and his community, as well as the private or public agency and school facility, now offer potential places for learning to take place.

The primary objectives of infant education today are: 1. comprehension of language through the development of auditory attention and the subsequent dynamic use of residual hearing and 2. the development of correct speech attitudes despite imprecise articulation.

The primary goal is the development of a child in harmony with his family, peer group, and environment; one who feels comfortable in being touched emotionally by them and who depends upon oral language as a functional social and cognitive tool for expression of individuality.

Thus, exemplary infant programs (Nashville, 1968; Calvert, 1969) pinpoint the characteristics of individual children in the selection of objectives, procedures, materials, and schedule of professional intervention for each. They emphasize a home-centered, parent-guided, natural language approach to the aural and oral education of all hearing impaired children during the brief infant years from birth to three.

Today, the recurring pattern is a focus upon the development of emotionally stable, confident, and competent families who can provide a supportive learning environment for the hearing impaired infant in his home. Under this rubric, a sustained program of parent guidance and education is an integral component of each comprehensive family-oriented infant education model which addresses to all facets of child growth and development through home training.

Definition of Terms

The term *infant* relates to a chronological age span from birth to the third birthday. The Nashville Conference on Current Practices in the Management of Deaf Infants (1968) added the interpretative phrase "0–3 Years" in its title.

The term *hearing impaired* is used by this author to include any child with a hearing loss which is handicapping educationally and developmentally. This term includes children who may later be educationally classified as hard of hearing as well as those who may later be classified as deaf (*Educational Guidelines,* 1968). Reed mentions the unsuitability of the audiological term "deaf" as applied to an infant who becomes operationally "partially hearing" through suitable training. "The same child without early training may appear to be operationally deaf and may be trained to remain so." (p. 543)

Sensitive Learning Periods

Evidence from the biological and psychological disciplines focuses attention upon the plasticity of infants and upon the importance of timing as well as type of environmental stimulation applied during the first few years of life when 50 percent of intellectual development occurs (Bloom, 1966) and the natural period for language learning reaches its peak (McNeill, 1966).

The central concept is the existence of critical developmental stages for infant learning which require appropriate stimulation and reinforcement in order to trigger the normal growth processes (Piaget, 1959). An examination of the interrelatedness of organic and experiential factors in early childhood development (Miller, 1950) highlights sensitive periods for learning when the infant is unusually dependent and highly motivated for environmental challenge. His learned responses from early experience have minimal interference from earlier established and inappropriate habits. During this period, the infant establishes his molarity and cognitive styles which are likely to persist into later life and contribute to subsequent intellectual and social behavior (Hunt, 1961). The premise has immense implications for the nature of preventive and compensatory programs of early childhood education (Biber, 1969).

Rationale for Parent Involvement

During the vulnerable years of infancy, family interaction sharply modifies the individual unfolding of a child's genetic pattern. The timing and intensity of parental responses to the infant's predictable intellectual, emotional, and physical requirements have survival value contributing to maturing social skills, emotional stability, and intellectual productivity (Erikson, 1963). During the second year of life when the child literally stands up for himself psychologically, the quality of parent support determines whether he will be encouraged to implement curiosity through exploration and know the joy of accomplishment or regress to more primitive behavior under frustration (Mowrer, 1960).

During the infant years the child's behavior reflects the emotional climate in his home (Spock, 1961) and the stability of the marriage and family interaction (Varwig, 1965). Comprehension and functional use of language in the hearing impaired infant may well have its origin in constructive positive relationships within the home (McCarthy, 1954; Smith, 1959). Projecting this premise into parent-child interaction in later years, the single most accurate predictor of general speaking ability has been identified (Marge, 1965) as the mother's educational expectations for her child.

When a mother and father are denied the role of normal parents to a normal child the trauma causes a distortion of reality and attendant inability to assess the deficit realistically or provide reasonable support in a rehabilitative program (Broomfield, 1967). Yet the vast majority of parents of deaf infants have no previous acquaintance with deafness and therefore possess no skill developed from prior experience to draw upon initially.

Since certain psychological adjustments and accomplishments are required of the mother and father as individuals before they can meet the responsibilities of young parenthood, their questions and fears must be answered so that subsequent adaptive responses to the infant can be positive (Solnit, 1961).

The need for immediate, parent-oriented therapy following the diagnosis of hearing loss in infancy is urgent (Fiedler, 1969), preferably synchronized with the mourning period to provide the psychological support parents require during the grieving that they experience (Smith, 1959). A sustained guidance program encourages a parent to maintain a reasonable degree of consistency in demands, expectations, and communication with her preschool child. Levine (1960) reports that given this support, there is every reasonable expectation for normal development despite delayed independence due to the hearing handicap.

Developments in Linguistics

Through an examination of verbal behavior in children, linguistic theorists and psycholinguists have come to view language acquisition as both an auditory and vocal process which integrates phonology, morphology, syntactics, and semantics. The premise is that every child is biologically programmed to learn language, being born with a linguistic competence or understanding of basic grammatical relationships which enable him to test his hypotheses about the rules of his grammar from the speech environment surrounding him (Chomsky, 1957; Lenneberg, 1964). The subsequent studies of expressive language in children (Bellugi, 1965; Brown and Bellugi, 1965; Braine, 1963) focus upon the child's ability to generate an infinite number of novel sentences by applying these internal rules.

Current theories of language acquisition cast a parent in the dynamic position of providing the child with enriched listening and speaking experience which expands his telegraphic speech, substantiates his word order, and hastens his conceptual development by linking language with child-centered activities. In turn, the child uses adult speech models to gain insight into the grammatical constructs of his language (Lenneberg, 1967). The deaf child must have "enough listening and speaking experience so that he can build up a knowledge of the sound system and of the statistics of the language" (Fry, 1963). The emphasis is upon comprehension as one facet of communication, although there is adult acceptance, positive reinforcement, and expansion of the child's expression with unconcern for the impreciseness of his responses.

Under this paradigm, the hearing impaired infant gains his first linguistic information about the grammar of his language from the prosodic patterns of speech that he hears—the rhythm, inflection, and stress of expressive language—presented in meaningful sentences. As he processes them through his own auditory and vocal mechanism, responding without intelligible words at first but conveying meaning through intonation patterns, valuable linguistic information is stored for future use (Simmons, 1968a).

Cognition and Language

A child's acquisition of language and his general cognitive growth are enmeshed and interact just as do memory and language. Categorically speaking, as a child increases in the capacity to grasp concepts, he simultaneously learns greater subtleties of distinction in speech. These in turn become important for further development of conceptual skills.

The research of Rosenstein (1960; 1964) indicates that the deaf child lags in linguistic performance, but that the mediational aspect of his understanding is unimpaired. Furth (1966) posits that cognition develops in proportion to the richness of the child's speech environment and the experiences accompanying it, since the deaf child's ability to reason and use imagination is intact.

Through play, the infant makes application of all his sensory modalities to structure his environment and perceive the regularities within it. Play elicits child language with its characteristic movement, gestures, mimicry, and words. It depends upon descriptive, vivid maternal language patterns to evoke cognitive judgments and mental discriminations from the hearing impaired infant in the sensorimotor stage of development. It is the quality of interpersonal relationships and verbal experience accompanying the child's associative selectivity of environmental experience which enables him to make a smooth transition to the concrete operational stage which follows (Piaget, 1959; 1969). The hearing impaired child receives direction for his movements from the language offered by his family which encourages him to think in terms of words, classify them into meaningful concepts, and finally through a gradual process of auditory, visual, and kinesthetic feedback to use them in order to manipulate his environment.

Today, remedial Head Start programs are visible reminders of the immature language patterns and poor auditory and visual discrimination found in children from homes which offer a barren linguistic and cognitive environment during the infant years (Hess and Shipman, 1965; Cazden, 1967).

The Role of Audition

The functional use of residual hearing as a primary modality for language acquisition and speech production is a basic objective of infant education programs today. The prognosis for success is dependent not upon the degree of hearing loss, but the "listening age" dating from the day auditory training is begun, preferably before the first birthday, and the richness of language environment accompanying the infant's listening experience (Huizing, 1961; Johnson, 1967; Nashville, 1968; Downs, 1968).

Discussants at the Toronto Conference (1964) cited mounting evidence from research studies of early sensory deprivation in support of a summary statement that the absence of early sensory stimulation causes neurological deterioration through disuse; which holds important clinical implications for educational management of the young child with sensory handicaps. It was emphasized that the initial auditory classification "deaf" or "hard of hearing" is assigned to an infant solely on the basis of an audiogram which records only the physiological measure of impairment. As a temporary label, subject to continuing reassessment for the addition of visual support as appropriate, it must not limit the initial prescription of a dynamic program of auditory rehabilitation to which all hearing impaired infants are entitled.

Reported evidence of the full statistical validity of definitive tests of hearing in neonates and infants (Toronto, 1964) supports the early prescription of a wearable hearing aid and the intensive instruction of parents in hearing training (Wedenberg, 1967; Downs, 1968). The benefits of amplified sound for infants in developing learned patterns of response to acoustic stimuli support the value of constant exposure to the sounds of speech and the environment. They indicate that the impaired auditory sense can become an effective channel for interpretation of contrastive patterns of speech, although the audiogram may indicate a profound loss (Griffiths, 1967; Pollack, 1967; Stewart, 1964).

The goal in auditory habilitation is the development of auditory attention and hearing perceptions leading to the dynamic use of residual hearing. It requires intensive auditory stimulation of the child's amplified hearing by his parents. Successful adjustment to a hearing aid and maximum benefit from amplification are directly related to the age at which it is fitted and parent guidance initiated (Sortini, 1959).

The present practice of diagnostic training in infant programs precludes the necessity of waiting for a precise threshold audiogram before checking auditory behavior in response to an enriched verbal environment (Nashville, 1968). It permits the systematic training of auditory perceptions during the infant's sensitive age for distinctive sound discrimination when he is naturally dependent upon the auditory function, although impaired, for linguistic information (Pollack and Downs, 1964; Downs, 1968). Tervoort (1961) concludes from longitudinal studies of young deaf children that, when appropriate acoustic stimulation is provided during the infant period of susceptibility to environmental influence, it prevents development of an esoteric system of gesture communication on a purely visual basis.

Speech

The focus in infancy is upon comprehension of language and the encouragement of the habit of verbal communication for expression of ideas and feelings.

Speech is recognized as the vehicle for expression of thought and the development of speech skills necessary to convey them. However, first-order priority is given to the provision of a variety of enriched auditory and visual stimuli associated with growth experiences in daily living which encourage improved approximations and imitations of the adult speech and language model (Vorce, 1958; Simmons, 1966). If well-inflected jargon and stabs at words are met with responsive adult expansion of the thought being expressed by a hearing impaired infant, the infant is motivated to acquire new language and vocabulary in the context of play and daily care. Through verbal and emotional reinforcement, he begins to perceive, abstract, generalize, and show self-expression about his environment in terms of words.

Phonemic drills, or a controlled vocabulary approach to language stimulation, are inappropriate for infants, who lack the required physical maturity and sustained attention and are in the discovery stage of learning (Toronto, 1964; Nashville, 1968). Pressure to make the young child letter-perfect in articulatory skills has psychological implications for resistance to later formal learning at an appropriate chronological age (Levine, 1960).

Historical Perspective

In a review of foreign literature, Quigley (1966) reported widespread emphasis in Europe upon infant education through home guidance with intensive concomitant use of high-quality amplification and auditory training. In England (Ewing, 1967) and the Scandinavian countries the ratio of infant caseload to availability of staff led to the present pattern of peripatetic teachers visiting parents of children of the 0–3 age group in their homes, supplemented by the Tracy Correspondence Course (Watson, 1967). "Short stay" institutes and "refresher courses" are offered parents, siblings, and hearing impaired infants in a central facility. These serve the dual purpose of guiding parents in daily management of the child and provision of an appropriate linguistic home environment as well as offering an opportunity for medical and audiological reassessment and evaluation. Illustrious examples are to be found at Ealing Hostel for Mothers and Children, of the Royal Throat, Nose, and Ear Hospital in London; Karolinska Hospital, Stockholm; Sint Michielsgestel (van Eijndhoven, 1967) The Netherlands; Bornekliniken, Copenhagen.

The beginnings of parent guidance at Manchester and other centers in the United Kingdom, Canada, and Australia are described by Ewing (1954), whose accumulated research evidence offers impressive support for educational intervention in infancy in terms of subsequent language performance, educational setting, and use of hearing aids (Ewing, 1957; 1958; 1964). Additional evidence is supplied by Reeves (1961), Owrid (1960), Stone (1961) and substantiated by extensive empirical and clinical experience in the United States (Griffiths, 1967; Pollack, 1967; Toronto, 1964; Nashville, 1968).

Conversely, Phillips (1963) and Craig (1964) found no long-range gains in academic achievement or social skills among residential school students in matched groups who entered school at nursery age and were offered a traditional child-oriented program without sustained support of parents.

In the United States as recently as the early 1960's preschool education was directed to hearing impaired children of nursery age who were "taught" in a clinic or school environment. The description of an exemplary child-oriented program for three- and four-year-olds is found in Groht's (1958) description of an enriched experiential nursery school provided by a trained nursery teacher at Lexington School for the Deaf as early as 1939, and supplemented by individual acoustic and linguistic stimulation offered by a teacher of the deaf. Dr. Groht concludes, "I hasten to add, however, that formal development of the speech sounds is not practiced here" (p. 18).

Elsewhere, the traditional formal speech and language drills and speechreading vocabulary of nouns and action verbs were provided nursery children still in the play-learning stage of development. Active parent guidance and group experience with hearing children, an integral component of the majority of present-day infant programs in the private sector, was not provided.

The annual parent institute was an early form of parent education for families of preschool children hosted, for instance, in Illinois, 1945; Kansas, 1947; and Minnesota, 1953, by a university and/or residential school for the deaf. They offered a program of lectures and parent discussion groups on facets of child growth and aural rehabilitation as well as demonstrations featuring a teacher of the deaf "working with" one or more nursery-age children on formal auditory training and lipreading.

Notable exceptions were the parent-oriented prenursery programs at the John Tracy Clinic, 1942, Central Institute for the Deaf, 1958, and a few hearing and speech centers. In 1961 at the Minneapolis Hearing Society, for example, Dr. and Mrs. Thomas Watson of England personally supervised implementation of their recommended shift of emphasis to a family-oriented prenursery program addressed to the support of parents through individual and group guidance.

The John Tracy Clinic, through its founder, Mrs. Spencer Tracy, and a notable professional staff has played an historic role in the development of present home-centered, parent-guided infant programs. Opening formally in 1943 as a "place where parents and children learn together" (Tracy, 1963) the Tracy Clinic offered a Parent's Correspondence Course without cost to the first of more than 31,000 families world-wide who have been enrolled to date. A summer training program offering university credit in preschool and parent education for teachers of the deaf was added in 1946, the parent film and recording series in 1962, and a demonstration home facility in 1965 with subsequent branches in Long Beach and Costa Mesa.

The parent-centered infant program at Central Institute for the Deaf began in 1958 in the clinic building under the leadership of the director of aural rehabilitation, Dr. Audrey Simmons, and initially made use of selected rooms of a second-floor apartment for experiential activities before the demonstration home was opened in 1965. During the past decade, Dr. Simmons has emerged as a central figure in focusing attention upon current research findings in linguistics and the behavioral sciences for application to the design and content of infant programs for hearing impaired children.

Federal "Seed Money"

The maternal rubella epidemic of 1964–1965 focused attention of the U.S. Department of Health, Education, and Welfare upon the unmet needs of handicapped children, many of whom suffered hearing loss as well as congenital anomalies. Beginning in 1965, a succession of federally funded national conferences addressed themselves to the compelling need for programs to serve a subpopulation of the hearing impaired—the very young deaf child. Two mandates emerged: 1. Early amplification and home training of the child; 2. Parental support to prevent secondary social and emotional stress relating to the defect.

The forerunner of these meetings was the international conference (Toronto, 1964) on *The Young Deaf Child: Identification and Management.* The *Proceedings* provide a definitive treatise on the identification, treatment, and educational management of deafness in young children. Health care specialists from the United Kingdom and Europe fully described the comprehensive program of parent guidance and education routinely provided in their countries. The emphasis is upon an *auditory* approach to the infant's acceptance and use of spoken language as a matter of course in connection with his daily home activities. Parents receive intensive instruction in hearing training and in the care and management of the infant's individual hearing aid.

A report to the Secretary of Health, Education, and Welfare by his Advisory Committee on Education of the Deaf (1965) urged programs for hearing impaired children as "young as one to two years of age" and sustained supportive services to their parents. The Conference of the Joint Committee on Audiology and Education of the Deaf (Tuscon, 1965) resolved that responsibility for identification, education, and training of the preschool hearing impaired child was a public one requiring public financial support.

Two years later, *The Challenge and the Charge* was issued at the National Conference on Education of the Deaf (Colorado, 1967), and echoed by the National Research Conference on Day Programs (1967) to convene a national conference on the hearing impaired child 0–3. The design of state plans was encouraged to provide educational services to children and support to their families without cost and regardless of minimum age.

In response, the invitational Nashville Conference* (1968) served as a forum and workshop for personnel actively teaching and offering parent counseling in operational programs for deaf infants, many of whom were staff members of various demonstration home projects initiated through federal grants. Detailed program descriptions, despite wide variation in infant populations, physical settings, and community support, revealed these commonalities: 1. An individually designed aural and oral program; 2. Utilization of child care and daily household activities for demonstration and home training; 3. Group experience with hearing children (all but three programs) and 4. Supportive medical, audiological, and psychological services.

Presently, a limited number of model service centers for preschool handicapped children are being developed under the Handicapped Children's Early Education Assistance Act (P.L. 90–538). These exemplary programs include a training and evaluation component and relate directly to child development and special education needs of the 0–5 age group while serving as catalysts for replication by local and state agencies assigning a high priority to pre-kindergarten programs. Although only five projects address primarily to hearing impaired and multiply handicapped children with hearing loss, each of the exemplary programs has emphasized an experiential basis for educational activities, a dynamic parent program, and nursery school experience with hearing children (Calvert, 1969).

Active parent participation ranging from membership on advisory

*Participants represented the listed agencies and institutions offering infant programs: Alexander Graham Bell Association for the Deaf; Atlanta Speech School; Bill Wilkerson Hearing and Speech Center; Central Institute for the Deaf; Emerson College; Gallaudet College; John Tracy Clinic; Lexington School for the Deaf; Minnesota Department of Education; Porter Hospital; Rochester Hearing and Speech Center; Rochester School for the Deaf; San Francisco Speech and Hearing Center; University of Kansas Medical Center; and Wichita State University.

councils to service as a teacher's aide is a design directive of the guidelines (Policies, 1969). Inadequate provision for parent participation was cited as a primary reason for disapproval of nearly three-fourths of the proposals submitted (Selected Data, 1969).

COMPONENTS OF EDUCATIONAL SERVICE: INFANT AND FAMILY

- comprehensive aural and oral program
- individual prescription of educational service
- medical, otological, audiological evaluation prior to entrance; re-assessment
- interdisciplinary professional team
- parent-child activities in home setting (family domicile, demonstration home or room)
- individual teaching (experiential setting; acoustic/linguistic stimulation)
- group educational activities (nursery school with hearing children)
- group educational activities (hearing impaired children only)
- parent guidance and parent education program

Individual Parent-Teaching Program

Premise: A parent is the nucleus of language input in every home, regardless of the child's auditory ability, and the climate for oral communication is dependent upon the parent's constructive coping skills developed through sustained guidance and support during the infant years.

> The Parent Teaching Program is not diluted preschool, but is itself a viable program in its own right, capitalizing on the child, where he is, what his interests are, and whatever materials and situations are available at hand. . . . The emphasis is upon natural language, natural learning, and natural listening. (McConnell, 1968 p. 65)

The methodology is multisensory, and the continual wearing of an individual hearing aid is assumed. The use of vision is encouraged, when appropriate, to supplement auditory clues for localization of environmental sounds and comprehension of speech. The relaxed atmosphere for the demonstration household activity may be offered in a complete demonstration home (Simmons, 1968b; Knox, 1968), a clinic or school setting, or through actual home visitation (Calvert, and Baltzer, 1967). The visits involving triangulation of parent, counselor, and hearing impaired infant are generally scheduled for one hour and at one-week intervals with exceptions as appropriate to permit desired behavioral changes to occur (McConnell, 1968; Horton, 1968).

Initially, the counselor demonstrates a specific experiential activity and the parent observes, being drawn gradually into the lead role through attention to the loudness, clarity, and frequency of auditory input by the counselor.

In making pancakes, for instance, the child carries on the actions involved in selecting utensils, beating the batter, eating the prepared food, and sharing the dishwashing activity with a parent who offers direction and control through conversation and/or eye clues. "We need a cup. . . . Can you find a cup? Good girl! . . . I'll hold the cup. . . . You pour the milk in. . . . Uh oh, you spilled some milk. . . . (Handing over a sponge) Wipe up the milk, please." The counselor provides the running commentary relating to the parent's intonation patterns, sentence length, choice of phrasing, use of vocal and visual clues, and expansion of the child's verbal expression (Northcott, 1967). Reinforcement of auditory perceptions and speechreading skills between guidance sessions is provided through home training which makes contrived use of daily experiences requiring cooperative action between parent and child. The accompanying language "Oh, it's so heavy. . . . It's my turn. . . . Come help me. . . . You're sleepy" and the circumstances gradually lead an infant to add a mediating link between speech and experience for conceptualization (Rosenstein, 1964).

Auditory stimulation begins with a mother's voice close to the infant's ear, rocking him in time to the rhythm of her singing, or speaking while using interesting intonation patterns. The infant's inflectional responses are reinforced and shaped through vocal play during the "talking times" of daily care (Pollack, 1967; Harris and Weber, 1967). At each developmental stage, the counselor provides parental support in the timing and substance of interesting auditory experience connected with the infant's toys and actions.

Following the activity specific guidance is given the parent concerning realistic oral home stimulation and the use of positive reinforcement in shaping his personal and linguistic behavior (Northcott, 1966). When discussion involves appropriate sentence length, the inflectional patterns or visibility factors of speech, the counselor relates it to the linguistic age of the child and the length of his present visual and auditory attention span. Grandparents and siblings may be invited to join in the parent-teaching sessions periodically. Separate meetings for fathers are desirable once a month (on Saturday) so that the entire family can contribute to the enrichment of the infant's oral home environment.

The Polaroid camera, video tape, and tape recorder offer a family support and reinforcement of their growing confidence in daily interaction with the infant.

A parent is encouraged to accept the child's gestures, facial expressions, and wordless and audible speech as well as words and phrases, however imprecise their articulation. At each stage of expressive language—vocalizing, babbling, holophrastic utterance, telegraphic speech—the infant depends upon appropriate *verbal reinforcement* and *expansion* to supplement his imperfect audition and sufficient *experience* to give it meaning. The emphasis is upon *spontaneity* and *purpose* in parent-infant vocal interaction, with attention to an individual cognitive style revealed in the content, not quality, of infant speech (Northcott, 1967).

Placement in a Regular Nursery School

Premise: Nursery school experience with hearing children offers a hearing impaired child the opportunity of responding with increased comprehension to the spontaneous language and lively intonation patterns of children of comparable age and interest levels.

The degree of parent and special education cooperation is the primary determinant for placement in a regular nursery school around the age of 2-1/2–3 years, rather than the severity of hearing loss. The decision is made by the special education personnel responsible for management of the infant's comprehensive program following consultation with the parents. Assignment to an appropriate group of hearing children depends upon the child's interests and abilities rather than his linguistic level (Northcott, 1970). Successful integration requires periodic site visitations for demonstration teaching and support of the nursery staff in addition to an invitation to attend selected inservice special education meetings (Cohen, 1963).

Three-quarters of the programs represented at the Nashville Conference (1968), in response to a questionnaire by this author, feature placement in an integrated nursery program, either in combination with group experience for hearing impaired children, or as a supplement to individual teaching of a supportive therapeutic nature. Lexington and Clarke schools for the deaf provide the integrated nursery on school premises; a similar nursery in the public school for the deaf in New York City was initiated in 1952 (Weinstein, 1968).

Visiting preschool programs in England and the Scandinavian countries in 1967, the author found hearing impaired children routinely placed in a regular nursery school in a ratio of one to three or four hearing children. They are served either through team teaching (nursery teacher and teacher of the deaf) or by a nursery teacher along with a supplemental weekly visit or two to a clinic for tutoring and parent guidance.

In Minnesota, tuition for a preschool hearing impaired child attending a regular private nursery school with hearing children is paid by the local school district, which can claim state aid in partial reimbursement. The nursery school teacher providing the service is required to hold currently valid N-K-P certification from the Minnesota Department of Education (Northcott, 1969).

An integrated nursery enables the hearing impaired child to observe appropriate behavior options for meeting the challenges of daily living. Here parents can realistically assess his abilities as well as his limitations (Stern, 1969). Placement serves to decrease an excessively dependent relationship which may have developed between a mother and her young hearing impaired child (Levine, 1955) and cushions the child against later developmental and learning problems often associated with the trauma of separation upon entrance into a residential program (Fiedler, 1969). In addition, the traditional preschool nursery for hearing children features individualized instruction, discovery learning, peer group stimulation, and use of intrinsic motivation which have enduring value for later interaction with a formal curriculum (Elkind, 1970).

Supplemental Instruction

A group nursery or tutorial program for the hearing impaired child supplements his placement in a regular nursery school. Provision of a linguistic environment in the supplemental program reinforces the earlier parent-teaching program more effectively than a traditional program of auditory training and speechreading (Stone, 1961; Nashville, 1968). Experiential activities to encourage divergent thinking are supplemented by symbolic materials, books, and experience charts which encourage selective auditory and visual attention and recall and provide opportunity for adult expansion and reinforcement of the child's expressive language. A diagnostic profile of each child's auditory and learning level is invaluable in designing each educational task.

Parent Guidance and Parent Education

Premise: The primary behavioral objective for parents is the development of emotional stability and resourcefulness in appropriate infant management based upon a realistic assessment of the child's abilities and hearing loss.

The central relationship between parent and counselor encourages a Rogerian (1961) atmosphere of trust and mutual respect which a parent can use for personal growth. Only gradually, as a parent's questions and anxieties about her effectiveness as an adult are met realistically, can attention be turned to the infant's needs (Smith, 1965). Natural humor, honesty, and adaptability are valuable assets to a counselor. Members of the interdisciplinary team and resource specialists can be utilized in the presentation of a common body of inter-disciplinary knowledge through individual and group parent discussions, lectures, and personal psychological counseling for selected families (Rotter, 1969).

CRITICAL AREAS OF PARENT GROWTH AND DEVELOPMENT

- attitudes and feelings of parents toward themselves and their children
- development of a stimulating home environment
- realistic acceptance of the infant's disability
- knowledge about the auditory function and its implications for the training of residual hearing
- stages of linguistic development in children
- physical, social, emotional, intellectual characteristics of preschool children

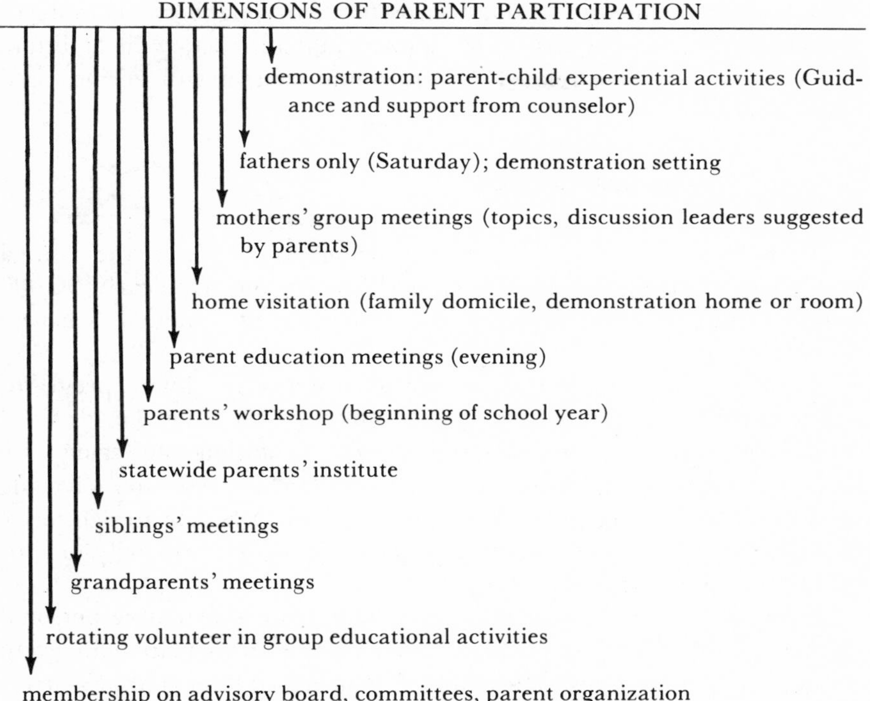

Evaluation

The psycho-educational diagnostician is usually and most desirably his teacher, functioning in the home or school setting, who appraises the child's response to learning tasks structured on the basis of behaviorally stated objectives and goals. As she teaches, she diagnoses to determine how the next learning task should be designed and the educational plan modified for the child and his parents (*Educational Guidelines,* 1968). Process evaluation data serves as a basis for appropriate individual program adjustments via continuing in-service training and case conferences involving the inter-disciplinary staff. Data may be accumulated in several forms: 1. standardized testing and objective measurement; 2. clinical observations and anecdotal description; 3. developmental log; time samples; 4. comparative video-taping and recorded speech samples.

The diagnostic opportunity provided in infant education programs ensures appropriate educational placement of a hearing impaired child when he reaches school age. It is expected that the number of hearing impaired children who will advance to their neighborhood nursery schools and kindergartens with supplemental instruction in audition, speech, and language related to curriculum content will be increased significantly.

Multiply Handicapped Infants

An epidemic of maternal rubella during pregnancy in the United States occurred during the winter of 1964–65 and left nearly 30,000 infants with handicaps, many of them with congenital anomalies as well as hearing loss.

Since diagnosis and evaluation are often imprecise, infant programs relate to the hearing impaired child who may give additional evidence of a physical, social, or mentally-handicapping condition interfering with normal speech and language development. A child suspected of being multiply handicapped is enrolled for diagnostic teaching to determine whether he would benefit from a program addressed primarily to children whose major deficit is hearing.

Parents of a multiply handicapped child require extensive personal guidance and counseling, but they may wish to also participate in group sessions with all parents. The child's demonstrated level of ability determines the goals and objectives designed to give realistic support to him and his family.

School-Community Relations

Widespread interest and support for extension of infant programs can be generated through carefully designed demonstration and dissemination activities. Ranging from mass media and convention participation to workshops for professional resource specialists, and descriptive summary sheets, each contributes to the gradual development of a supportive philosophical and financial climate necessary for proliferation of infant education programs.

Needs and Issues: Portent for the Future

The single most pressing need today is the availability of public school programs for hearing impaired individuals from birth to 21 years. Administered under the aegis of an integrated philosophy, a common set of goals, and a measurable set of objectives, this design would ensure complete management of the strategic timing of acoustic and linguistic input for its enrollees. It would permit diversity of educational options accommodating the individual needs of children. A new service model for the hearing impaired infant as an integral component of the comprehensive service matrix, would feature an individually designed program for each child and his family offered in an individual or inter-district facility or intermediate unit, or by an itinerant professional worker in a program of home visitation.

The premise of free public instruction from "diaper to diploma" carries an implicit mandate for change in existing legal, financial, and administrative patterns undergirding public support of programs for hearing impaired pupils today. The focus is upon the promotion of new relationships and new affiliations between individuals and institutions. The unanswered questions are many.

Can agreement be reached on operational definitions of nomenclature: hearing impaired, deaf, and hard of hearing? Can downward extension of entrance age be ensured through comprehensive state planning or does it require legislative change? What alterations would be required in present recruitment practices, certification standards, and special education state aid patterns? Should the educational program of a residential school, as one station in the cascade of state educational services, continue to be offered outside the purvue of the department of education as in some states today? Can the interest and organization of the medical community be broadened to provide routine neonatal screening? What are the logical first steps to achieve the necessary regionalization of public school educational services for the 0–3 subpopulation? What available monies under various titles of the Elementary and Secondary Education Act and other federal sources can be tapped for inauguration of pilot public school infant programs for hearing impaired children and restructured university coursework to develop a specialized staff? Can facilities and staff be located for the burgeoning numbers of multiply handicapped children requiring specialized educational services?

The efficiency of *initial* and *primary* emphasis upon *auditory* stimulation in parent-oriented infant programs is supported by significant European research findings and clinical and empirical evidence in the United States. It is imperative that this substantial evidence in support of early oral and aural intervention be examined with reason and objectivity by the professional community relating to the education of preschool hearing impaired children today. A published position paper would provide the conceptual framework for the functional design of future public school educational services for that subpopulation of the preschool hearing impaired, the infant in his first three years of life.

Research for the Future

The topics inviting research are legion and include: the benefits of early binaural amplification; conditions sustaining the increased rate of language performance noted in infants found in parent-oriented educational programs; studies of convergent and divergent thinking for matched groups of hearing impaired infants in a linguistic or controlled-vocabulary educational environment; inborn modality preference and its implications for early educational intervention.

Significant numbers of hearing impaired infants of deaf parents are currently making notable progress in the development of oral communication skills as participants in the comprehensive parent-oriented infant program at Lexington School for the Deaf. Longitudinal studies of this subpopulation and descriptive articles in professional journals detailing unique features of parent counseling are invited.

The children in Quigley's (1969) longitudinal research on the influence of fingerspelling on the development of language, communication, and achievement in deaf children were between the ages of 3-1/2 and 4-1/2 at the beginning of the study. Replication is appropriate in the light of availability of matched groups of hearing impaired infants, 0–3, today and might be linked with the risk of an incomplete visual function for those programmed to depend primarily upon visual clues. The 12.64-month mean age of onset of hearing loss in infants provided fingerspelling in contrast to the 1.79-month figure for the control subjects was not deemed meaningful by Quigley in the behavioral sense, in the context of current educational provisions for hearing impaired children. This offers additional opportunity for scientific investigation.

The present-day explosion of knowledge requires a teacher to be a manager of learning strategies and a resource person serving children with individual cognitive styles rather than a dispenser of factual information. Research addressed to the ways in which children learn, the characteristics of an effective learning environment, and the structure and spacing of educational tasks matching content to cognitive development offers great promise of an inviting educational environment for every hearing impaired child, 0–21, in the future.

BIBLIOGRAPHY

Audiology and education of the deaf. *Proceedings, National Conference on Audiology and Education of the Deaf.* Tucson, Arizona: V.R.A. Department of H.E.W., 1965.

Bellugi, U. The development of interrogative structures in children's speech. Report #8, *The development of language functions.* Ann Arbor: University of Michigan, 1965.

Biber, B. *Challenges ahead for early childhood education.* Washington, D.C.: National Association for Education of Young Children, 1969.

Bloom, B. *Stability and change in human characteristics.* New York: John Wiley and Sons, 1966.

Braine, M. D. S. The ontogeny of English phrase structures: list phas. *Language,* 1963, **39,** 1–13.

Broomfield, R. M. Guidance to parents of deaf children—a perspective. *British journal of disorders of communication,* 1967, **2,** 112–113.

Brown, R., and Bellugi, U. Three processes in the child's acquisition of syntax. In E. H. Lenneberg (Ed.), *New directions in the study of language.* Cambridge, Mass.: M.I.T. Press, 1964.

Calvert, D. R., and Baltzer, S. Home management in a comprehensive preschool program for hearing-impaired children. *Exceptional children,* 1967, **34,** 253–258.

Calvert, D. R., Olshin, G. M., DeWeerd, M. J., and Berson, M. P. Office of Education describes model projects for young handicapped children. *Exceptional children,* 1969, **36,** 229–248.

Cazden, C. B. Some implications of research on language development for preschool education. In Hess, R. O., and Bear, R. (Eds.), *Early education: Current theory, research and practice.* Chicago: Aldine Pub. Co., 1967.

Chomsky, N. *Syntactic structures.* The Hague, The Netherlands: Mouton and Co., 1957.

Cohen, E. S. Teaching and guidance of preschool deaf children. *Report of the Proceedings of the International Congress on Education of the Deaf.* Washington, D.C.: U.S. Government Printing Office, 1964, 842–847.

(Colorado, 1967) *Proceedings, National Conference on Education of the Deaf.* Washington, D.C.: U.S. Dept. of H.E.W., 1967.

Conference on Current Practices in Management of Deaf Infants (0–3 years). *Proceedings.* Nashville, Tenn.: Bill Wilkerson Speech and Hearing Center, 1968.

Craig, W. N. Effects of preschool training on the development of reading and lip-reading skills of deaf children. *American annals of the deaf,* 1964, **109,** 280–296.

Downs, M. P. Identification and training of deaf child: Birth to one year. *Volta review,* 1968, **70,** 154–158.

Elkind, D. The case for the academic preschool: Fact or fiction? *Young Children,* 1970, **21,** 132–139.

Education of the deaf. A report to the Secretary of H.E.W. by his Advisory Committee on Education of the Deaf. U.S. Department of H.E.W., March, 1965.

Educational guidelines: A family-oriented preschool program for hearing-impaired children in Minnesota. Approved by State Board of Education, April 1968.

Erikson, E. Childhood and society (2nd ed.) New York: W. W. Norton and Co., 1963.

Ewing, A. W. G., and Ewing, I. R. *Speech and the deaf child.* Manchester, England: University Press, 1954.

Ewing, A. W. (Ed.) *Educational guidance and the deaf child.* Manchester, England: University Press, 1957.

Ewing, I. R., and Ewing, A. W. G. *New opportunities for deaf children.* Springfield, Ill.: Charles C Thomas, 1963.

Ewing, A. W., and Ewing, E. C. *Teaching deaf children to talk.* Washington, D.C.: The Volta Bureau, 1964.

Ewing, E. C. Parent guidance. *Proceedings of International Conference on Oral Education of the Deaf.* Washington, D.C.: Alexander Graham Bell Association for the Deaf, 1967, 318–328.

Fiedler, M. F. Developmental studies of deaf children. *ASHA Monographs No. 13.* Washington, D.C.: American Speech and Hearing Association, 1969.

Fifth Congress of the World Federation of the Deaf. Warsaw, 1967. The very young hearing-impaired child (Selected papers). Washington, D.C.: Alexander Graham Bell Association for the Deaf, 1967.

Fry, D. B. Speech. *Report of the Proceedings of the International Congress on Education of the Deaf.* Washington, D.C.: U.S. Government Printing Office, 1964, 183–191.
Furth, H. *Thinking without language.* New York: The Free Press, 1966.
Griffiths, C. *Conquering childhood deafness.* New York: Exposition Press, 1967.
Groht, M. A. *Natural language for deaf children.* Washington, D.C.: Alexander Graham Bell Association for the Deaf, 1958.
Harris, G., and Weber, L. Babies with hearing losses. *Volta review,* 1967, **69,** 604–609.
Hess, R. D., and Shipman, V. C. Early experience and the socialization of cognitive modes in children. *Child development,* 1965, **36,** 869–883.
Horton, K. B. Home demonstration teaching for parents of very young deaf children. *Volta review,* 1968, **70,** 97–101; 104.
Huizing, H. C. Audition—its basic skills in early childhood. *Proceedings of 2nd International Course in Paedo-Audiology.* Groningen University, June 1961, 51–60.
Hunt, J. *Intelligence and experience.* New York: Ronald Press, 1961.
International Conference on Oral Education of the Deaf. *Proceedings.* Vol. I and II. Washington, D.C.: Alexander Graham Bell Association for the Deaf, 1967.
Johnson, E. W. Let's look at the child not the audiogram. *Volta review,* 1967, **69,** 306–310; 344.
Knox, L. K., and McConnell, F. Helping parents to help deaf infants. *Children,* 1968, **15,** 183–187.
Lenneberg, E. H. *New directions in the study of language.* Cambridge, Mass.: M.I.T. Press, 1964.
Lenneberg, E. H. Prerequisites for language acquisition. *Proceedings of International Conference on Oral Education of the Deaf.* Washington, D.C.: Alexander Graham Bell Association for the Deaf, 1967, 1302–1363.
Levine, E. S. Emotional problems of deaf children. *Fanwood Journal,* 1955.
Levine, E. S. *The psychology of deafness.* New York: Columbia University Press, 1960.
Levine, E. S. *Youth in a soundless world.* New York: New York University Press, 1956.
Marge, M. The influence of selected home background variables on the development of oral communication skills in children. *Journal of speech and hearing research,* 1965, **8,** 291–309.
McCarthy, D. Language disorders and parent-child relationships. *Journal of speech and hearing disorders.* 1954, **8,** 514–523.
McConnell, F. (Ed.) Proceedings: Current practices in educational management of the deaf infant (0–3 years). Nashville, Tenn., 1968.
McNeill, D., The capacity for language acquisition. *Volta review,* 1966, **68,** 17–33.
Miller, N. E. Some implications of modern behavior theory for personality change and psychotherapy. In Lindzey, G., and Hall, C. S. (Eds.), *Theories of personality: Sources and research.* New York: John Wiley and Sons, 1965, 413–429.
Mowrer, O. H. *Learning theory and behavior.* New York: John Wiley and Sons, 1960.
National research conference on day programs for hearing-impaired children. *Proceedings.* Washington, D.C.: Alexander Graham Bell Association for the Deaf, 1968.
Northcott, W. Language development through parent counseling and guidance. *Volta Review,* 1966, **68,** 356–360.
Northcott, W. Counseling parents of preschool hearing-impaired children. *Proceedings of the International Conference on Oral Education of the Deaf.* Washington, D.C.: Alexander Graham Bell Association for the Deaf, 1967, 424–442.
Northcott, W. Head Start program . . . implications for deaf children. *Volta review,* 1968, **70,** 106–113.
Northcott, W. Education of the hearing impaired. *Bulletin, Education for the Hearing Impaired.* Washington, D.C.: American Organization for Education of the Hearing Impaired, Winter 1969, 22–23.
Northcott, W. Candidate for integration: A hearing-impaired child in a regular nursery school. *Young children,* 1970, **25,** 367–380.
Owrid, H. L. Measuring spoken language in young deaf children. *Teacher of the deaf,* 1960, **58,** 124–128.
Phillips, W. D. The influence of preschool language on achievement in language arts, arithmetic concepts and socialization of young deaf children in residential schools. Unpublished dissertation, Teachers College, Columbia University, 1963.

Piaget, J. *The language and thought of the child* (3rd ed.) Translated by M. Gabain. London: Routledge & Kegan Paul, 1959.
Piaget, J., and Inhelder, R. *The psychology of the child.* New York: Basic Books, 1969.
Policies and procedures. Handicapped Children's Education Assistance Act. P.L. 90–538. Bureau of Education for the Handicapped, U.S.O.E. February 1969.
Pollack, D. The crucial year: A time to listen. *International audiology,* 1967, **6,** 243–247.
Pollack, D. C., and Downs, M. P. A parent's guide to hearing aids for young children. *Volta review,* 1964, **66,** 745–749.
Quigley, S. P. Language research in countries other than the U.S. *Volta review,* 1966, **68,** 68–83.
Quigley, S. P. *The influence of fingerspelling on the development of language, communication, and educational achievement in deaf children.* Urbana: Institute for Research on Exceptional Children, University of Illinois, 1969.
Reed, M. Preprimary education. *Report of the Proceedings, International Congress on Education of the Deaf.* Washington, D.C.: U.S. Government Printing Office, 1964, 543–550.
Reeves, J. K. The use of hearing aids by children with defective hearing. *Teacher of the deaf,* 1961, **59,** 181–190.
Rogers, C. R. *On becoming a person.* Boston: Houghton Mifflin, 1961.
Rosenstein, J. Cognitive abilities of deaf children. *Journal of speech and hearing research,* 1960, **3,** 108–119.
Rosenstein, J. Concept development and language instruction. *Exceptional children,* 1964, **30,** 337–343.
Rotter, P. The parents' role in encouraging speech growth. *Volta review,* 1955, **57,** 53–57.
Rotter, P. *A parents' program in a school for the deaf.* Lexington School for the Deaf Education Series Book VI. Washington, D.C.: The Alexander Graham Bell Association for the Deaf, 1969.
Selected data from project proposals, fiscal year 1969. Handicapped children's early education assistance act, P.L. 90–538, Bureau of Education for the Handicapped, U.S.O.E., September 1969.
Simmons, A. Language growth for the pre-nursery deaf child. *Volta review,* 1966, **68,** 201–205.
Simmons, A. A. teaching aural language. *Volta review,* 1968, **70,** 26–30 (1968a)
Simmons, A. A. Home demonstration program at Central Institute for the Deaf. In *Proceedings,* Conference on Current Practices in Management of Deaf Infants (0–3 years). Nashville, Tenn.: Bill Wilkerson Speech and Hearing Center, 1968. (1968b)
Smith, A. J. Parent counseling. *Proceedings,* 39th meeting, Convention of American Instructors of the Deaf. Colorado: 1959, 246–250.
Smith, A. J. Understanding parents. *Proceedings.* A guidance and counseling program for parents of preschool deaf children. Minnesota Department of Education Special Study Institute, Minneapolis, 1965.
Solnit, A. J., and Stark, M. J. Mourning and the birth of a defective child. *The psychoanalytic study of the child* New York: International University Press, 1961, **16,** 523–537.
Sortini, A. Importance of individual hearing aids and early therapy for preschool children. *Journal of speech and hearing disorders,* 1959, **24,** 346–353.
Spock, B. *On being the parent of a handicapped child.* Chicago: National Society for Crippled Children and Adults, Inc., 1961.
Stern, V. W. Fingerpaint on the hearing aid. *Volta review,* 1969, **71,** 149–154.
Stewart, J. L., Pollack, D., and Downs, M.P. A unisensory program for the limited-hearing child. *ASHA,* 1964, **6,** 151–154.
Stone, L. J., Fiedler, M. F., Fine, C. G. Preschool education of deaf children. *Journal of speech and hearing disorders,* 1961, **26,** 45–60.
Tervoort, B. T. Esoteric symbolism in the communication behavior of young deaf children. *American annals of the deaf,* 1961, **106,** 436–480.
(Toronto, 1964) The young deaf child: Identification and management. *Proceedings.* Acta Otolaryngologica, Supplementum 206, Stockholm, 1965.
Tracy, L. Preschool. In *Report of the Proceedings of the International Congress on Education of the Deaf.* Washington, D.C.: U.S. Government Printing Office, 1964, 483–494.
van Eijndhoven, Father J. Sint Michielsgestel. *Proceedings of International Conference on Oral*

Education of the Deaf, Washington, D.C.: Alexander Graham Bell Association for the Deaf, 1967, 67–76.

Varwig, R. Social considerations of preschool hearing impaired children. *Volta review,* 1965, **67,** 434–439.

Vorce, E. Speech in the preschool for the deaf. *Volta review,* 1958, **60,** 478–481; 506.

(Warsaw, 1967) The very young hearing impaired child. Selected papers from the Fifth Congress of the World Federation of the Deaf, Warsaw, 1967. Compiled by A. G. Bell Association for the Deaf, Washington, D.C.

Watson, T. C. *The education of hearing-handicapped children.* London: University of London Press, 1967.

Wedenberg, E. Experience from 30 years of auditory training. *Proceedings of International Conference on Oral Education of the Deaf.* Washington, D.C.: Alexander Graham Bell Association for the Deaf, 1967, 2089–2100

Weinstein, G. W. Nursery school with a difference. *Parents,* 1968, **43,** 66–69.

The young deaf child: Identification and management. *Proceedings.* Acta Otolaryngologica, Supplementum 206, Stockholm, 1965.

CHAPTER XVI

Speech for the Deaf Child: Knowledge and Usage Trends

William G. Hardy, Ph.D.

Sincere and careful attention to the topic of *trends* relative to speech for the deaf child probably requires a kind of prescience that this writer does not claim to have. On the other hand, he does have some beliefs and some comments to make about speech for the deaf child,—all based, naturally, on common sense and pure reason. Even a start in this direction is probably all that can be reflected in the many verbal excursions on this topic which are so freely indulged in these days.

Some Negative Observations

It might or might not be wise and fair to introduce these remarks with a quite negative expression of opinion about some things (ideas, attitudes, expressions of opinion) that are currently going on. A basic point is that there is in action a kind of "putsch" in the name of signs and manual methods of teaching the deaf. Unfortunately, in lieu of sober consideration and reflection, some of the "putschers" appear to be both aggressive and arrogant, quite unwilling to undertake an argument from common ground, well satisfied with assertion. This is unfortunate, indeed. For one, I have no particular antipathy toward either of these methods of training a deaf child, provided that they are not applied in place of a serious effort to help the child to understand and utilize speech early in life. The usual response to this opinion is a rejoinder to the effect that so many children cannot learn to talk early in life. So be it; I suspect that the experienced audiologic clinician is rather more clearly aware of this fact than is the average teacher of the deaf, for if he is really experienced in this field he is looking for and at much more than ears and deafness-by-definition. There is a potent effort these days to offer a multiple defense about manual spelling and signing, and a very considerable amount of offense. One reads and hears much about the "simultaneous method" and, more recently, "total communication." As I have watched mature people utilizing either of these (they seem to amount to much the same thing), it seems apparent that what is going on might better be called the "spontaneous method," typically based on a mature lifetime of acquaintance with manual communication. One must wonder seriously whether it is possible for either a preschool-age child or a first grader to utilize this form of communication with facility. Communicative reflexes usually take quite a while in development, speech as well as manual devices.

As a working clinician in audiology, one must believe that there are particular children who, for various reasons, cannot learn speech well. One must also observe, however, that the problems these children present—often summed up with the use of the term *learning disability*—are really particular, to a degree that makes it important to learn to talk within a normal or usual course of development. This is, however, a very large order. It is predicated upon a thorough knowledge of the child's capacities and limitations. (This is surely true about all children, not simply those who are deaf.) This latter appraisal can rarely be accomplished in a single clinical session. It usually requires a sequential analysis which is not uncommonly called *diagnostic teaching*. One authority on the education of the deaf child was recently heard to describe a quite single-minded approach to the diagnosis of deafness in the young preschool-age child. The descriptors were very direct: one asks the child to close his eyes and if he does not respond to a verbal-symbolic stimulus he is considered to be deaf. In terms of what we know about the measurement of hearing and its uses at the integrative level of the brain, this can only be considered a non-intellectual approach to the problem, with much non-sense. The early and sensible use of hearing aids, the selection of which is appropriately adapted to the acoustic spectrum available to the child, should entirely change this kind of attitude toward these problems.

Some Positive Observations

To turn to some of the more positive aspects of speech for the deaf, there is much to be said. First, contrary to the expressed belief of some educators of deaf children, there are increasingly lesser distinctions between *the deaf* and *the hard of hearing*. This simply reflects what is happening these days in terms of sustaining and maintaining life in the young child which heretofore was not possible. When one is able to work from a high-risk register, to take advantage of knowledge about prenatal and perinatal conditions that long remained unknown, and to apprehend the fact of responsiveness to sound early in an infant's life, he has the possibility of utilizing much information in helping a family to understand a problem and to undertake to meet it. At stake here is a realization that lack of response to an acoustic signal may represent many kinds of behavioral limitations other than, but sometimes including, deafness. As one of our colleagues has recently commented, "Oralism is as much an attitude as it is a method." (One might include auralism, as well.)

These other limitations may involve many aspects of learning disabilities, only part of which can plausibly be related to hearing impairment. It is surely true that many children who exhibit difficulties in learning language do indeed have impaired hearing. But it is surely not true that something like deafness is necessarily their primary deviation in terms of incapacity to undertake to learn language normally.

It follows, then, that early screening of infants relative to acoustic responses and differentiation (long before they could be expected to demonstrate language) is an absolute requirement to describe at least one clinical aspect of their capacities for learning. This we now know how to do, not with infallibility but with reasonably good assurance that this is a necessary early step in the long process of follow-up in finding out how a very small child can learn. This kind of early screening by 6 to 10 months of age, which has been well described in the literature, is the foundation both of behavioral diagnosis and of prediction about any child's capacities and limitations. This sort of inquiry and description cannot be accomplished by intuition alone, nor through the use of a medium or other non-worldly unrealities.

A Useful Program

Based on a thorough program of screening for the infant and adequate otologic attention (for many infants are subject to upper respiratory infections which, unattended, can affect their acoustic responses), there is implied in the previous remarks the need for programs of home training and parental guidance for both infants and very young preschool-age children. Already such programs have been started in many communities. Relative to the education of the deaf child and of the hard of hearing child, it seems to make sense that a very careful sequence of training and learning be established.

First, home guidance with the mother, already referred to: this means some careful direction of her capacities and interest, accomplished within the home, relative to the fundamentals of learning language and speech. This requires specific concentration on a mother's part in the use of communicative experiences through which she is able to help her child both to expand vocabulary and to develop normal syntax.

Second, the use of training and teaching in small groups; this can certainly well be undertaken by the age of 30–36 months. This is an extremely important step relative to the child's development of auditory monitoring and to the sociology of knowledge relative to language. This is an inescapable aspect of all learning. Without it no child can develop the capacity for critical control that is probably the brain's highest integrative capacity in learning whatever involves verbal-symbolic communication and the development of cognition that is related to this.

These generalizations apply to all children. Obviously, there are many more limitations in children who are deaf or severely hard of hearing. It is important to remember, however, that a child ordinarily learns language through conversation. Linguistic structure, in the sense of the brain's capacity to learn syntax in any useful degree, is utterly dependent on expressed oral language, not on signs and fingerspelling.

In our black and white ghettos this is referred to as a step in child guidance, and these are called child centers in the communities where they exist.

A third stage in developmental generation with children is what in recent years has been called Head Start. This is a step that has proved to be important in several thousand communities. A further step has to do with training in kindergarten as a precursor of a more formal school curriculum.

Rather as an aside, but surely pertinent, is the idea that an early introduction to reading is good for all children, let alone those who have severe or profound impairment of hearing. It has been clearly demonstrated within the past few years that a child with reasonably normal developmental potentials (particularly one who has an auditory deficit) can learn to read long before "statutory" school age. His capacities and limitations must be understood. This can be done at least by the age of 4 years, other psychosocial aspects of his development being reasonably good.

The Beginnings of Speech

There is now going on very extensive study of early vocalization and beginning speech sounds. This work is being carried on in several centers. Among other things, it involves the direct recording and observation of birth cries. Very soon in the infant's life these kinds of data can be translated into some very useful observations about the basic biologic and neurologic system of the child. Still later, with the use of careful tape-recording and interpretation of the results much is being learned about other relations between hearing and hearing impairment. There is much to be done in this aspect of inquiry. It will be done, of course, and should prove of tremendous value in relation to ways and means of teaching the hearing impaired child. What is at stake here (not always admitted by at least some special educators) is the possibility of learning much more than we now know about the relationships among genetics, etiology of disability, and the behavior of the child.

Aids for Learning

Relative to some of the ideas pertinent to these complex disturbances in learning and behavior, it might be well once again to emphasize the need for concentration on the capacity to read. Among other things, the child whose problems have been caused by prenatal rubella is apt to be wizened, an underachiever, faced with varieties of biologic deficits. It is clear from recent studies that he needs all the help he can get in language learning. Within his capacities reading will be one of his greatest attributes in the development of learning. Most current studies of reading readiness and achievement support this point of view.

Cued Speech

Another aspect of learning in the deaf child currently enjoying considerable professional favoritism is an attitude toward his learning that is centered in the thesis of *cued speech*. As an idea, this is no newer than gestural behavior. It has simply been organized in an orderly fashion and has, therefore, become more available for popular use. In a value judgment one may well believe that this is good.

In the system of cued speech, speech and hand signals are used simultaneously. Unlike the signals of fingerspelling or conventional signing, however, the hand signals of cued speech do not have independent symbolic value. By themselves, they convey no meaning. Instead, they are used to resolve ambiguities for the lipreader—especially for the lipreader who has little experience in language usage—by differentiating look-alike gestures of the lips, tongue, and jaw.

For the vowels of American English, four different hand positions are used. These help to differentiate:

1. The vowels with an open mouth position (in the International Phonetic Alphabet: ɑ :, or :a:, : æ :, and : ɔ :);
2. The vowels with a flattened-relaxed position (in I.P.A. : ʌ :, :ɪ:, or : ə :, : ɛ :, and :i:);
3. The vowels with a rounded position (in I.P.A. :o:, :ʊ:, :u:, and : ɜ :).

These hand positions are:

A. *Base* (i.e., to one side at the level of the larynx);
B. *Larynx* (i.e., in the midline at the level of the larynx);
C. *Chin* (i.e., at the level of the chin in the midline);
D. *Mouth* (i.e., at one corner of the mouth).

Diphthongs are represented by a shift of hand position from that appropriate to the first element of the dipthong to that appropriate for the last element.

For the consonant positions of American English, seven different hand configurations are used. (The hand is always placed with the palm toward the person signaling.) Each configuration is identified with three or four different consonants which do not look alike on the lips, e. g., pointing of the index finger is used to indicate :d:, :p:, and : ʒ :. The configuration will be quite different for consonants which look like :d:, :p:, or : ʒ :. For example, all fingers are extended for :t:.

As far as one can tell, the rule is that when a hand configuration for a consonant is given, the hand *position* must be that of the following vowel, whether or not it belongs to the same word. However, if there is no following vowel, i. e., the sentence ends with a consonant, the base position is used with the proper hand configuration for that final consonant. Also, (as with a vowel), if there is no preceding consonant, i. e., the sentence begins with a vowel, the hand configuration appropriate to the "t group," or :t:, :m:, and :f:, is used with the hand position appropriate to this initial vowel sound. Presumably lipread information resolves possible confusions in these instances.

The system is based on the broad phonetic values of American English, not on its orthography. The Initial Teaching Alphabet forms the basis for the signals described above. The system is intended to bridge the gap between the proponents of oral and of manual methods of teaching the deaf. While it is ingenious, it seems unfortunate that it was not tried out on a small scale first, so that modifications might have been made as these were suggested in practice.

It is claimed that the capabilities of the deaf in speech production are improved by use of this system, as well as capabilities in speech perception. This claim seems to be exaggerated. The use of phonetic transcription or of the Initial Teaching Alphabet would go equally far toward accomplishing this end, and possibly better than does the system of cued speech.

Some Combinations

A not unrelated concept is that of the "simultaneous method." One must wonder how this can be done by a confused 6-year-old who is deaf, or at least is without adequate acoustic information. The method is undertaken, however, and its basic concepts have received much more than lip service from many educators of the deaf. So far as this writer understands it, the method employs the simultaneous use of speech, lipreading, hearing aids, fingerspelling, and signing in communicating with the deaf. The student using this system needs a background with the oral, manual, and auricular methods, or any combination of these.

Teaching the mechanics of oralism or manualism is not the basic concern of this method, but rather the task of getting ideas across clearly and meaningfully. The user of the simultaneous method speaks, fingerspells, and signs every word in logical and correct syntax. The deaf person attempts to understand the message by watching the speaker's lips, as well as gaining additional information from the accompanying signs and fingerspelling. The use of all these cues is supposed to minimize the likelihood of misunderstanding and reduces the need for repetition.

Proponents of this approach to communication indicate that its use need not detract from the development of speech. Deaf persons have frequently commented that this method has helped to build up their lipreading ability. Individual and group hearing aids may also be utilized in this approach. Various psychologists have stated that deaf children who have been using signs and fingerspelling in the early years come to school with an experiential background which prepares them for other communicative skills. So be it. Any audiologist with extended experience with "deaf" children can point to many, with average intelligence, who have been started by the age of one to two years in auditory and speech learning, who are quite fully verbal by the time they begin school. Research from Russia has indicated that the carefully selected deaf child at 30 months of age knows the alphabet and can read, and accumulates a vocabulary of more than 2,000 words by the time he goes to school. This is accomplished in at least four state schools, with the children removed from the home by age two. One doubts that the system would work here.

One can only hope that the simultaneous method will indeed prove to be useful for the deaf child, and can only encourage its use as a form of the development of language understanding and communication. As well, however, there exists the need for dedicated educators of the deaf to demonstrate its success not only with select groups, but also with children who express all ranges of multiple problems. That as a basic concept it can contribute critically to the development of speech and oral syntax remains to be demonstrated. One can only hope this is possible.

Technical Developments

Another idea to which attention should be paid is the concept of speech-analyzing aids for the deaf. It seems apparent that speech education for the deaf may benefit greatly from two lines of research presently being undertaken. The first is the development of analyzing aids; the second is the study of the normal development of speech in the first year of life.

Much interest is currently shown in analyzing aids. These may display any or all of the following attributes: (1) pitch and/or intensity levels; (2) pitch and/or intensity contours over time; (3) degree of nasality; (4) static patterns representing steady-state vowel and consonant sounds; and (5) spectral patterns which relate to movements of articulation in a real speech context. There is evidence to show that the displays which include information relative to time are most useful for the deaf child.

Displays of visual speech remain in a fairly early stage of development. It is possible, however, to analyze a speech signal with the aid of an on-line computer and the use of a storage oscilloscope as an output device. With this technique much flexibility can be achieved in developing a useful critique about different modes and formats of display. The procedure makes possible a selection of those of optimal value.

The value of any speech-analyzing aid in instruction for the deaf depends on the development of sound procedures for its use. Logically, these must be based on knowledge of the procedures of speech development in both the normal and the hearing impaired infant. As yet, we do not know how or when the development of speech sounds in the hearing impaired infant departs from a normal developmental course. As this can be identified, it seems probable that speech instruction for the deaf child should begin and should thereafter follow a modified developmental course. It seems logical that the sounds taught first to the infant with impaired hearing should be those which are not only easy to see by direct vision but also easy with respect to the manner of production. There is evidence to indicate that these are the sounds typically produced by infants from 6 to 9 months of age. From these bases, a severely hearing impaired child (or deaf, as one chooses to use the term) should learn to build upon early sound-types in much the same steps as are used by the infant with normal hearing.

Studies of the vocalization of infants are being carried out in a number of centers. Both normal and hearing impaired infants have been studied. Obviously, however, with infants suspected of hearing loss it has oftentimes not been possible to document its nature and degree. In the center with which I am most familiar, methods of describing and measuring early sound-types produced by normal infants are being developed. In the future, information from all these studies will be applied in using speech-analyzing aids in instruction for the deaf.

Audiologic Matters

One cannot thoughtfully address these various concepts, particularly from a conviction that a very great many deaf children can learn speech, without paying attention to the idea that audiologic measurements are critical determinants for the prospectus of the education of the deaf child. In any case, the child is in trouble and he needs all of the best help he can get. One hears or reads a damning comment about pseudo-hearing, but many of those who are most verbal in this regard never mention pseudo-deafness. Without the capacity to use what residual hearing remains, and without any attempt to help him use it, any severely impaired child will become deaf in the course of several years of un-use. It has become clearly apparent in recent years that children with severe or profound hearing impairment can do far better by way of learning language with the use of hearing aids which accentuate low frequencies, and often with the use of binaural aids.

Where To?

Two-earedness is something we all employ and regard in daily living. The child with severe hearing impairment needs at least major access to all these attempts to develop the kinds of learning from audition, however limited, that we who hear take for granted. If the child who closes his eyes and cannot understand is considered to be deaf, we may at least try to become less deaf than those who cannot see.

As was suggested at the beginning of this discussion, any analysis of trends genuinely pertinent to the present context requires certain commitments, and perhaps a form of advocacy. Nobody doubts that every conscientious person, teacher or clinician, is concerned deeply with the lifelong well-being of every child who cannot well learn language and speech through hearing. Trade unionism relative to the details of attitudes and procedures does not necessarily aid and abet this concern. A special modern trend is a capacity to know more and to know better how to think about each child's needs, with only historical attention to the doctrines of yesteryear which presented the best that could be done at the time.